$$S_{G.} \ Hg = 13.55$$

$$S.G \ OIL = 0.8 \ , \ 0.9$$

$$S.G. \ CCl_4 = 1.59$$

$$\rho = \frac{SLUGS}{FT^3}$$

$$COS \ \pi = -1$$

$$V = \sqrt{2gh} \quad FOR \quad FRICTIONLESS \quad FLOW$$
$$FROM \ HEIGHT \ h$$

CONTINUITY
$$0 = \frac{dM'}{dt} + \int_A \rho V \cos\theta \cdot dA$$

BERNOULI
$$\frac{V_2^2 - V_1^2}{2} + \frac{P_2 - P_1}{\rho} + g(z_2 - z_1) = 0$$

$$N_R = \frac{\rho \overset{VEL}{\overset{\downarrow}{V}} \overset{\text{PIPE DIAM}}{\overset{\downarrow}{d}}}{\underset{\text{VISCOSITY}}{\mu}} \quad \overset{\text{DENSITY}}{}$$

$$\overset{\text{ACCOUNTS FOR FRICTION}}{}$$

$$\frac{V_2^2 - V_1^2}{2} + \frac{P_2 - P_1}{\rho} + g(z_2 - z_1) + gh_L = 0$$

$$h_L = f \frac{LV^2}{D2g} \quad (PAGE \ 220) + C \frac{V^2}{2g}$$
$$(PAGE \ 225)$$

$$D = C_D \frac{\rho A V^2}{2}$$

ELEMENTARY
THEORETICAL
FLUID
MECHANICS

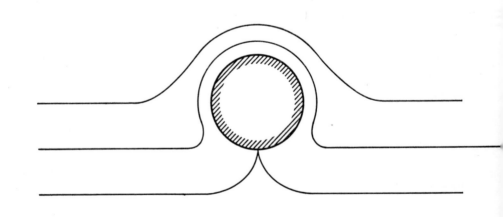

ELEMENTARY THEORETICAL FLUID MECHANICS

Karl Brenkert, Jr.
Associate Professor of Applied Mechanics
Michigan State University

New York . London . JOHN WILEY & SONS, INC.

To my beloved wife, Betty

PREFACE

The fundamentals of fluid mechanics form one of the areas of engineering science essential to the background of every engineer. In this book these fundamentals are developed with a minimum of attention to practical applications, in order to provide a basis for the study of applications in many fields of advanced specialization. Although I have introduced some discussion of applications that serve to illustrate and augment the student's grasp of principles, I have been guided by my belief that a beginning student can easily lose sight of basic ideas if he becomes engrossed too soon in the details of application or in the techniques of problem solution. This does not imply that applications are unimportant; on the contrary, I believe that the applied work of today's engineer is becoming increasingly important at the same time that it is becoming increasingly complex.

I have presented the basic topics of fluid mechanics that will be as useful in the applications of the future as they are in today's technology. The choice of the extent to which the basic equations may be reduced for specific applications is left to the teacher. For instance, in the chapter on fluid statics the equations for computing the magnitude and location of the pressure forces have been left out deliberately. Methods for computing forces on curved surfaces have also been omitted. If the teacher wishes to use these he can develop them from the fundamental equations and let the class use the formulas. If they were developed in this text the student might use them whether the teacher wanted him to or not.

The student is assumed to have completed a year of calculus, and I have used calculus in most of the derivations and proofs. Some partial differential equations appear in Chapter 2 but a short explanation of them is given. Because the fundamental equations in this book are as general as possible in elementary fluid mechanics, many of them are repeated several times in illustrative problems and special examples in order to ease the difficulty of student comprehension. The illustrative problems are worked out numerically so that the student has no formulas to use but must return again and again to the basic equations.

In deriving the general equations of continuity, energy, momentum, and angular momentum, the control volume approach is used because it is the most general and the most useful. This control volume approach to fluid mechanics is similar to the free body approach used in the other fields of mechanics.

The chapter on friction is meant to give the student an understanding of the causes of friction and some different ways in which friction is handled. It will not be enough for the student to solve practical problems in friction flow. But with this background he should readily grasp friction concepts in his own field.

Dimensional analysis and dynamic similitude are included in the main part of the text because they are becoming extremely important tools in solving engineering problems. The treatment of dimensional analysis is not as rigorous as is Langhaar's, but the general approach is the same.

The chapter on potential flow is included to let the student know that such a theory exists and to give him an insight into its workings. This chapter will give the student an opportunity to start his education on wing theory.

At the end of each chapter are presented problems of varying degrees of difficulty. Approximately three times as many problems are offered as will be needed to cover the material adequately. They vary from easy problems to routine problems to problems that will challenge the best students.

I wish to thank Dr. Charles O. Harris for giving me the freedom in organizing class material necessary to develop elementary fluid mechanics as presented in this book; Dr. Dennis Strawbridge and Mr. Dale Taulbee for their proofreading assistance and helpful suggestions; Fred Landis for his pertinent, pointed, constructive criticisms; Mrs. Strawbridge for her excellent job of typing the manuscript; and my wife, Betty, for her constant help and encouragement.

KARL BRENKERT, JR.

June, 1960

CONTENTS

1. INTRODUCTION, DEFINITIONS, and CONCEPTS   1

    1. Introduction to Fluid Mechanics   1
    2. Definitions   2
    3. Perfect Fluid   3
    4. Density   3
    5. Pressure   5
    6. Surface Tension   7
    7. Vapor Pressure   11
    8. Bulk Modulus   11

2. FLUID STATICS   16

    9. Introduction   16
   10. Derivation of Basic Equation   17
   11. Manometry   20
   12. Forces on Plane Surfaces   27
   13. Forces on Curved Surfaces   33
   14. Buoyancy   37
   15. Stability   42
   16. Compressible Fluid Statics   47
   17. Acceleration   50
   18. Rotation   53

3. CONSERVATION of MATTER and EULER EQUATION   71

19. Introduction 71
20. Definition of Terms 72
21. One- and Two-Dimensional Flow 74
22. Control Volume Derivation of Continuity 77
23. Derivation of Euler Equation 86
24. Applications of Bernoulli's Equation 91
25. Pipe Flow 93
26. Submerged Bodies 96
27. Compressible Flow 103
28. Summary 109

4. MOMENTUM and ANGULAR MOMENTUM   123

29. Introduction to Momentum Analysis 123
30. Derivation of Momentum Equation 123
31. Derivation of Angular Momentum 146
32. Summary 160

5. CONSERVATION of ENERGY   173

33. Introduction 173
34. Derivation of General Energy Equation 173
35. Comparison of the Energy Equation and
    the Euler Equation 184
36. Compressible Flow in Diverging and
    Converging Nozzles 188
37. Critical Pressure Ratio 192
38. Summary 195

6. FRICTION   202

39. Introduction 202
40. Definition of Viscosity 202
41. Reynolds' Experiment 213
42. Exchange of Momentum between Layers 215
43. Pipe Flow 217
44. Friction on Submerged Bodies 226
45. Secondary Flow 233

7. DIMENSIONAL ANALYSIS and MODEL STUDY   241

46. Introduction   241
47. Dimensional Homogeneity   241
48. Dimensional Analysis   245
49. Dimensionless Ratios or π Terms   251
50. Determination of Minimum Number of π Terms   254
51. Model Testing   262
52. Incomplete Dynamic Similarity   267

8. POTENTIAL FLOW   276

53. Introduction   276
54. Continuity   277
55. Irrotational Flow   281
56. Solution to the Laplace Equation   290
57. Application to Flow of Fluid in a Corner   293
58. Application of Bernoulli Equation   295
59. Comparison of Theoretical and Actual Pressure
    Distribution on Cylinders   305
60. Source and Vortex   308
61. Flow Around a Cylinder with Circulation   313
62. Airfoil Theory   317
63. Summary   317

APPENDIX A.   ACOUSTIC VELOCITY   323

APPENDIX B.   CAVITATION   327

APPENDIX C.   THERMODYNAMICS   329

APPENDIX D.   BOUNDARY LAYER THEORY   331

APPENDIX E.   REFERENCES   340

INDEX   345

INTRODUCTION, DEFINITIONS, and CONCEPTS

chapter **1**

1. Introduction to Fluid Mechanics

Since life began, man's very existence has depended upon two fluids—water and air. His first problems in fluids were with water; air was to play a vast role in later history. Long before he had had a chance to develop theories and principles of fluid mechanics he was faced with the immediate problems of procuring water to drink, finding water to irrigate crops, and developing waterways for commerce. Almost all of man's early knowledge of fluids, then, dealt with hydraulics, as water problems are known today. Because it was necessary to solve problems promptly, his early experience had to be of an empirical nature, a trend in hydraulics which has continued into recent times. The tendency to look upon empirical work with some scorn still exists, but we should keep in mind that such work led to the famous irrigation systems in Egypt, aquaducts in ancient Rome, windmills in Holland, canals in the United States, and the famous clipper ships of the nineteenth century.

At the time some men were solving hydraulics problems, others, mainly mathematicians and physicists, were delving into mathematical and theoretical approaches to the behavior of frictionless fluids. The fine work they accomplished seemed wholly impractical until near the beginning of the twentieth century, when Ludwig Prandtl conceived the boundary layer theory. For the first time the work of the two groups had a common meeting ground—friction inside the boundary layer, frictionless fluid outside the boundary layer.

Fluid mechanics plays an ever-increasing part in the complicated technology of the present-day world. From the age-old problems of water supply to the exotic problems of today, involving such things as the pumping of liquid oxygen or the directing of the flow of exhaust gases near 2000°F, new enigmas in fluid mechanics arise daily and almost every division of engineering is faced with fluid flow problems in one form or another. Even the civil engineer who builds massive steel structures realizes that a knowledge of the fundamentals of fluid mechanics can save him from a disaster such as the collapse of the Tacoma Narrows bridge under wind loading. The field of fluid mechanics offers the young engineer an outstanding, challenging opportunity. This book attempts to give the student a thorough background in the fundamental principles of fluid mechanics. These principles will enable him to undertake further work on specialized problems in any of the many fields of fluid mechanics, with the accuracy of his solutions depending upon his grasp of the practical difficulties involved in his field. Subsequent courses will delve into the special difficulties which are purposely omitted in this book.

2. Definitions

The main difference between a solid and a fluid is that a solid material subjected to a shearing stress will deform to a certain point and then stop deforming whereas a fluid subjected to the same shearing stress will deform at a certain rate and continue to deform at the same rate as long as the stress is applied.

The two categories of fluids are liquids and gases. A liquid is practically incompressible compared to a gas. A liquid poured into a container, if it has a volume less than the volume of the container, will fill the container only partially and will assume the shape of the container on all sides of the liquid except the free surface at the top. A gas poured into a container, regardless of the amount of the gas or the size of the container, will fill the container completely. As Sir Oliver Lodge stated it: "A solid has volume and shape; a liquid has volume but no shape; a gas has neither."

This difference between a gas and a liquid is very well explained by a simplified molecular theory, which is that all fluids are mainly empty space with a scattering of billions of molecules per cubic inch. Even with this large number of molecules, a cubic inch of gas at standard atmospheric conditions has more space empty than is occupied by molecules. The true nature of the molecules is complicated, but for our purposes we shall assume that they are spheres. The molecules have an attraction for each other as long as they are further apart than approximately one diameter of the molecule, but they have a strong repulsion for each other when the distance between them is approximately one diameter or less. This repulsion acts as a great force to keep molecules from colliding.

The molecules in gases are so far apart in relation to their diameter that they travel in straight lines, and, when they pass within one diameter of each other, the repulsive force makes them act as if they had collided.

The molecules are much closer together in liquids than in gases, so close, in fact, that they continually attract and repel each other, which causes them to travel in wavy, curved paths. Liquid molecules are attracted to one another in such a way that they tend to maintain a certain shape, which accounts for the fact that liquids will occupy a definite volume; whereas gas molecules are so far apart that the attraction between them is negligible.

3. Perfect Fluid

To simplify the analysis of many problems, we must use an imaginary fluid called a perfect fluid which is nonviscous, meaning that there are no shearing stresses during motion of the fluid. The concept of a perfect fluid enabled mathematicians to solve many fluid problems, but until the advent of the boundary layer concept by Prandtl the solutions obtained by this concept were of little practical value. Although no such thing as a perfect fluid exists, many problems involving gases can be solved approximately by assuming the gas to be a perfect fluid, and for simplicity many problems in this book will deal with assumed perfect fluids.

4. Density

The amount of mass per unit of volume is one of the most important properties of any fluid. In elementary solid dynamics we isolate a specific unit of mass and study its motion due to external forces. In fluid mechanics a particular unit of mass as it moves through the system can change shape and size and even become broken up into many smaller units of mass, making analysis difficult. To overcome this difficulty, a certain volume is selected within the fluid through which the fluid continuously passes. The density of the fluid within the volume at any specific time t is the mass within the volume divided by the amount of the volume. If the volume ΔV selected is very small, the amount of mass ΔM within the volume at any particular time is also very small.   The average density ρ_a of the fluid within the volume is then $\Delta M / \Delta V$.

To define density at a point, the volume ΔV must become smaller and smaller until it approaches zero.   We define density ρ at a point in a fluid as

$$\rho = \lim_{\Delta V \to 0} \frac{\Delta M}{\Delta V}$$

Obviously, the density of a fluid is a function of its location and time, and it can be written as

$$\rho = f(x, y, z, t)$$

In most fluid mechanics problems, such a definition of density is practical and accurate.   We must keep in mind, however, that in any fluid the density is a function of the number of molecules in an infinitesimal volume.   The molecules are changing continuously within the volume, and the slight fluctuation in the number of molecules has no practical effect except in certain processes requiring a high vacuum.   Problems of this nature are rather rare, but, as man travels further into outer space, they will increase in number and importance.   For this book, we shall assume the foregoing definition of density to be correct.

Just as density is a measure of mass per unit volume, temperature is a measure of the mean value of kinetic energy of the molecules per unit mass.   Temperature also is assumed to vary continuously with time and from point to point within the fluid.

Having defined density, we can define specific weight as the product of density and gravitational acceleration.   Thus, specific weight has all the properties of density except that, because of the change of gravitational acceleration with extreme changes of location, the specific weight of a particular unit of mass will vary.   Density for any specific substance will vary only by changing the number of molecules per unit volume, whereas specific weight may change by increasing or decreasing the number of molecules per unit volume and/or changing the gravitational acceleration.   In the problems of a few years ago this was an interesting technical point used mainly to trip students on examinations.   In the space age, it is no longer a fine technical point but a practical reality that every engineer should know and understand.

The reciprocal of the specific weight is called the specific volume.

The ratio of the density of a liquid to the density of pure water is the specific gravity of the material.   The specific gravity will vary with temperature, and, to be accurate, the temperature should be given for the specific gravity. The density of any material is its specific gravity times the density of pure water. The specific gravity of mercury is 13.55. The density ρ_{Hg} of mercury is

$$\rho_{Hg} = (\text{s. g.})_{Hg}(\rho_{H_2O}) = (13.55)(1.938) = 26.26 \text{ slugs/ft}^3$$

5. Pressure

A solid can rest unenclosed upon any platform that will support its weight, whereas a fluid must be kept in a container because an unenclosed fluid tends to spread out, indicating that the fluid exerts a force on the walls of the container. The intensity of the force varies from point to point in the fluid and is called the pressure.

The force that the surrounding fluid exerts on the faces of a small cube of fluid, isolated as a free body, must be shown as an external force on that free body. Considering only one face of the cube, the average pressure acting on that face is the force due to the surrounding fluid divided by the area of the face. To define pressure at a point, it is necessary to take the limit of the average pressure as the area over which the force acts tends to zero; that is,

$$p = \lim_{\Delta A \to 0} \frac{\Delta F}{\Delta A} = \frac{dF}{dA}$$

which may be rewritten as

$$dF = p \, dA$$

or

$$F = \int_A p \, dA$$

Thus, we can compute the force due to a fluid on any area when pressure due to the fluid is completely defined.

We assume that, unless otherwise stated, the pressure, like density and temperature, is a continuous function of time and space within the fluid, an assumption that is true in the majority of problems. Most problems in which it is not true, such as those involving shock waves and water hammer, are beyond the scope of this book.

No definition of pressure is complete until we know the direction in which the pressure acts. The weight of any body always acts toward the center of the earth, but, to find in which direction the pressure at a certain point acts, we shall select an x and y axis system somewhere in the fluid. Figure 1a is a sketch of an element taken from the fluid,

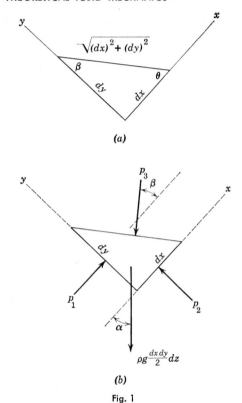

(a)

(b)

Fig. 1

and Fig. 1b is a free body diagram of this element. By summing forces in the x direction, we obtain

$$\Sigma F_x = m a_x$$

$$p_1 \, dy \, dz - \rho g \frac{dx \, dy}{2} \, dz \cos \alpha - p_3 \, dz \sqrt{(dx)^2 + (dy)^2} \cos \beta$$

$$= \rho \frac{dx \, dy}{2} \, dz \, a_x$$

From Fig. 1a

$$\cos \beta = \frac{dy}{\sqrt{(dx)^2 + (dy)^2}}$$

$$p_1 \, dy \, dz - \rho g \frac{dx \, dy}{2} \, dz \cos \alpha - p_3 \, dz \sqrt{(dx)^2 + (dy)^2} \, \frac{dy}{\sqrt{(dx)^2 + (dy)^2}}$$

$$= \rho \frac{dx \, dy}{2} \, dz \, a_x$$

Dividing by $dy\,dz$, we obtain

$$p_1 - \rho g \frac{dx}{2} \cos \alpha - p_3 = \rho a_x \frac{dx}{2}$$

Since dx is an infinitesimal, the terms containing dx may be neglected when compared to the finite term. This leaves

$$p_1 - p_3 = 0$$

or
$$p_1 = p_3$$

Now we sum forces in the y direction to get

$$p_2 = p_3$$

Therefore,

$$p_2 = p_3 = p_1$$

This proves that the pressure is the same in all directions because the direction of the axis system was arbitrary.

The free body diagram in Fig. 1b shows the pressure as normal to the surface because pressure is always normal to the surface and always acts against the surface in a manner similar to a compression stress. The force due to pressure is just one of the forces that make up the resultant force on the surface, and it should not be confused with the resultant force. Fluids in motion may cause other forces.

6. Surface Tension

Molecules of a liquid have a certain attraction for each other and also are attracted to molecules of other materials. When small amounts of mercury are spilled on a smooth, horizontal surface such as clean glass, the mercury tends to form into small beads because the molecules of mercury have a greater attraction for each other than they have for the material of the horizontal surface. They try to draw into a shape (in the absence of other forces, a sphere) that will place all their molecules as close to the center of gravity of the mercury bead as possible. This attraction has the same effect as if the surface of the sphere were in a state of tension, explaining why this phenomenon is called surface tension.

When water is poured on the same smooth, horizontal surface, the water spreads out to a thin uniform thickness because the water molecules have a greater attraction for the material of the surface than for each other.

Figure 2a shows a wire that has been immersed in a liquid and slowly withdrawn so that it has a length l held above and parallel to the surface of the liquid.   This piece of wire although held above the surface of the liquid has a thin film of the liquid passing over it.   A certain force F required to break the thin film, divided by the total length of

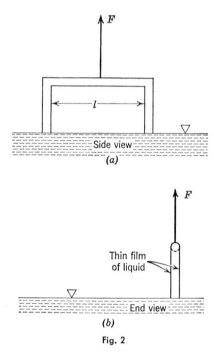

Fig. 2

film, is called the surface tension.   Since the film covers both sides of the wire, the total length is $2l$, and the surface tension σ is

$$\sigma = \frac{F}{2l}$$

Obviously, the dimensions of surface tension are force per unit length.

Let us immerse one end of a clean glass tube in water.   Since the water molecules have greater attraction for the glass than for each other, the water will rise in the tube (Fig. 3a), a common example of surface tension.   The pressure on the surface of the water is atmospheric both inside and outside of the tube.   The water in the tube rises above the free surface of the remaining water.   Figure 3b is a simplified free body diagram of this water.   The pressure on the top and bottom of the free body diagram is atmospheric and cancels out and so it does not appear in the figure.   Since the forces designated by σ are forces per unit length, they act all the way around the tube.   When the vertical forces are summed, the surface tension forces are $\sigma\pi d$.   Therefore,

$$\Sigma F_V = 0 \quad +\uparrow$$

$$\sigma\pi d \cos \alpha - \rho g \frac{\pi d^2}{4} h = 0$$

$$h = 4\frac{\sigma \cos \alpha}{\rho g d}$$

The angle α is dependent upon the liquid and the material of the tube. For water $\alpha = 0°$, and for mercury $\alpha = -129°$ when the water and the mercury are in contact with glass.

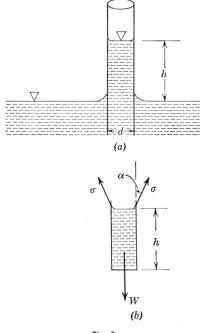

(a)

(b)

Fig. 3

If the liquid had been one in which the molecules had a greater attraction for each other than for the wall of the glass tube (Fig. 4), the liquid would not have risen in the tube.   Since we are unable at this time to handle the pressure forces in the tube, we shall not solve this problem.

From the foregoing discussion it should be clear that the surface tension σ is a function not only of the liquid itself but also of the material adjacent to the liquid.   Since molecular attraction depends upon the kinetic energy of the molecules, the surface tension also must depend upon the kinetic energy of the molecules.   Thus, the surface tension depends upon the liquid itself, the material with which it is in

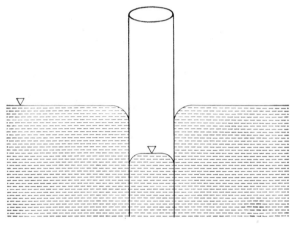

Fig. 4

contact, and the kinetic energy of the molecules which is measured by temperature.

▶**Illustrative Problem 1.**   A drop of water 0.01 in. in diameter is suspended in a liquid of specific gravity equal to 1.   The surface tension of the water in contact with this liquid is $\sigma = 4.98(10)^{-3}$ lb/ft.   What

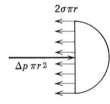

Sketch 1

is the difference between the pressure inside and outside of the drop?

Solution: The only forces acting upon the drop will be forces due to surface tension and pressure because the liquid and the water have the same density.

The surface tension for water in this case is $4.98(10)^{-3}$ lb/ft.   The radius is $0.01/(2)(12)$ ft.   The simplified free body diagram of one half of the drop appears in Sketch 1.

$$\Sigma F_h = 0 \quad \overset{+}{\leftarrow}$$

$$-\Delta p\, \pi r^2 + 2\sigma\pi r = 0$$

$$-\Delta p \left(\frac{0.01}{24}\right)^2 + (2)(4.98)(10)^{-3}\left(\frac{0.01}{24}\right) = 0$$

$$\Delta p = 23.9 \text{ lb/ft} \qquad \blacktriangleleft$$

7. Vapor Pressure

A closed container is filled partially with a liquid, and then the container is pumped free of other material, leaving the liquid and a vacuum acting upon the liquid surface. The molecules of the liquid travel at a velocity that allows some of them to break through the liquid surface into the vacuum. Some of those that break through into the vacuum will pass through the liquid surface again and return to the liquid. This process continues with more molecules leaving than entering the liquid. The number of molecules in the space above the liquid increases until the number of molecules leaving the liquid is equal to the number of molecules re-entering the liquid. The liquid molecules in the space above the liquid are not dense enough to be a liquid but form a vapor that exerts a pressure called vapor pressure on the surface of the liquid. The greater the vapor pressure, the greater must be the velocity of the molecules to break through the liquid surface. Thus, the greater the vapor pressure, the greater the kinetic energy of the molecules. The kinetic energy of the molecules is measured by temperature; an increase in temperature means an increase in vapor pressure.

A liquid boils when its temperature is increased so that the pressure acting upon its surface is equal to its vapor pressure. Water boils at 212°F at standard atmospheric pressure. Since the outside pressure would be less if the water were at a higher elevation, the temperature would not have to be so great in order to make the outside pressure equal to the vapor pressure, and the water or any liquid would boil at a lower temperature.

Vapor pressure is very important in problems of liquid flow. When the pressure in a liquid drops below the vapor pressure, the liquid vaporizes forming gas bubbles in the liquid. When the pressure returns to above the vapor pressure, the gas returns to a liquid and extremely high pressures result. This is called cavitation and must be avoided.

8. Bulk Modulus

A plot of stress versus strain in solid materials gives a line whose slope is called the modulus of elasticity. We apply the stress and measure the strain along a single axis. In dealing with fluids, we cannot apply stress in only one direction because fluid would immediately flow in another direction. Therefore, we must apply a stress in all three directions which means the strain is a volume strain, not the longitudinal strain we use in solid materials. The stress is the force divided by the area upon which the force acts, which in fluids at rest is just the pressure. Figure 5 is a plot of the pressure p versus the volume V at p divided by the volume V_o at atmospheric pressure. The negative slope of the curve at any point is the bulk modulus β or modulus of elasticity, defined as

$$\beta = \lim_{\Delta V \to 0} - \frac{\Delta p}{\Delta V / V_o} = \frac{-dp}{dV / V_o} \qquad (1\text{-}1)$$

The bulk modulus is a positive number because the change in volume dV is a negative number. Fluids will not support tension to any appreciable degree; therefore, to define a negative pressure as tension is impractical.

We determine the bulk modulus at or near the atmospheric pressure in most practical engineering problems. We must keep in mind, also, that the bulk modulus is not only a property of the fluid but also a

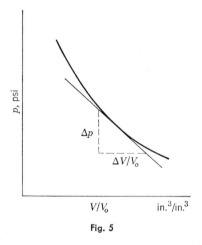

Fig. 5

function of the pressure and temperature. Even though the bulk modulus of water at atmospheric pressure (approximately 310,000 psi) indicates that water is by no means incompressible, the exceedingly small changes in volume for normal changes in pressure make us consider water and other liquids as incompressible. Exceptions occur only when the liquid is subject to severe accelerations, which cause compression waves, or when ice or steam is involved.

One important use of the bulk modulus in modern problems arises when we consider the liquid in a hydraulic system as a spring. We must investigate the possibility that loading may be in resonance with the hydraulic system, giving rise to much greater pressures and deflections than would appear possible.

The bulk modulus is not often used in gases because the thermodynamic processes involved determine the relation between the pressure and the specific volume. To compute the bulk modulus for an isothermal process (constant temperature), we already know the following relation among the pressure, specific volume, and temperature for a perfect gas

$$pv = RT$$

where R is the engineering gas constant. When the temperature is constant,

$$pv = \text{constant}$$

We can take the differential to get

$$v\,dp + p\,dv = 0$$

$$p = -\frac{dp}{dv/v}$$

which is the definition of the bulk modulus. Therefore,

$$\beta = p$$

for an isothermal process.

PROBLEMS

1-1. The specific weight of alcohol is 43.5 lb/ft³. Determine the density, specific gravity, and specific volume of the alcohol.

1-2. A room 8 ft high, 10 ft wide, and 14 ft long is filled with air. The total weight of the air is 85.7 lb. Compute the specific weight, density, and specific volume of the air.

1-3. A gas that weighs 0.024 lb is in a cylinder 8 in. in diameter with the piston 4 ft from the closed end of the cylinder. Compute the specific weight, the specific volume, and the density of the gas.

1-4. In Problem 1-3 how far from the end of the cylinder must the piston be moved for each of the following conditions:

(a) The specific weight of the gas is doubled.
(b) The specific volume of the gas is tripled.
(c) The density of the gas is cut in half.

Assume no gas leaks around the piston.

1-5. A certain liquid has a density of 1.5 slugs/ft³. Determine the specific weight, the specific volume, and the specific gravity of the liquid on the earth and the moon. The gravitational acceleration on the moon is 5.47 ft/sec². What is the density of the liquid on the moon?

1-6. Gas A is in cylinder 1 which has a volume of 6 ft³, and gas B is in cylinder 2 which has a volume of 8 ft³. The specific weight of gas A is 0.003 lb/ft³, and the specific weight of gas B is 0.0027 lb/ft³. Calculate the ratio of the volume of cylinder 1 to the volume of cylinder 2 when the specific weight of the two gases is the same. Assume that the volume of the cylinders can vary but that the amount of gas inside each cylinder is constant.

1-7. What is temperature? What does zero degree Rankine mean in terms of molecules?

1-8. Surface tension is often measured by determining the force necessary to lift a wire from the surface of the liquid in question. If we wish to lift a 10 ft long wire from a tank of water, what force will be needed to overcome the surface tension? The surface tension of water is 0.00498 lb/ft.

1-9. An unknown liquid has a surface tension of 0.026 lb/ft and a density of 2 slugs/ft³. In an $\frac{1}{8}$ in. dia. tube the liquid rises $\frac{1}{4}$ in. above the free surface of the liquid outside the tube. Calculate the angle α between the liquid and the wall of the tube.

1-10. In Problem 1-8 calculate the force if the water and the wire are both on the surface of the moon. The gravitational acceleration on the moon is 5.47 ft/sec², the mass of the moon is 0.01228 times the mass of the earth, and the diameter of the moon is 3476 km.

1-11. A liquid that has a surface tension of 0.026 lb/ft and a density of 2 slugs/ft³ rises a distance h in a $\frac{1}{8}$ in. dia. glass tube. The angle α between the tube and the surface of the liquid is $\pi/6$. Compute h.

1-12. Compute h in Problem 1-11 when the liquid is on the surface of the moon. The gravitational acceleration on the surface of the moon is 5.47 ft/sec².

1-13. A 30 ft pipe is filled with a hydraulic fluid which has a bulk modulus of 210,000 psi. Calculate the diameter of the pipe that would give the system a spring constant of 314 lb/in. Assume that the pipe is rigid.

1-14. What additional pressure must be exerted on 100 ft³ of water at atmospheric pressure to compress the water into a volume of 99.9 ft³? The bulk modulus of water is 300,000 psi.

1-15. Compute the bulk modulus of a perfect gas during a process that obeys the law

$$pv^{1.4} = \text{constant}$$

where p = pressure, in lb/ft²
v = specific volume, in ft³/lb

1-16. Compute the bulk modulus of a perfect gas during a process that obeys the law

$$pv^{n} = \text{constant}$$

where p = pressure, in lb/ft²
v = specific volume, in ft³/lb
n = constant $\neq 1$

1-17. A $\frac{1}{2}$ in. dia. pipe that is 10 ft long is filled with a hydraulic fluid.

Assume that the walls of the pipe are rigid and that the bulk modulus of the fluid is 250,000 psi. Considering the fluid as a stiff spring, compute the spring constant.

1-18. Derive the value of the spring constant for a rigid pipe that is L ft long and D in. in diameter when the bulk modulus of the fluid is β psi.

1-19. A very long 1 ft dia. rigid pipe is used to pump a fluid cross-country. The pipe becomes plugged at some unknown point so that no fluid can flow. Since the pipe is buried, it will be necessary to find how far from one end it is plugged. A piston that slides in the pipe without leaking moves a distance along the pipe of 24 in. and increases the pressure of the liquid in the pipe by 20 psi. The bulk modulus of the liquid is 200,000 psi. How far down the pipe would you recommend that they look for the obstruction?

1-20. In Problem 1-19 derive the general expression for the distance L to the obstruction in terms of the diameter of the pipe, the length the piston travels, the bulk modulus of the liquid, and the increase in pressure. Be certain to specify the unit of each variable.

1-21. A very large irregularly shaped rigid body is sealed except at one point. Determine the inside volume of the body when an increase of 50 psi in pressure will decrease the volume of the liquid by 0.05 ft³. The bulk modulus of the liquid which completely fills the inside of the body is 300,000 psi.

1-22. A drop of liquid is suspended in a different liquid of the same density The drop forms a sphere which has a diameter of 0.015 in. The pressure inside the drop is 50 lb/ft² greater than the pressure outside the drop. What is the surface tension of the liquid in the drop?

FLUID STATICS

chapter **2**

9. Introduction

Fluid statics is the special case of fluids at rest with respect to the earth or at rest with respect to an axis system moving in rectilinear translation at a constant velocity with respect to the earth. The acceleration is zero, and the sum of all forces acting on a body must be zero in every direction.

In Chapter 1 we pointed out that all fluids consist of empty space and molecules, a difficult concept to use for solving engineering problems. It is impossible to describe conditions at a given point that at one instance might lie in empty space and in the next instance in a molecule; for such a case all properties of the fluid at a point would be meaningless. To circumvent such difficulties in solving engineering problems, we assume that a fluid is continuous and not made up of molecules. This assumption works well because the small particles used in the solutions contain millions of molecules, causing the properties of a particle to change continuously rather than discontinuously from particle to particle. When all the properties of the fluid are continuous functions of time and location, we call the fluid a continuum.

In only one instance can a fluid not be considered a continuum, that is, when the density of molecules is reduced to a very low level. Two examples are the atmosphere at great elevations and the gases in some very low pressure, high vacuum processes. Unless specified otherwise, every fluid mentioned in this book is considered to be a continuum.

We derive the basic equation of fluid statics by accounting for the two limitations, zero acceleration and the continuum. From this basic equation we may develop through the use of statics many secondary equations covering different applications. A great temptation exists to develop secondary equations and to solve fluid statics problems by plugging numbers into equations, and it becomes expedient to do so when necessary to solve many problems of the same type. In this book, however, we do not develop the secondary equations. We solve examples of different applications by the basic equations and statics to unburden the student from trying to remember secondary equations.

10. Derivation of Basic Equations

The study of friction in Chapter 6 shows that shear forces can exist only when there is relative motion between particles of fluids. Since there is no relative motion between fluid particles in fluid statics, there can be no shear forces. Body forces and pressure forces, therefore, are the only forces that we need to consider. A body force is a force that depends on the mass or volume of the body. The most important body force is weight, but others we could consider are magnetic forces and electrodynamic forces. The axis system in fluid statics does not rotate and so the centripetal acceleration is zero, which eliminates inertia effects due to this acceleration. We need not consider the magnetic forces and electrodynamic forces at this time. Therefore, the only body force will be weight.

We use an axis system, with a vertical z axis and horizontal x and y axes, at rest with respect to the earth or moving with a constant velocity in translation. A cube of fluid (Fig. 6a) is immersed completely in a body of fluid at rest with respect to the axis system. Figure 6b is a free body diagram of the fluid in the cube. The only forces acting on this free body are the pressure forces on each face and the weight of the cube which acts at the center of the cube. Since the fluid is considered to be a continuum, the pressure and density may be considered as continuous functions of x, y, z, and t. We take the pressure at the center of the cube as p. The pressure at the top of the cube is the pressure at the center plus some infinitesimal increment of pressure. We call the change of p with respect to a change in z the partial derivative of p with respect to z and write it as $\partial p/\partial z$. The partial derivative is the rate of change of p in the z direction. When we multiply the rate of change of p in the z direction by the distance moved in the z direction, we obtain a close approximation to the change of p. Therefore, we write the pressure on the top of the element as

$$p + \frac{\partial p}{\partial z}\frac{dz}{2}$$

and, in a similar manner, the pressure at the bottom of the element as

$$p - \frac{\partial p}{\partial z}\frac{dz}{2}$$

Figure 7 better demonstrates this point by showing the variation of pressure in the z direction near the center of the cube.   Pressure in

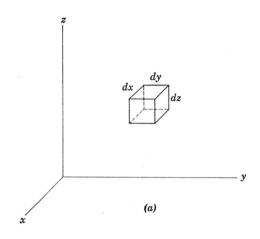

(a)

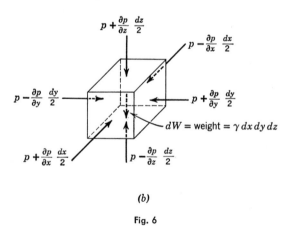

(b)

Fig. 6

the center of the cube is p and at face 1 is $[p + (\partial p/\partial z)(\Delta z/2)]$.   This is an approximation until the limit is taken as $\Delta z \to 0$ and the pressure becomes the exact pressure at face 1 or $[p + (\partial p/\partial z)(dz/2)]$.   We determine the pressure at the bottom of the cube $[p - (\partial p/\partial z)(dz/2)$ and on the other faces by using the same procedure.

We sum the forces on the cube in the z direction.

$$\Sigma F_z = 0 \quad \uparrow +$$

or $\quad \left(p - \frac{\partial p}{\partial z}\frac{dz}{2}\right)dx\,dy - \left(p + \frac{\partial p}{\partial z}\frac{dz}{2}\right)dx\,dy - dW = 0$

where dW = weight of fluid in cube = $\gamma\,dx\,dy\,dz$

Therefore $\qquad -\frac{\partial p}{\partial z}dx\,dy\,dz = \gamma\,dx\,dy\,dz$

$$\frac{\partial p}{\partial z} = -\gamma$$

When we sum the forces in the x and y directions, we obtain two

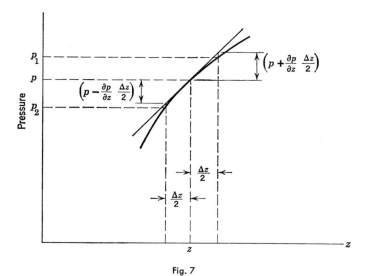

Fig. 7

additional equations which give the following three:

$$\frac{\partial p}{\partial x} = 0 \qquad\qquad (2\text{-}1)$$

$$\frac{\partial p}{\partial y} = 0 \qquad\qquad (2\text{-}2)$$

$$\frac{\partial p}{\partial z} = -\gamma \qquad\qquad (2\text{-}3)$$

Equations 2-1 and 2-2 demonstrate that no change of pressure exists with a change of x or y. Thus, p does not depend upon x or y and is a function only of z. Since p is a function of z alone, we can write the partial derivative of p with respect to z as the derivative of p with respect to z and rewrite Equation 2-3 as

$$\frac{dp}{dz} = -\gamma \quad \text{or} \quad \int dp = - \int \gamma\, dz \qquad (2\text{-}3a)$$

Equation 2-3a is the basic fundamental equation of fluid statics.

In setting up the original axis system, we took z as positive in the upward direction, but the minus sign in the basic equation indicates that the pressure increases in the downward direction contrary to the original assumption.

The fact that p is a function of z alone shows that the pressure is a constant for each value of z. Since each value of z represents a horizontal plane, the pressure is a constant for each horizontal plane. For example, the surface of bodies of water is exposed to air at a constant pressure; therefore, the water surface will be horizontal. Two main exceptions are very large surfaces where the curvature of the earth must be taken into consideration and very small surfaces where the capillary action at the walls keeps the surface from being a horizontal plane.

Because p is a function of z alone, dp/dz is also a function of only z and remains constant for each value of z and for each horizontal plane. From Equation 2-3a we see that, when dp/dz is a constant, γ is also a constant. Therefore, the specific weight γ of a fluid must be constant along a horizontal plane.

The fact that the density is constant in a horizontal plane is obvious when we consider a fluid of constant density. However, the foregoing shows that two or more mixed fluids form horizontal layers of constant density when they come to rest. The $-\gamma$ in Equation 2-3a means that the fluid of lowest density will be on the top progressing to the fluid of highest density on the bottom. A compressible fluid will be of constant density in each horizontal plane with the density varying from a maximum at the bottom to a minimum at the top. The equation of this variation will depend on the equation of state of the gas.

11. Manometry

The first applications of the basic Equation 2-3a which we shall consider are for fluids of constant density, which include all liquids. For a fluid of constant density the specific weight independent of z may be taken outside of the integral sign.   Equation 2-3a may be integrated to give

$$\int dp = - \int \gamma \, dz = -\gamma \int dz$$

or

$$p_2 - p_1 = \gamma(z_1 - z_2) \tag{2-4}$$

Equation 2-4 is the basic equation of incompressible fluid statics.

Next we consider the special case of pressure computation at a point distance h_1 below the surface of water.   The pressure at the surface of the water equals atmospheric pressure p_a and the pressure at distance h_1 below the water surface is p.   The surface of the water is the xy plane and z is positive upward by definition.   The limits of integration on the right-hand side of the equation become $-h_1$ to zero and on the left-hand side p to p_a.

$$\int_p^{p_a} dp = -\gamma \int_{-h_1}^0 dz$$

$$p_a - p = -\gamma h_1$$

$$p = \gamma h_1 + p_a \tag{2-5}$$

Pressure at point P equals the pressure at the surface of the water plus the change in pressure between $-h_1$ and 0.

Because many pressure gages do not measure pressure but measure the difference in pressure between a point in the fluid and the atmosphere, gage pressure has come to mean the difference between the pressure being measured and atmospheric pressure.   Absolute pressure is known as the atmospheric pressure plus the gage pressure.

When the absolute pressure becomes less than zero, the pressure forces become tension forces instead of compression forces.   One property of a fluid is that it cannot support tension forces; thus, it is impossible for the absolute pressure to go below zero.   The gage pressure, however, may become negative until the magnitude equals the magnitude of the atmospheric pressure.   When the gage pressure equals negative atmospheric pressure, the absolute pressure is zero and the pressure cannot go lower.   We see that it is important to know the atmospheric pressure which can be measured by means of the mercury manometer.

Figure 8a shows a schematic sketch of a mercury manometer.   The surface of the mercury at point a is open to the atmosphere and is subject to atmospheric pressure.   The surface of the mercury at point b is completely enclosed and is subject only to the vapor pressure of the mercury.   We can neglect the vapor pressure of mercury because it is exceedingly low.   Point c is at the same elevation as point a.   The fluid from c to a is a continuum because it is possible to go from c to a without leaving the fluid which itself is a continuum.   The pressure at point c equals the pressure at point a (atmospheric pressure).

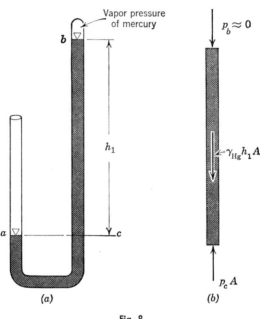

(a)   (b)

Fig. 8

Figure 8b shows a free body diagram of the column of mercury between b and c.   We sum the forces in the vertical direction and set them equal to zero to arrive at

$$p_a(A) - \gamma_{\text{Hg}} h_1 A = 0$$

$$p_a = (\gamma_{\text{Hg}})(h_1) \qquad (2\text{-}6)$$

where A is the cross-sectional area of the mercury column.   Equation 2-6 shows that atmospheric pressure equals the specific weight of mercury times some height; it is customary to measure atmospheric pressure in inches of mercury.   If water had been used and the water vapor pressure assumed to be zero, we could make the same analysis to arrive at a relation between atmospheric pressure and the height of a column of water.   Atmospheric pressure, then, could be expressed as so many feet of water.

   The assumption of zero vapor pressure for any liquid is sufficient to derive a relation between pressure and height of liquid.   The more valid this assumption, the more accurate an instrument of this type would be in measuring atmospheric pressure.   The following example demonstrates these calculations for various liquids at standard atmospheric conditions.

We consider a manometer similar to the one in Fig. 8a except that the liquid in the manometer has a specific weight equal to γ and the vapor pressure at point b is zero.   We draw a free body diagram similar to the one in Fig. 8b and sum forces in the vertical direction.

$$p_a = \gamma h_1$$

$$h_1 = \frac{p_a}{\gamma}$$

By substituting 14.696 psia (lb/in.^{2} absolute) for the atmospheric pressure in the equation and a specific weight of the liquid for γ, we can compute the height h_1 of the column of liquid.   We substitute the specific weight of water (62.4 lb/ft^3) for γ and evaluate h_1 as follows:

$$h_{1_{H_2O}} = \frac{(14.696)(144)}{62.4} = 33.913 \text{ ft of water}$$

Then we use the same equation by substituting the specific weight of mercury 848 lb/ft^3 to compute the value of h_1 of mercury.

$$h_{1_{Hg}} = \frac{(14.696)(144)}{(848)} = 2.493 \text{ ft} = 29.92 \text{ in. of mercury}$$

The standard atmosphere of 14.696 psia is expressed as 29.92 in. of mercury or 33.913 ft of water.   Any liquid can be handled in a similar manner.   For simplicity we use 14.7 psia as standard atmospheric pressure in this book.

A manometer can be used to measure the pressure difference between any two points just as it has been used to measure the pressure difference between atmospheric pressure and absolute zero, as Illustrative Problems 1 and 2 demonstrate.

▶Illustrative Problem 1.   A gage attached to a completely enclosed container filled with water and air (Fig. 9) reads the gage pressure of the air.   Assume as constant the pressure of the air inside of the container because the specific weight of gases is so small that pressure changes due to variation of less than 500 ft elevation can be neglected in most problems.   Water fills a mercury manometer down to point c; from c to k to b to a, mercury fills it.   Atmospheric pressure, p_a acts on the surface of the mercury at a because the tube is open at the top. Compute the gage pressure of the air in the tank.

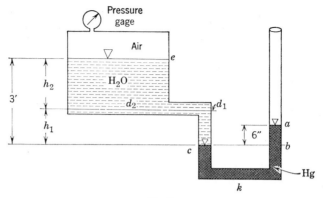

Fig. 9

Solution: Draw a free body diagram of the fluid from b to a (see Sketch 2), and compute the pressure at b by summing vertical forces.

$$\Sigma F_V = 0 \quad +\downarrow$$

$$p_a A + (\tfrac{6}{12})\gamma_{\text{Hg}} A - p_b A = 0$$

$$p_b = p_a + \tfrac{1}{2}\gamma_{\text{Hg}}$$

Because points b and c lie in a horizontal plane and it is possible to go

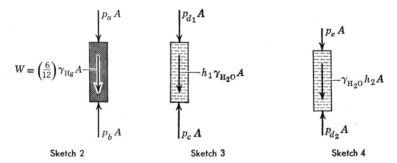

from point b to point c without leaving the mercury, the pressure at c equals the pressure at b.

$$p_c = p_b = p_a + \tfrac{1}{2}\gamma_{\text{Hg}}$$

Sketch 3 is a free body diagram of the water between c and d_1.

$$\Sigma F_V = 0 \quad \downarrow +$$

$$p_{d_1} A + \gamma_{\text{H}_2\text{O}} h_1 A - p_c A = 0$$

$$p_c - p_{d_1} = \gamma_{\text{H}_2\text{O}} h_1$$

Points d_1 and d_2 are in the same horizontal plane in a continuum, the water. Pressure everywhere in this plane is constant. Therefore,

$$p_{d_1} = p_{d_2} = p_d$$

Summing the vertical forces in the free body diagram in Sketch 4, a column of water drawn between d_2 and the liquid surface at e, gives the results

$$\Sigma F_V = 0 \quad +\downarrow$$

$$p_e A + \gamma_{H_2O} h_2 A - p_{d_2} A = 0$$

$$p_{d_2} - p_e = \gamma_{H_2O} h_2$$

When the results of the last two free body diagrams (Sketches 3 and 4) are combined, the heights h_1 and h_2 are eliminated. From Figure 9 $h_1 + h_2 = 3$. Therefore,

$$p_c - p_{d_1} + p_{d_2} - p_e = \gamma_{H_2O} h_1 + \gamma_{H_2O} h_2 = \gamma_{H_2O}(h_1 + h_2) = 3\gamma_{H_2O}$$

$$p_c - p_e = 3\gamma_{H_2O}$$

Notice that the difference in pressure between point e and point c is the same as if point c were directly under the water surface. In further problems involving a continuum do not calculate the intermediate step but calculate only the pressure difference between two points in a continuum as if one were directly above the other.

Determine the pressure p_e at point e by substituting the pressure at p_b for p_c in the last equation

$$p_b - p_e = 3\gamma_{H_2O}$$

and from above

$$p_b = p_a + \tfrac{1}{2}\gamma_{Hg}$$

so that

$$p_a - p_e = 3\gamma_{H_2O} - \tfrac{1}{2}\gamma_{Hg}$$

The gage reads the difference between p_e and the atmospheric pressure p_a. Therefore, the gage pressure will be $p_e - p_a = \tfrac{1}{2}\gamma_{Hg} - 3\gamma_{H_2O}$.

$$\text{Gage reading} = \tfrac{1}{2}\gamma_{Hg} - 3\gamma_{H_2O} \qquad \blacktriangleleft$$

▶Illustrative Problem 2. Figure 10 is a schematic drawing of a mercury manometer connected between two parallel pipes, A filled with water and B filled with carbon tetrachloride. The manometer fluid in between is mercury. From this schematic drawing determine the pressure difference between the centerlines of the two pipes.

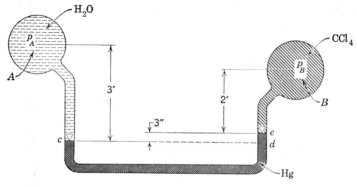

Fig. 10

Solution: Draw a *schematic* free body diagram (Sketch 5) between points A and c.

$$\Sigma F_V = 0 + \downarrow$$

$$p_A A_1 + 3\gamma_{H_2O} A_1 - p_c A_1 = 0$$

$$p_c = p_A + 3\gamma_{H_2O}$$

In the same horizontal plane are c and d. Since it is possible to go from c to d without leaving the mercury, the pressure at c equals the

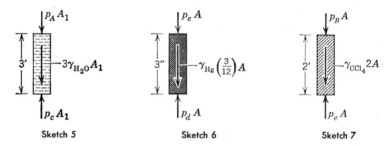

| Sketch 5 | Sketch 6 | Sketch 7 |

pressure at d. Therefore, $p_c = p_d$ and $p_A = p_d - 3\gamma_{H_2O}$. Draw a free body diagram of the fluid from d to e (Sketch 6) and another of the fluid from e to B (Sketch 7).

$$\Sigma F_V = 0 \quad +\uparrow$$

$$-p_e A - \gamma_{Hg}(\tfrac{3}{12})A + p_d A = 0$$

$$p_d = p_e + \tfrac{1}{4}\gamma_{Hg}$$

$$\Sigma F_V = 0 \quad +\downarrow$$

$$p_B A + 2\gamma_{CCl_4}A - p_e A = 0$$

$$p_e = p_B + 2\gamma_{CCl_4}$$

Substitute these equations for p_e and p_d into

$$p_A = p_d - 3\gamma_{H_2O}$$

which gives $p_A - p_B = \tfrac{1}{4}\gamma_{Hg} + 2\gamma_{CCl_4} - 3\gamma_{H_2O}.$ ◀

12. Forces on Plane Surfaces

Up to now, we have computed the pressure of the fluid only for the point. In this section we show how to compute the magnitude and location of the resultant force due to pressure acting on a plane surface which is inclined to the horizontal. This is really only a problem in distributed load that can be handled by statics. The problems of a horizontal plane surface or a vertical plane surface are special ones that can be handled by this new approach.

We select a differential area dA so that the pressure on the area is a constant. The product of this pressure, computed from Equation 2-3a, and the area dA equals a differential force dF. Since there is an infinite number of these forces, we sum all of them by integrating to get the magnitude of the resultant force. We know that the resultant force must act normal to the plane surface because the pressure is normal to the plane surface. We locate the point of application by taking moments about two perpendicular axes in the plane. The sum of the moments of the differential forces dF must equal the moment of the resultant about the same axis.

$$Fx_F = \int x(dF) \tag{2-7}$$

When we integrate Equation 2-7, x_F may be evaluated; it determines a plane. The intersection of this plane with the inclined plane gives a line. By repeating the procedure for another axis, we determine another line in the inclined plane. The point of intersection of the two lines will be the point of application of the resultant force.

We could develop equations to handle this type of problem by plugging in numbers, but we shall apply just Equation 2-3a and elementary statics by the procedure shown in Illustrative Problems 3 and 4.

▶**Illustrative Problem 3.** Calculate the total force on one side of a 3 ft by 6 ft plate submerged completely in water. A line along the 6 ft side of the plate extended to the surface of the water makes a 30° angle with the water surface, and the 3 ft side of the plate parallels the water surface. This problem and a projection of the plate *abcd* appear in Sketch 8. Atmospheric pressure is 15 psia.

Solution: The pressure on the water surface in Sketch 8 is atmospheric pressure p_a.   Sketch the plate with the pressure distribution (see Sketch 9).

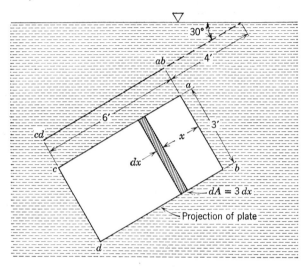

Sketch 8

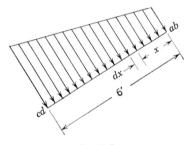

Sketch 9

Measure a distance x along the plate parallel to ac and select an area dA which is dx thick and 3 ft wide so that the pressure is constant on the area.   With Equation 2-3a, the pressure on the area is

$$p_x = p_a + \int_0^{h_x} \gamma \, dh_x = p_a + \gamma h_x$$

where h_x is the vertical distance from the area dA to the liquid surface. The product of this pressure and the area dA on which it acts is the differential force due to the pressure.

$$dF = p_x \, dA = (p_a + \gamma h_x)3 \, dx$$

The force due to the total pressure is the sum of all differential forces which is the integral over the entire plate.

$$F = \int dF = \int_0^6 (p_a + \gamma h_x)3 \, dx$$

where h_x = vertical distance from dA to liquid surface
$$= (4 + x) \sin 30$$

Therefore,

$$F = \int_0^6 [15(144) + 62.4(4 + x) \sin 30]3 \, dx$$

$$= 3\left(2160x + (31.2)(4)x + 31.2\frac{x^2}{2}\right)_0^6$$

$$= 3[2285(6 - 0) + 15.6(36 - 0)] = 42{,}811 \text{ lb}$$

Here is the magnitude of the total pressure force due to both the water and the air pressure. Now, locate this resultant force on the plate. By symmetry resultant must act somewhere $1\frac{1}{2}$ ft from a 6 ft long edge. The question is where.

From statics you know that the moment of a resultant force about any axis must be equal to the moment of the distributed load about the

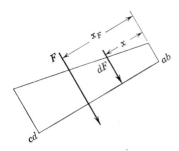

Sketch 10

same axis. Since it can be any axis, you had better choose one that will reduce the amount of work. In this case choose the top edge of the plate as shown in Sketch 10.

$$Fx_F = \int x \, dF$$

$$dF = (p_a + \gamma h_x)3 \, dx$$

$$Fx_F = \int_0^6 x(p_a + \gamma h_x)3 \, dx$$

$$= 3 \int_0^6 [15(144) + 62.4(4 + x) \sin 30]x \, dx$$

$$= 130{,}118.4 \text{ ft-lb}$$

Therefore, $$x_F = \frac{\int x \, dF}{F} = \frac{130{,}118.4}{42{,}811} = 3.04 \text{ ft}$$

The force F acts at $(3.04 + 4) \sin 30 = 3.52$ ft below water surface. ◀

▶**Illustrative Problem 4.**   A flat plate AB (Fig. 11) acts as a gate in a liquid, water.   Atmospheric pressure acts upon the upper side of the

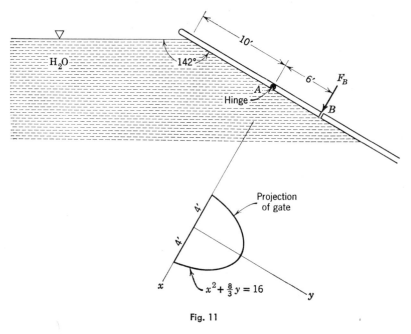

Fig. 11

gate and upon the water surface.   Compute the normal force at B necessary to hold the gate closed.

Solution: Draw a free body diagram of the gate (see Sketch 11). The distributed pressure loading resolves into a resultant force F. Taking moments about the hinge A in the free body diagram (Sketch 11) allows you to solve for F_B.

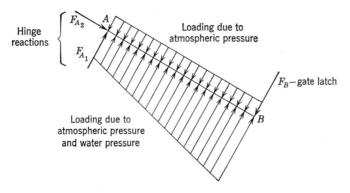

Sketch 11

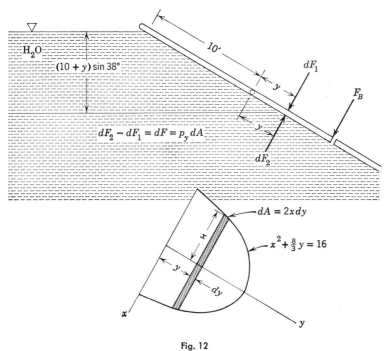

Fig. 12

Choose the elemental area dA to assure pressure p_y constant everywhere on the area. The sum of the pressures on the lower and upper sides of the gate is p_y (Fig. 12).

From Equation 2-3a for an incompressible liquid

$$p_y = p_a + \gamma h_y - p_a = \gamma h_y$$

where γ = sp. wt. of water = 62.4 lb/ft^3

h_y = vertical distance to water surface

$= (10 + y) \sin(180 - 142) = (10 + y) \sin 38$

$dF = p_y \, dA$, where p_y is the gage pressure on the area dA and is constant over dA

$= p_y 2x \, dy = \gamma h_y 2x \, dy = 2\gamma(10 + y) \sin 38 \, x \, dy$

$$F = 2\gamma \sin 38 \int_0^6 (10 + y)x \, dy$$

but $x^2 + (\tfrac{8}{3})y = 16$

so that $\qquad\qquad x = (16 - \tfrac{8}{3}y)^{\frac{1}{2}} = (\tfrac{8}{3})^{\frac{1}{2}}(6 - y)^{\frac{1}{2}}$

Therefore:

$$F = 2\gamma \sin 38 \int_0^6 (10 + y)(\tfrac{8}{3})^{\frac{1}{2}}(6 - y)^{\frac{1}{2}} \, dy = 15{,}220 \text{ lb}$$

From statics

$$Fy_F = \int dM_a = M_a$$

Solve for M_a

$$dM_a = y \, dF = y[2\gamma(10 + y) \sin 38 x \, dy]$$

$$M_a = 2\gamma \sin 38(8/3)^{\frac{1}{2}} \int_0^6 (10 + y)(6 - y)^{\frac{1}{2}}y \, dy$$

$$= 39{,}600 \text{ ft-lb}$$

$$y_F = \frac{39{,}600}{15{,}220} = 2.6 \text{ ft in } y \text{ direction}$$

By symmetry the resultant lies on line $x = 0$.

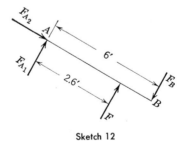

Sketch 12

Replace the distributed load in the free body by the resultant force shown in Sketch 12.

$$\Sigma M_A = 0 \quad \curvearrowleft_+$$

$$6F_B - 2.6F = 0$$

$$F_B = \frac{(2.6)F}{6} = \frac{(2.6)(15{,}220)}{6} = 6600 \text{ lb}$$

Instead of locating the resultant force of the pressures, you could compute the moment about the hinge of the pressure loading and use it in the $\Sigma M_a = 0$ without solving for the resultant pressure force. ◀

13. Forces on Curved Surfaces

Calculations of forces on curved surfaces are more complicated than those on plane surfaces because it is more difficult to mathematically describe the elemental area dA and because the forces do not all act in the same direction.   However, we can use the same general approach on both types of problems.   To simplify the work, we engineers have to use some ingenuity in selecting the elemental area dA.   We should keep in mind that the area must be such that the pressure is constant over the area.   The differential force dF is a vector, and, therefore, we must sum it as a vector.   In forces on plane surfaces, all differential forces act in the same direction, and the resultant is merely the algebraic sum of these forces.   The infinitesimal forces acting on a curved surface will in general act in all directions.   To use integration, forces must be all in the same direction.   We take the components of these forces in one direction and sum them to get the resultant component in that direction.   So doing for all three directions gives three components of the resultant force.   We can add these three components vectorially to get the resultant force.   Also, we must locate each of the components of the resultant force.   Since each set of components is a parallel force system, we compute the point of application of the resultant component as in Art. 12, a general approach best demonstrated by Illustrative Problems 5 and 6.

▶Illustrative Problem 5.   The water level is 4 ft from the top of the cylindrical gate shown in Fig. 13.   Calculate the resultant water pressure force acting on the gate per unit length.   (See Sketch 13.)

Solution:

$$dF = p\, dA = \gamma(16 \sin \theta - 4)(1)r\, d\theta = 4\gamma(4 \sin \theta - 1)(16)\, d\theta$$

$$= 64\gamma(4 \sin \theta - 1)\, d\theta$$

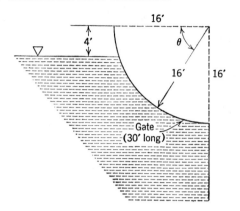

Fig. 13

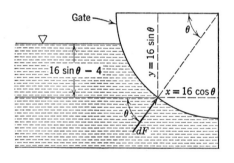
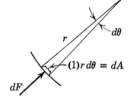

Sketch 13

Because integration is an algebraic sum, you must add all the forces in the same direction. Sum the horizontal components (x direction) and then the vertical components (y direction).

$$\overset{+}{\rightarrow} \quad dF_x = \cos \theta \, dF = \cos \theta \, [64\gamma(4 \sin \theta - 1)] \, d\theta$$

$$F_x = 64\gamma \int_{\theta = \text{arc sin } \frac{1}{4}}^{\theta = \pi/2} (4 \sin \theta - 1) \cos \theta \, d\theta$$

$$F_x = 72\gamma \text{ lb/ft of length}$$

$$+\!\uparrow \quad dF_y = \sin \theta \, dF = \sin \theta \, [64\gamma(4 \sin \theta - 1)] \, d\theta$$

$$F_y = 64\gamma \int_{\text{arc sin } \frac{1}{4}}^{\pi/2} (4 \sin^2 \theta - \sin \theta) \, d\theta$$

$$F_y = 137.8\gamma \text{ lb/ft of length}$$

To find the location of the resultant, take moments about center of cylinder at 0.

$$F_x y_F = \int y \, dF_x = \int (16 \sin \theta) \, dF_x$$

$$= \int_{\text{arc sin } \frac{1}{4}}^{\pi/2} (16 \sin \theta) 64\gamma (4 \sin \theta - 1) \cos \theta \, d\theta$$

$$= 864\gamma \text{ ft-lb/ft of length}$$

$$y_F = \frac{864\gamma}{F_x} = \frac{864}{72} = 12 \text{ ft below } 0$$

$$F_y x_F = \int x \, dF_y = \int_{\text{arc sin } \frac{1}{4}}^{\pi/2} 16 \cos \theta \sin \theta [64\gamma (4 \sin \theta - 1)] \, d\theta$$

$$= 864\gamma \text{ ft-lb/ft of length}$$

$$x_F = \frac{864}{137.8} = 6.27 \text{ ft to left of } 0$$

$$\tan \alpha = \frac{137.8\gamma}{72\gamma}$$

$$\tan \alpha = 1.915$$

For the magnitude of resultant,

Sketch 14

$$F = [F_x^2 + F_y^2]^{\frac{1}{2}}$$

$$= \gamma[(137.8)^2 + (72)^2]^{\frac{1}{2}}$$

$$= 155.5\gamma = 9700 \text{ lb/ft length}$$

From the location of the point of application and the angle, notice that the resultant force acts through center 0, as you could have predicted had you remembered that the pressure force must be normal to the surface. This means that each differential force dF is normal to the surface and, therefore, through the center of the cylinder. ◀

▶Illustrative Problem 6. Determine the magnitude and direction of the resultant water pressure force F acting on the parabolic section of the barrier of width t shown in Sketch 15.

Solution: By direct integration

$$dF = p \, dA = \gamma(h - y)t \, ds$$

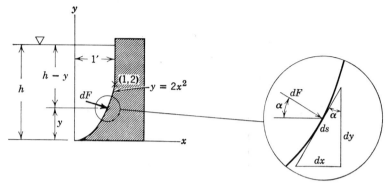

Sketch 15

For the horizontal component,

$$dF_x = \cos \alpha \, dF = \gamma(h - y)(ds)t \frac{dy}{(ds)} = \gamma(h - y)t \, dy$$

$$F_x = \int dF_x = \int_0^2 \gamma(h - y)t \, dy = 2\gamma t(h - 1)$$

For the vertical component,

$$\int dF_y = \int \sin \alpha \, dF = \int \gamma(h - y) \, ds \, t \frac{dx}{ds} = \gamma \int_0^1 (h - y)t \, dx$$

$$F_y = \gamma t \int_0^1 (h - 2x^2) \, dx = \gamma t(h - \tfrac{2}{3})$$

$$\tan \theta = \frac{F_y}{F_x} = \frac{\gamma t(h - \tfrac{2}{3})}{2\gamma t(h - 1)} = \frac{1}{2} \left(\frac{h - \tfrac{2}{3}}{h - 1} \right)$$

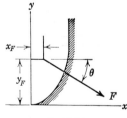

Sketch 16

For the location of the resultant,

$$F_x y_F = \int y \, dF_x = \int_0^2 \gamma(h - y)yt \, dy = 2\gamma t(h - \tfrac{4}{3})$$

$$y_F = \frac{2\gamma t(h - \frac{4}{3})}{2\gamma t(h - 1)} = \frac{h - \frac{4}{3}}{h - 1}$$

$$F_y x_F = \int x \, dF_y = \int_0^1 \gamma(h - y)xt \, dx = \gamma t \int_0^1 (h - 2x^2)x \, dx = \frac{\gamma t}{2}(h - 1)$$

$$x_F = \frac{(\gamma t/2)(h - 1)}{\gamma t(h - \frac{2}{3})} = \frac{h - 1}{2(h - \frac{2}{3})} \qquad \blacktriangleleft$$

14. Buoyancy

Fluid exerts a pressure on the surfaces of a body partially or completely submerged in it. The net effect of this pressure is a vertical force called buoyant force. In this article we analyze buoyant force

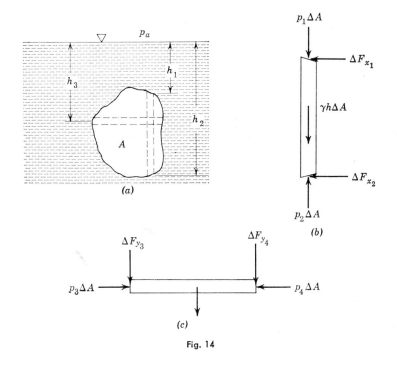

Fig. 14

by using the basic equation of fluid statics and the principles of statics. Figure 14a shows the body A completely submerged in a fluid of constant density. Figure 14b is a free body diagram of a vertical column taken from the body. This column has a height h and a constant cross-sectional area ΔA. The pressure on the top of the column is $(p_a + \gamma h_1)$, taken from Equation 2-5 for a constant density fluid, and the pressure on the bottom is $(p_a + \gamma h_2)$. The vertical component of these pressure forces is the product of the pressure and the cross-sectional area. Since the horizontal components are not used in this analysis, they appear as dF_{x1} and dF_{x2}. We are interested only in the pressure forces, and all others may be neglected.

We sum the vertical pressure forces on the free body diagram (Fig. 14b).

$$+\uparrow \quad \Delta F_v = -p_1 \, \Delta A + p_2 \, \Delta A = (p_2 - p_1) \, \Delta A$$

$$= (p_a + \gamma h_2 - p_a - \gamma h_1) \, \Delta A = \gamma(h_2 - h_1) \, \Delta A$$

which gives the resultant vertical pressure force on only the small column. The sum of the resultant pressure forces on all the small columns that make up the body is the vertical component F_v of the buoyant force F.

$$F_v = \Sigma \gamma(h_2 - h_1) \, \Delta A$$

$$= \gamma \Sigma(h_2 - h_1) \, \Delta A = \gamma \Sigma h \, \Delta A$$

In this equation $\Sigma h \, \Delta A$ is the volume of body A. Since γ is the specific weight of the liquid, $\gamma \Sigma h \, \Delta A$ is the weight of the water which the body displaces.

Figure 14c shows as a free body diagram a horizontal element of volume similar to the vertical column. We determine the forces on this volume in the same manner as those on the vertical column. This element is also of constant cross-sectional area ΔA, and the pressure at each end of the element is the same $(p_a + \gamma h_3)$. The sum of the horizontal pressure forces is

$$\xrightarrow{+} \quad \Delta F_h = (p_a + \gamma h_3) \, \Delta A - (p_a + \gamma h_3) \, \Delta A = 0$$

On this elemental volume the horizontal force component due to pressure is zero, and, therefore, the sum of all the horizontal components due to pressure is zero. The buoyant force, then, has no horizontal component and is a vertical force that acts upward with a magnitude equal to the weight of the water displaced. This is called Archimedes' principle because he was the first to define it. By knowing the magnitude and direction of the buoyant force, we need only to find the point of application to completely define the force.

We take the y axis as vertical and the x and z axes as horizontal. The pressure forces acting on the elemental vertical columns make up a parallel force system. To locate the point of application of the resultant force, we use the principle that the moment of a resultant force about an axis is equal to the sum of the moments of all the forces about the same axis. First, we take moments about the z axis.

$$Fx_F = \gamma \Sigma xh \, \Delta A$$

but
$$F = \gamma \Sigma h \, \Delta A$$

Therefore,

$$x_F = \frac{\gamma \Sigma xh \, \Delta A}{\gamma \Sigma h \, \Delta A} = \frac{\Sigma xh \, \Delta A}{\Sigma h \, \Delta A} = \frac{\Sigma x (\text{Vol.})}{\Sigma (\text{Vol.})}$$

We recognize this as the definition for the x coordinate of the center of gravity of a body of uniform density. We follow the same procedure to determine the z distance to the buoyant force and obtain the same result, the distance to the center of gravity of the body if it is of constant density. We can conclude from this that the buoyaht force acts through the center of gravity of the volume of the body. We define the buoyant force as one which acts upward through the center of gravity of the fluid displaced by the body and has a magnitude equal to the weight of fluid displaced.

A body submerged in such a manner as to lay on the interface between two fluids must be treated in two separate sections. The first would be that part of the body in the upper fluid, and the second that in the lower fluid. We compute the buoyant forces for each section and add them vectorially to obtain the total buoyant force.

▶Illustrative Problem 7. A 4-in.-dia. steel ball is suspended by a string in a liquid composed of two layers of different liquids. The bottom layer 6 in. deep is carbon tetrachloride, and the upper layer 8 in. thick is water. Calculate the tension in the string when (a) the ball is half submerged in water and half in carbon tetrachloride; (b) the ball is completely submerged in carbon tetrachloride; (c) the ball is submerged half in air and half in water.

Solution: (a) For the free body diagram of the ball shown in Sketch 17

$$\gamma_s = \text{specific weight of steel} = 487 \text{ lb/ft}^3$$

$$\gamma_{CCl_4} = \text{specific weight of carbon tetrachloride} = 99.5 \text{ lb/ft}^3$$

$$W = \gamma_s \tfrac{4}{3}\pi R^3 = (487)\tfrac{4}{3}(3.1416)(\tfrac{2}{12})^3 = 9.45 \text{ lb}$$

$$F_w = \tfrac{1}{2}\gamma_{H_2O}\tfrac{4}{3}\pi R^3 = \tfrac{1}{2}(62.4)\tfrac{4}{3}\pi(\tfrac{2}{12})^3 = 0.61 \text{ lb}$$

$$F_c = \tfrac{1}{2}\gamma_{CCl_4}\tfrac{4}{3}\pi R^3 = \tfrac{1}{2}(99.5)\tfrac{4}{3}\pi\left(\tfrac{2}{12}\right)^3 = 0.96 \text{ lb}$$

$$\Sigma F_V = 0 \quad +\uparrow$$

$$T + F_w + F_c - W = T + 0.61 + 0.96 - 9.45 = 0$$

$$T = 7.88 \text{ lb}$$

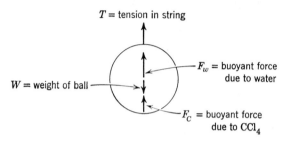

T = tension in string

F_w = buoyant force due to water

W = weight of ball

F_c = buoyant force due to CCl_4

Sketch 17

(b) For the free body diagram of the ball shown in Sketch 18

$$W = 9.45 \text{ lb}$$

$$F_c = \tfrac{4}{3}\pi R^3 \gamma_c = \tfrac{4}{3}\pi\left(\tfrac{2}{12}\right)^3 99.5 = 1.93 \text{ lb}$$

$$\Sigma F_V = 0 \quad +\uparrow$$

$$T + F_c - W = 0$$

$$T = W - F_c = 9.45 - 1.93 = 7.52 \text{ lb}$$

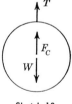

T

F_c

W

Sketch 18

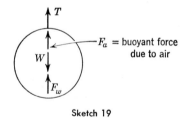

T

F_a = buoyant force due to air

W

F_w

Sketch 19

(c) For the free body diagram of the ball shown in Sketch 19

$$\Sigma F_V = 0 \quad +\uparrow$$

$$T + F_a + F_w - W = 0$$

$$W = 9.45 \text{ lb}$$

$$F_w = 0.61 \text{ lb}$$

$$F_a = \tfrac{1}{2}(\tfrac{4}{3}\pi R^3)\gamma_a = \tfrac{1}{2}\tfrac{4}{3}\pi(\tfrac{2}{12})^3(0.0763) = 0.00074$$

$$T + 0.0074 + 0.61 - 9.45 = 0$$

$$T = 8.83 \text{ lb}$$

The bouyant force of air is so small when it is compared to liquid buoyant forces that you can neglect it. Hereafter in problems in which buoyant forces include liquids, neglect the buoyant forces of gases. ◀

▶**Illustrative Problem 8.** A hollow steel gondola 10 ft in diameter, weighing 24,000 lb, swings by rope from a helium-filled gas bag. The gas bag and rope weigh 1000 lb. Calculate the volume V of helium in the balloon for equilibrium of the system. The specific weight γ_h of helium is 0.0106 lb/ft³, and the specific weight γ_a of air is 0.0763 lb/ft³.

Solution: For the free body diagram which is shown in Sketch 20

$W_B = 1000 \text{ lb} = \text{weight of bag and rope}$

$W_G = 24{,}000 \text{ lb} = \text{weight of gondola}$

$W_h = \gamma_h V = 0.0106V = \text{weight of helium}$

$F_G = \tfrac{4}{3}\pi R^3 \gamma_a = \tfrac{4}{3}\pi(5)^3(0.0763) = 40 \text{ lb}$

$F_B = \gamma_a V = (0.0763)V$

$$\Sigma F_V = 0 \quad +\uparrow$$

$$F_B - W_B - W_h + F_G - W_G = 0$$

Sketch 20

$$(0.0763)V - 24{,}000 - 0.0106V + 40 - 1000 = 0$$

$$(0.0763 - 0.0106)V = 25{,}000 - 40 = 24{,}960$$

$$V = 379{,}900 \text{ ft}^3 \qquad ◀$$

When the weight of a completely submerged body is less than the weight of the fluid it displaces, an unbalanced vertical force will tend to accelerate the body upward until the body rises to a position where the buoyant force equals the weight of the body. A vessel floating on water is an example of this because the vessel is submerged completely in a mixture of water and air. In Illustrative Problem 7 we saw that the buoyant force of the air can be neglected for bodies floating freely in an interface of water and air. Thus, the body will displace its weight in water. We handle the problem of floating bodies directly from the weight and buoyant force.

15. Stability

In Art. 14 we devised a method of calculating the buoyant force and solved problems in equilibrium using that method. This article discusses the stability of equilibrium which was not previously mentioned. First we consider the stability of floating submerged bodies.

The buoyant force on a body which is completely submerged in a fluid acts through the center of gravity of the displaced fluid. The

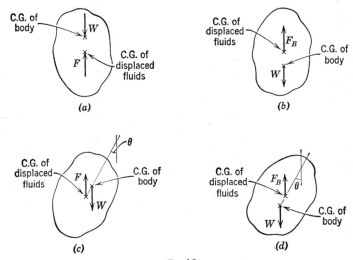

Fig. 15

only other force acting is the weight of the body which must act through the center of gravity of the body. The body itself may be of any size, shape, and weight distribution. If it contains living animals, they will move from place to place inside of the body and so change its center of gravity. Many bodies are hollow with weight added for ballast to move the center of gravity to a desired location. Thus, we see that the location of the center of gravity of the body does not have to coincide with the location of the buoyant force.

The two forces, buoyancy and weight, must be colinear to keep the body in equilibrium. Figures 15a and b show two positions of equilibrium for a body floating completely submerged. Figures 15c and d show the body in a position rotated an angle θ out of equilibrium.

The two forces (Fig. 15c) form a couple which tends to turn the body so as to increase the angle θ. Thus, in the case of the center of gravity of the body above the center of gravity of the displaced fluid, any rotation of the body away from the equilibrium position causes the body to get further away from equilibrium. This is unstable equilibrium. The two forces (Fig. 15d) form a couple which tends to turn the body back into equilibrium position. In this case, the center of gravity of the displaced water is above the center of gravity of the body. This is stable equilibrium. When the centers of gravity coincide, no matter how the body turns there is no couple. Thus, the body will be in equilibrium for any position. We call this neutral equilibrium. To be in stable equilibrium, therefore, a completely submerged body must be floating with the center of gravity of the body below the center of gravity of the displaced fluid.

The problem of stability of a body floating at the interface of two different fluids is more complicated although basically the same. Will a rotation of the body away from its equilibrium position cause forces to act and return the body to its equilibrium position, or will the forces cause the body to move away from the equilibrium position? The body floating at an interface is more difficult to analyze because rotation of the body causes a change in the center of gravity of the displaced fluid. This change makes it possible for the center of gravity of the displaced fluid to be below the center of gravity of the body and still to have the body in stable equilibrium. In the remaining discussion of bodies floating at an interface, the upper fluid is air and the lower fluid is water. From Illustrative Problem 7 we know that we can neglect the buoyant force of the air. Therefore, we consider only the buoyant force of the water.

A barge floating in water (Fig. 16a) has a width w and depth h. Point G is the center of gravity of the body, and point B is the center of gravity of the displaced water. The body is in equilibrium. In Fig. 16b the body has rotated about point O through a small angle θ. Point G stays in the same place in the body, but the center of gravity of the displaced water moves to point B_1. The weight and the buoyant force form a couple that tends to return the barge to its equilibrium position. Thus, the barge is in stable equilibrium.

When a floating body has rotated to a different position, a vertical line drawn through the new center of gravity of the displaced water crosses the former vertical line BG at a point M, called the metacenter. Whenever the metacenter lies above the center of gravity of the body, the body will tend to return to its equilibrium position. If the angle θ is increased enough, the metacenter will fall below the point G. The

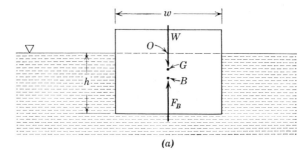

(a)

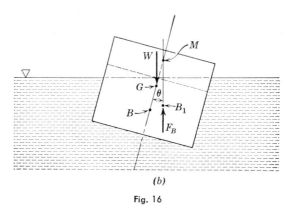

(b)

Fig. 16

body will then turn away from the equilibrium position and will be unstable.

▶**Illustrative Problem 9.** A barge 6 ft high, 6 ft wide, and 20 ft long has straight, perpendicular sides. The center of gravity of the barge and its load is in the middle of the barge 3 ft from the bottom. Calculate the safe load range for stable equilibrium when the center of gravity of the barge and its load remain fixed.

Solution: The weight of the barge shown in Sketch 21 equals the weight of water displaced and so $W = F_B$.

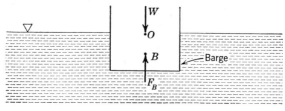

Sketch 21

Rotate the barge through an angle θ as shown in Sketch 22.

The magnitude of the buoyant force must be the same, and the new buoyant force may be considered as the old one plus a couple. The new displacement of water causes the couple. The old water line was AC; the new one is DE. Rotation displaces a wedge of water OEC by 20 ft long.

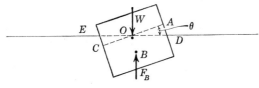

Sketch 22

On the other side of the barge the wedge of water AOD by 20 ft long displaced before is no longer displaced. Therefore, add a new buoyant force F_{B_1} because of the water OEC displaced, and subtract a buoyant force F_{B_2} because of the water no longer displaced. (See Sketch 23.)

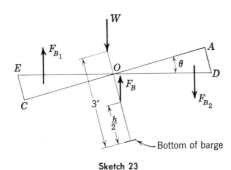

Sketch 23

The sum of the vertical forces must be zero.

$$\Sigma F_V = 0 \quad +\uparrow$$

$$-W + F_B + F_{B_1} - F_{B_2} = 0$$

but

$$F_B = W$$

therefore

$$F_{B_1} = F_{B_2} = 3(\theta)3(\tfrac{1}{2})(20)62.4 \text{ lb}$$

The moment of the couple due to F_{B_1} and F_{B_2} tries to return the barge to equilibrium, while the moment of the couple due to F_B and W tries to overturn the barge.

For stable equilibrium the moment due to F_{B_1} and F_{B_2} must be greater than the moment due to F_B and W

$$F_{B_1}(3 + 3)\tfrac{2}{3} > W\left(3 - \frac{h}{2}\right)\theta$$

where $(3 + 3)\tfrac{2}{3}$ and $[3 - (h/2)]\,\theta$ are moment arms and

$$W = h(20)(6)(62.4)$$

$$F_{B_1} = (3\theta)(3)(\tfrac{1}{2})(20)(62.4)$$

For stability $(62.4)(3\theta)(3)(\tfrac{1}{2})(20)(6)\tfrac{2}{3} > h(20)(6)(62.4)\left(3 - \frac{h}{2}\right)\theta$

$$3 > 3h - \frac{h^2}{2}$$

For neutral equilibrium $\dfrac{h^2}{2} - 3h + 3 = 0$

$$h^2 - 6h + 6 = 0$$

$$h = 3 \pm \sqrt{3} = 4.732 \text{ ft or } 1.268 \text{ ft}$$

Thus, for $h = 4.732$ ft or 1.268 ft, $3 = 3h - (h^2/2)$, and the equilibrium is neutral.

For $h < 1.268$, try $h = 1.2$ to see if $3 > 3h - (h^2/2)$.

$$3h - \frac{h^2}{2} = 3.6 - \frac{1.44}{2} = 2.88 < 3.00$$

Therefore, the equilibrium is stable since $3 > 3h - (h^2/2)$

For $1.268 < h < 4.732$, try $h = 2$

$$3h - \frac{h^2}{2} = 6 - 2 = 4$$

This does not satisfy $3 > 3h - (h^2/2)$ and so the equilibrium is unstable.   For $h > 4.732$, try $h = 5$

$$3h - \frac{h^2}{2} = 15 - \tfrac{25}{2} = 2.5$$

This satisfies $3 > 3h - (h^2/2)$ and so the equilibrium is satisfied for all h greater than 4.732.   Of course, when h reaches 6 ft the barge will sink anyway.

The barge, therefore, is safe for all loads that will not cause it to sink deeper than 1.218 ft or

$$W < (6)(20)(1.268)(62.4) = 9495 \text{ lb}$$

The barge is also safe for $h > 4.732$ ft or $W > (6)(20)(4.732)(62.4)$

$$W > 35{,}433 \text{ lb}$$

For $9495 < W < 35{,}433$, the barge is unstable.   All in all, this is a very poor barge.   ◀

16. Compressible Fluid Statics

We derived the basic Equation 2-3a for any fluid but have worked since then with only incompressible fluids or compressible fluids in which the change in elevation was small.   We neglected the compressible effects for small changes in elevation.   When we consider the case of the atmosphere, the changes in elevation are large.   The basic equation is

$$\frac{dp}{dh} = -\gamma \tag{2-3a}$$

When the specific weight γ is not constant, we must know the relation between the specific weight and the height.   Air near atmospheric conditions may be considered a perfect gas.

$$\frac{p}{\rho} = g_c R T$$

where p = pressure, in lb/ft^2 absolute
$\quad \rho$ = density, in slugs/ft^3
$\quad g_c$ = Newton's proportionality constant, in lb$_m$-ft/lb$_f$ sec^2
$\quad T$ = temperature, in degrees Rankine (°R)
$\quad R$ = engineering gas constant, in lb$_f$-ft/lb$_m$ °R
$\quad g$ = acceleration due to gravity, in ft/sec^2

We divide by g

$$\frac{p}{\rho g} = \frac{g_c}{g} RT; \qquad \frac{p}{\gamma} = \frac{g_c}{g} RT$$

$$-\gamma = -\frac{p}{RT} \frac{g}{g_c}$$

and substitute this into Equation 2-3a

$$\frac{dp}{dh} = \frac{-p}{RT}$$

since $g/g_c = 1$ lb$_f$/lb$_m$ on the earth, or

$$\frac{dp}{p} = -\frac{dh}{RT}$$

For an isothermal process the temperature T is a constant.

$$\int \frac{dp}{p} = -\frac{1}{RT} \int dh$$

$$\log_e p = -\frac{1}{RT} h + C_1$$

When $h = 0$, $p = p_a$.   Therefore,

$$\log_e p_a = 0 + C_1 \qquad \text{or} \qquad C_1 = \log_e p_a$$

$$\log_e p = -\frac{h}{RT} + \log_e p_a$$

$$\log_e p_a - \log_e p = \log_e \frac{p_a}{p} = \frac{h}{RT} \qquad\qquad (A)$$

We use Equation A to calculate pressure at any elevation h in a constant temperature atmosphere.   In this equation we measure h from the surface of the earth, a mandatory procedure based upon the basic equation and the boundary condition.

The atmosphere is not isothermal so that this is an oversimplification.   The temperature of the atmosphere decreases with an increase in elevation up to about 5 miles.   From 5 miles to about 13 miles the temperature of the atmosphere is constant near 529°R.   Between 13 miles and 50 miles above the earth's surface, conditions are not known, but research is continuing.   Above 50 miles the atmosphere is strongly ionized and is called the ionosphere.   To calculate the pressure in an atmosphere of this complexity is beyond the scope of this book.   We shall calculate the pressure only for simplified conditions.

▶**Illustrative Problem 10.**   Calculate the pressure 25,000 ft above sea level for an isentropic atmosphere.   At sea level the pressure is 14.7 psia and the temperature is 70°F.

Solution:

$$\frac{p}{\gamma^k} = \text{constant}$$

where $k = 1.4$ for an isentropic atmosphere

$$\frac{p}{\rho g} = \frac{p}{\gamma} = \frac{g_c}{g} RT = RT$$

where $g_c/g = 1$ lb_f/lb_m near the earth

$$\frac{p}{\gamma} = RT$$

where $R = 53.3$ for air

Therefore, $\dfrac{p_a}{\gamma_a} = RT = (53.3)(460 + 70) = (53.3)(530)$

$$\frac{1}{\gamma_a} = \frac{(53.3)(530)}{(14.7)(144)}$$

$$\frac{1}{\gamma_a{}^k} = \left[\frac{(53.3)(530)}{(14.7)(144)}\right]^k = 37.5$$

$$\frac{p_a}{\gamma_a{}^k} = (14.7)(144)(37.5) = 79{,}400$$

$$\frac{p}{\gamma^k} = \frac{p_a}{\gamma_a{}^k} = 79{,}400$$

Now $\gamma = p^{1/k}/3160$. Therefore,

$$\frac{dp}{dh} = -\gamma = \frac{-p^{1/k}}{3160}$$

$$\int_{p_a}^{p} \frac{dp}{p^{1/k}} = - \int_{0}^{25{,}000} \frac{dh}{3160}$$

$$\int_{p_a}^{p} \frac{dp}{p^{1/k}} = \frac{1}{-(1/k)+1} p^{(-1/k)+1} \Big|_{p_a}^{p} = \frac{k}{k-1} (p^{(k-1)/k} - p_a{}^{(k-1)/k})$$

Now $k = 1.4$. Therefore,

$$\int_{p_a}^{p} \frac{dp}{p^{1/k}} = \frac{1.4}{1.4-1} (p^{1.4-1/1.4} - p_a{}^{(1.4-1/1.4)})$$

$$= - \int_{0}^{25{,}000} \frac{dh}{3160} = -7.91$$

$$3.5[p^{2\!/\!7} - (14.7)^{2\!/\!7}](144)^{2\!/\!7} = -7.91$$

$$p^{2\!/\!7} = (14.7)^{2\!/\!7} - \frac{7.91}{(3.5)(144)^{2\!/\!7}} = (14.7)^{2\!/\!7} - 0.545$$

$$p = 5.28 \text{ psia}$$

The actual pressure at this point is 5.46 psia based on the standard sea level atmosphere, 58°F.   ◄

17. Acceleration

No shear forces arise when a body of liquid is subjected to constant acceleration such that there is no relative motion between the liquid particles.   The problem can be handled quite easily.   In general, we

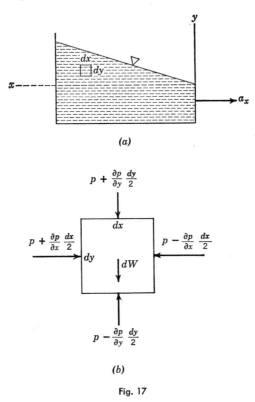

(a)

(b)

Fig. 17

consider here two types of acceleration: linear acceleration in a direction normal to the gravitational acceleration, and liquid rotation with its axis in the direction of the gravitational acceleration.

A large tank, filled with an incompressible liquid, is accelerated to the right, with a magnitude a_x (Fig. 17a).   A free body diagram (Fig. 17b), drawn for the elemental cube taken out of the liquid from point x, y, and z, shows a pressure p in the center of the cube and the weight

dW of the cube. We determine the pressures on each face of the cube in the same manner as the pressures on the cube in Fig. 6b. We sum the forces on the cube in the vertical and horizontal directions to calculate the equation of the pressure anywhere in the liquid.

$$\Sigma F_V = 0 \quad +\downarrow$$

$$dW + \left(p + \frac{\partial p}{\partial y}\frac{dy}{2}\right) dx\,dz - \left(p - \frac{\partial p}{\partial y}\frac{dy}{2}\right) dx\,dz = 0$$

$$dW = \frac{\partial p}{\partial y} dx\,dy\,dz$$

The weight of the cube $dW = \rho g\, dx\,dy\,dz$

$$\rho g\, dx\,dy\,dz = -\frac{\partial p}{\partial y} dx\,dy\,dz$$

$$\frac{\partial p}{\partial y} = -\rho g$$

Thus $p = -\rho gy + f_1(x)$ where $f_1(x)$ is some unknown function of x. We prove this by holding x constant and differentiating with respect to y which $\partial p/\partial y$ by definition.

$$\frac{\partial p}{\partial y} = -\rho g \frac{\partial y}{\partial y} + \overset{0}{\overbrace{\frac{\partial f_1(x)}{\partial y}}} = -\rho g$$

This checks. Now

$$p = \rho gy + f_1(x)$$

We return to the free body diagram and sum forces in the x direction.

$$\Sigma F_x = ma_x \quad \overset{+}{\leftarrow}$$

$$\left(p - \frac{\partial p}{\partial x}\frac{dx}{2}\right) dy\,dz - \left(p + \frac{\partial p}{\partial x}\frac{dx}{2}\right) dy\,dz = -\rho\,dx\,dy\,dz\,(a_x)$$

$$-\frac{\partial p}{\partial x} = -\rho a_x$$

Because a_x is a constant,

$$p = \rho a_x x + f_2(y)$$

where $f_2(y)$ is some unknown function of y. Therefore, we have two separate equations for p.

$$p = -\rho gy + f_1(x) = \rho a_x x + f_2(y)$$

and $$p = -\rho gy + \rho a_x x + C \qquad \text{(B)}$$

Equation B satisfies both of these equations for p where C is an arbitrary constant.

In the axis system in Fig. 17a the surface of the liquid goes through the origin. The pressure on the surface of the liquid is constant and equals atmospheric pressure p_a. The boundary condition is $p = p_a$ when $x = y = 0$. We make this substitution in equation B and solve for C.

$$p_a = 0 + 0 + C$$

$$C = p_a$$

$$p = -\rho gy + \rho a_x x + p_a$$

Therefore, we can calculate the pressure in the tank.

To find the equation of the liquid surface, we set $p = p_a$ and solve for y.

$$p_a = -\rho gy + \rho a_x x + p_a$$

$$y = \frac{a_x}{g} x$$

which is the equation of the liquid surface. It is also the equation of a straight line of slope a_x/g. Thus, planes of constant pressure are no longer horizontal planes but are planes with a slope a_x/g. When the acceleration is in the direction of the gravitational acceleration, we can use this same approach. Any other linear acceleration we consider as a combination of these two cases.

▶Illustrative Problem 11. Some types of aircraft depend upon gravitational acceleration to cause the fuel to flow through the fuel line from the fuel tank to the carburetor (Fig. 18). The fuel tank has an opening at point A to maintain atmospheric pressure in the tank. For this aircraft, determine the maximum forward acceleration which will not stop fuel flow to the carburetor.

Solution: Acceleration of the aircraft causes the free surface of the gasoline to slope at some angle α (Fig. 18). The pressure at the carburetor depends upon the height of the liquid free surface above the carburetor. When acceleration is great enough to extend the free surface below the carburetor, the gasoline will no longer flow from tank to carburetor.

The equation of the free surface of the gasoline is

$$y = \frac{a_x}{g} x$$

In Fig. 18, when $y = 2$ ft and $x = 4$ ft, the free surface goes through the carburetor which means that the gasoline will not flow to the carburetor by gravity alone.

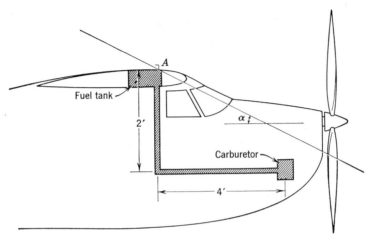

Fig. 18

When you substitute these values in the equation, you get

$$2 = \frac{a_x}{g} 4$$

Thus, the maximum acceleration is

$$a = \tfrac{1}{2}g = 16.1 \text{ ft/sec}^2$$

If the plane is catapulted with an acceleration greater than $g/2$, the fuel will not flow to the carburetor, and the plane will stall.   This is called carburetor stall.   ◀

18. Rotation

A large cylindrical tank, partially filled with a liquid, rotates at a constant angular velocity ω about its vertical axis of revolution (Fig. 19a).   We choose an axis system with a z axis vertical through the center of the cylinder and positive upward and with an r direction perpendicular to the z axis and positive away from it.   We measure the angle θ from a set line in the r direction through the z axis.   We shall select the location of the ordinate of the system later.   Figure 19b is a free body diagram of a fluid element, and Fig. 19c is a top view of

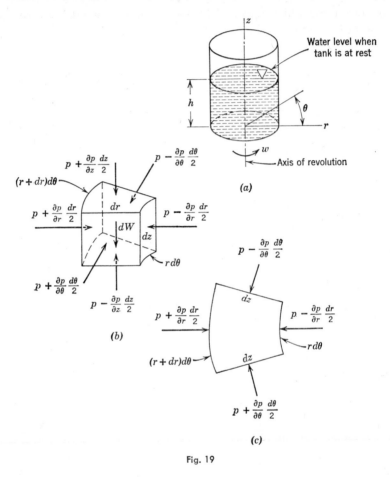

Fig. 19

the fluid element.   The fluid rotates as a solid because there is no relative motion between the fluid particles.   The only acceleration of the fluid is the normal acceleration $a_n = \omega^2 r$ directed toward the center of rotation.   The sum of the forces in the r direction, as shown in Fig. 19c, equals the product of the mass and the normal acceleration.

$$\Sigma F_r = ma_n$$

where outward is positive.

$$-\left(p + \frac{\partial p}{\partial r}\frac{dr}{2}\right)(r + dr)\,d\theta\,dz + \left(p - \frac{\partial p}{\partial r}\frac{dr}{2}\right)r\,d\theta\,dz +$$

$$\left(p - \frac{\partial p}{\partial \theta}\frac{d\theta}{2}\right)dr\,dz\,\frac{d\theta}{2} + \left(p + \frac{\partial p}{\partial \theta}\frac{d\theta}{2}\right)dr\,dz\,\frac{d\theta}{2} = -\rho r\,d\theta\,dz\,dr\,a_n$$

This reduces to

$$-p\,dr\,d\theta\,dz - \frac{\partial p}{\partial r}r\,dr\,d\theta\,dz - \frac{\partial p}{\partial r}dr\,dr\,d\theta\,dz + p\,dr\,d\theta\,dz$$

$$= -\rho r\,d\theta\,dz\,dr\,(\omega^2 r)$$

We divide by $r\,d\theta\,dr\,dz$ to get

$$-\frac{\partial p}{\partial r} - \frac{\partial p}{\partial r}\frac{dr}{r} = -\rho\omega^2 r$$

Because dr is an infinitesimal, the term containing it is infinitesimal, and we neglect it. Thus,

$$\frac{\partial p}{\partial r} = \rho\omega^2 r$$

By the same method as used to solve the differential equation in linear acceleration we solve for p.

$$p = \frac{\rho\omega^2 r^2}{2} + f_3(z)$$

Because of symmetry p is not a function of θ but is a function only of r and z.

We repeat the above procedure for the z direction.

$$\Sigma F_z = mg \quad \downarrow +$$

From Fig. 19b

$$\left(p + \frac{\partial p}{\partial z}\frac{dz}{2}\right)r\,d\theta\,dr + dW - \left(p - \frac{\partial p}{\partial z}\frac{dz}{2}\right)r\,d\theta\,dr = 0$$

$$dW = \rho gr\,d\theta\,dr\,dz$$

By substituting for dW and rearranging, we obtain

$$\frac{\partial p}{\partial z}r\,d\theta\,dr\,dz + \rho gr\,d\theta\,dr\,dz = 0$$

$$\frac{\partial p}{\partial z} = -\rho g$$

This is the same as before and so

$$p = -\rho g z + f_4(r)$$

We combine the two equations for p

$$p = \frac{\rho \omega^2 r^2}{2} + f_3(z) = -\rho g z + f_4(r)$$

The following equation for p satisfies both the above equations for p.

$$p = \frac{\rho \omega^2 r^2}{2} - \rho g z + C_1$$

Now we select the ordinate of the axis system so that it coincides with the liquid surface. At this point the pressure is p_a.

When $z = 0$, $\theta = 0$, $r = 0$

Then $p = p_a$

We substitute this in the last equation and solve for C_1.

$$C_1 = p_a$$

Then we place this value of C_1 in the pressure equation to get

$$p = \frac{\rho \omega^2 r^2}{2} - \rho g z + p_a$$

The liquid surface is subject to a constant atmospheric pressure p_a and so, to determine the equation of the liquid surface, the pressure p_a is substituted into the last equation.

$$p_a = \frac{\rho \omega^2 r^2}{2} - \rho g z + p_a$$

$$z = \frac{\omega^2 r^2}{2g}$$

which is the equation of a liquid surface.

It is also the equation of a parabola of revolution.

PROBLEMS

2-1. Calculate the gage pressure above the liquid in the closed tank shown in the Fig. P.2-1. The barometer reads 30 in. of mercury.

2-2. In Fig. P.2-2 calculate the pressure difference between A and B.

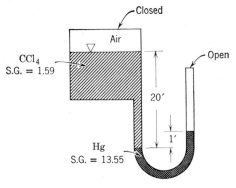

Fig. P.2-1

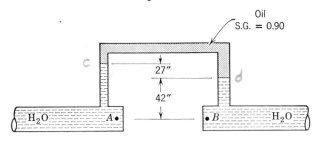

Fig. P.2-2

2-3. In Fig. P.2-3 pipe A contains water under a pressure of 10 psig and pipe B contains oil, specific gravity $= 0.80$, under a pressure of 18.4 psig. Calculate h, the difference in the height of the mercury columns.

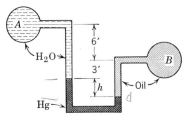

Fig. P.2-3

2-4. In order to measure small pressure changes in a high pressure water line, a mercury–oil manometer is used as shown in Fig. P.2-4. Calculate the pressure at the center of the pipe for the conditions shown. Specific gravity of mercury is 13.55 and of oil is 0.8.

2-5. In Problem 2-4, if the pressure at the center of the pipe is lowered 0.5 psi, at what height will the top of the oil be? Also what will be the height if the pressure is lowered 0.05 psi? (*Hint:* This problem may be simplified by assuming that the mercury does not change heights. Is this a good assumption?)

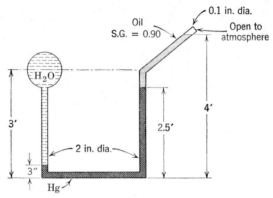

Fig. P.2-4

2-6. The pressure at A is 30 psia. Compute the pressure at B for the following values:

$$h_1 = 6 \text{ in.}, \quad h_2 = 1 \text{ yd}, \quad h_3 = 8 \text{ in.}, \quad h_4 = 5 \text{ ft}, \quad h_5 = 26 \text{ in.}, \quad h_6 = 2 \text{ ft},$$
$$h_7 = 4 \text{ ft}, \quad h_8 = 3 \text{ ft (Fig. P.2-6)}.$$

2-7. The pressure at B is reduced to 28 psia; the pressure at A remains 30 psia. Calculate the values of h_1, h_2, h_3, h_4, h_5, and h_6. The manometer tube is all the same diameter. (Fig. P.2-6.)

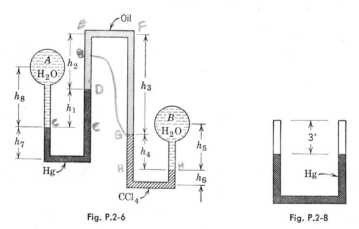

Fig. P.2-6   Fig. P.2-8

2-8. The U tube which is open at both ends is partially filled with mercury as shown in Fig. P.2-8. Water is poured into the left side of the U tube until a column of water 2 ft high is in the tube. Calculate the distance from the top of the U tube to the mercury in the right side of the U tube. Assume that the U tube is of constant cross-sectional area.

2-9. In Fig. P.2-8 what will be the height of the column of water when water is poured into the left leg until the water surface is at the top of the leg.

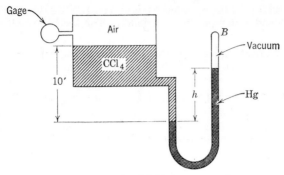

Fig. P.2-10

2-10. The gage in Fig. P.2-10 reads 21.3 psig, and atmospheric pressure is 14.7 psia.   Compute the height h.   Assume that the pressure in the vacuum is zero.

2-11. Determine the height h in Problem 2-10 if the tube at B were open to the atmosphere instead of being a vacuum.

2-12. As shown in Fig. P.2-12 a wall 9 ft high by 20 ft long holds back water. Calculate the force of the water on the wall.

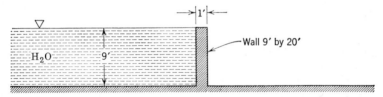

Fig. P.2-12

2-13. Figure P.2-13 is a sketch of a door 5 ft square that is hinged at A and has a simple latch at B.   The force of the latch acts normal to the door. Determine the force the latch exerts on the door.

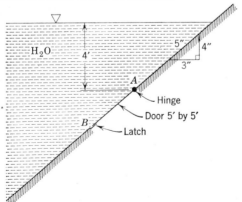

Fig. P.2-13

2-14. Calculate the force on the latch in Fig. P.2-13 if the liquid is oil for the top 4 ft and water for the remainder. The specific gravity of the oil is 0.90.

2-15. Calculate the force on the latch shown in Fig. P.2-13 if the liquid is oil for the top 6 ft and water for the remainder. The specific gravity of the oil is 0.90.

2-16. The gate ABC is hinged at A as shown in Fig. P.2-16. The weight at B holds the gate closed against the stop because the gate ABC is one rigid piece. Determine the magnitude of the weight which will allow the gate to open when the depth of water back of the gate is 3 ft.

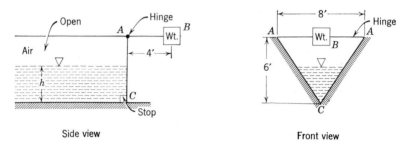

Side view   Front view

Fig. P.2-16

2-17. The channel in Fig. P.2-16 is filled with water to a depth of 2 ft and on top of the water is 3 ft of oil (specific gravity = 0.90). Compute the minimum weight at B to hold the gate closed.

2-18. In Fig. P.2-18 determine the force on the sill if the door is 6 ft by 4 ft. The specific gravity of CCl_4 is 1.59.

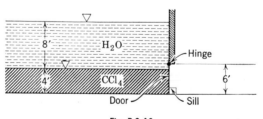

Fig. P.2-18

2-19. The gate shown in Fig. P2-19 is rigidly attached to the weight W and is hinged at A. Thus, the gate and the weight W rotate together about A. The gate is 4 ft wide. Determine the minimum depth of water h which will cause the gate to open when W is 500 lb.

2-20. What weight W is necessary in order that the gate in Fig. P.2-20 will open when h is 6 ft? The gate, lever arm AB, and the weight W are all one unit. The unit is hinged at A, and the gate is 6 ft wide.

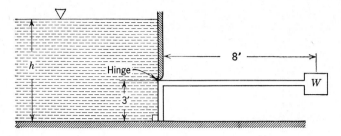

Fig. P.2-19

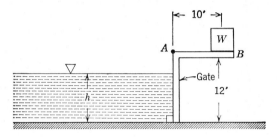

Fig. P.2-20

2-21. The water in the channel with the cross section shown in Fig. P.2-21 is dammed by the gate shown. The depth of water is 6 ft. Calculate the minimum weight W that will keep the gate closed.

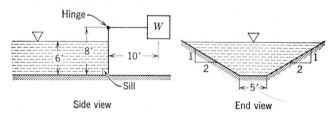

Fig. P.2-21

2-22. In Fig. P.2-22 calculate the horizontal force the wall exerts on the door to keep the door in equilibrium. The door is square.

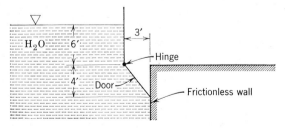

Fig. P.2-22

2-23. Figure P.2-23a shows the cross section of a river bed at a dam. Figure P.2-23b shows the side view. When the water is 9 ft deep at the deepest point, calculate the force on the dam.

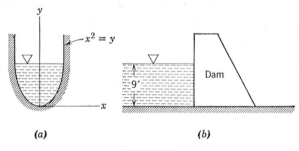

(a)   (b)

Fig. P.2-23

2-24. The flat plate in Fig. P.2-24 is hinged at C and acts as a dam. The cord AB passes over the pulley at A so that the plate may be raised or lowered. When the angle $\theta = 45°$ and the angle $\alpha = 90°$, calculate the tension in the cord.

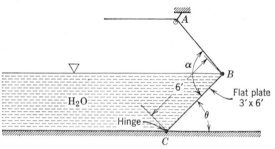

Fig. P.2-24

2-25. In Problem 2-24 the cord is reeled in until the angle $\theta = 60°$ and the angle $\alpha = 100°$. Compute the tension in the cord when the water level is at the top of the flat plate.

2-26. In Problem 2-25 the cord can withstand a maximum load of 750 lb. What is the maximum safe depth of water the plate can dam?

2-27. A circular pipe is 10 ft in diameter. The pipe is horizontal with a flat plate over one end as shown in Fig. P.2-27. Determine the force on the flat plate when the depth of the water $h = 5$ ft and the space above the water is filled with air at atmospheric pressure.

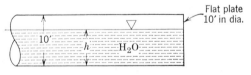

Fig. P.2-27

2-28. Calculate the force on the flat plate in Problem 2-27 when the space above the water is filled with air at 2 psig.

2-29. Calculate the force on the flat plate in Fig. P.2-27 when $h = 7$ ft and the space above the water is filled with air at atmospheric pressure.

2-30. In Fig. P.2-30 a very unusual liquid is held in a reservoir by a dam. Calculate the force at the sill on the gate of the dam. The specific weight of the liquid is $(50 + 4h)$ lb/ft³, where h is the distance in feet from the liquid surface. The gate is 3 ft by 4 ft.

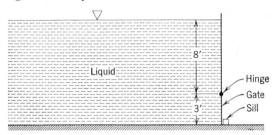

Fig. P.2-30

2-31. A very unusual liquid is held in check by a dam. A gate near the bottom of the dam is hinged at A and held closed by a sill at B. Calculate the force of the sill on the gate for the liquid height shown in Fig. P2-31. The specific weight of the liquid is

$$\gamma = 70 + \tfrac{1}{2}h$$

where γ is specific weight in pounds per cubic feet and h is the distance below the liquid surface in feet. The gate is 4 ft by 4 ft.

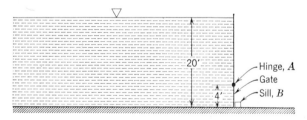

Fig. P.2-31

2-32. Calculate the resultant force per unit width on the dam shown in Fig. P.2-32.

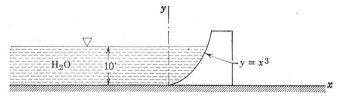

Fig. P.2-32

2-33. Compute the force at A necessary to hold the parabolic dam of Fig. P.2-33 in place.   The force at A is vertical.

2-34. Calculate the force at A in Problem 2-33 if the force at A is horizontal.

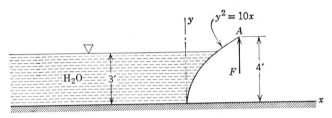

Fig. P.2-33

2-35. Determine the moment M required to keep the gate shown in Fig. P.2-35 in equilibrium.   The gate is 5 ft wide.

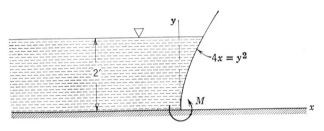

Fig. P.2-35

2-36. Calculate the minimum height h of water necessary to open the gate shown in Fig. P.2-36.

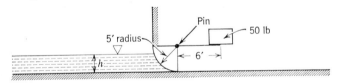

Fig. P.2-36

2-37. Calculate the force necessary to hold the quarter circular gate in place.   The width of the gate is 10 ft as shown in Fig. P.2-37.

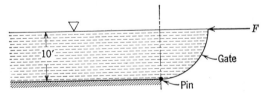

Fig. P.2-37

2-38. Determine the force F (Fig. P.2-38) necessary to hold the gate in place when $\theta = \pi/2$ and $h = 5$ ft.   The gate is 4 ft wide.

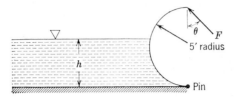

Fig. P.2-38

2-39. Compute the force F of Problem 2-38 when $h = 8$ ft.

2-40. When the depth of water (Fig. P.2-38) is $h = 6.28$ ft, determine the angle θ that will make the equilibrium force F a minimum.

2-41. Calculate the force F shown in Fig. P.2-41 when $h_1 = A/2$ and the dam is free to slide on the surface without friction.   The dam is 4 ft long.

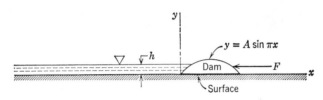

Fig. P.2-41

2-42. Calculate the minimum force F in Fig. P.2-41 when the coefficient of friction between the surfaces is $\frac{1}{10}$ and $h_1 = A$.   The material in the dam weighs 190 lb/ft^3.

2-43. In Problem 2-42 compute the minimum coefficient of friction necessary to hold the dam in place when the external force is equal to zero.

2-44. A barge is loaded with steel bars.   The barge is floating freely in a canal lock.   When there is no water leaving or entering the canal lock, the steel bars fall into the water in the canal.   Does this cause the water level in the canal to change?   If so, does the water level rise or fall?

2-45. A cylindrical pine log that is 1 ft in diameter and 12 ft long is floating horizontally in water.   How deep is the log submerged in the water?   The specific gravity of pine is 0.54.

2-46. In Problem 2-45 change the shape of the log to 1 ft square and change the wood to beech which has a specific gravity of 0.80.

2-47. A ball of density 1.00 slug/ft^3 is floating in a liquid in which the density varies linearly from 0.7 to 1.3 slugs/ft^3 as the depth of the liquid varies from 0 to 3 ft.   How far below the surface will the center of the floating ball be?   (The ball is completely submerged).

2-48. Figure P.2-48 is the sketch of the side view of a barge.   Calculate the distance from the top of the barge to the water surface when the barge is floating freely.   The barge weighs 10 tons and is 8 ft wide.

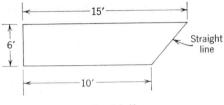

Fig. P.2-48

2-49. A large drum 3 ft in diameter and 6 ft high is open at the top end. The drum is filled with water to a depth of 4 ft. A wooden disk 2 ft in diameter and 5 in. thick is placed in the drum so that it floats on the water surface with a flat side up. The specific gravity of the wood is 0.80. Determine the change in elevation of the water surface.

2-50. A rectangular barge 24 ft by 40 ft by 6 ft deep is floating in a canal lock 30 ft by 50 ft by 10 ft deep. The bottom of the barge is 2 ft beneath the surface of the water which is 6 ft deep. When 120,000 lb of steel is placed in the barge, what is the new depth of the water?

2-51. A 15 in. dia. ball which weighs 1 lb is floating on the surface of the water in a 3 ft dia. oil drum. The depth of the water is 2 ft when the ball is floating on it. Compute the change in depth of water if a vertical force of 40 lb is applied downward on the ball.

2-52. A large box 5 ft by 12 ft by 30 ft floats on water as shown in Fig. P.2-52. The diagonal plane 13 ft by 30 ft is parallel with the water surface and the center of mass of the box is located at the center of volume of the box. The cord attached at A holds the point A 1 ft below the water surface. Calculate the weight of the box.

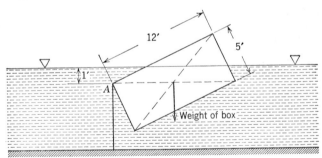

Fig. P.2-52

2-53. A cylinder 24 in. in diameter and 6 ft long is held under the surface of the water as shown in Fig. P.2-53. The cord attached to the bottom at A is wrapped half way around the cylinder and attached to a steel weight at B. Steel weighs 480 lb/ft³. Determine the weight of steel necessary to hold the cylinder in position when the cylinder weighs 600 lb.

2-54. A hollow square log 1 ft by 1 ft by 20 ft is floating on the surface of water. The center of mass of the hollow log is located $\frac{1}{2}$ ft from each side

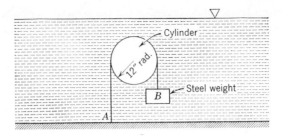

Fig. P.2-53

and 10 ft from the ends. There are three positions of equilibrium for this log which has a specific gravity of $\frac{1}{2}$. What are these positions and which are stable?

2-55. A barge that is 20 ft long and 6 ft high has a center of gravity which is 3 ft from the bottom of the barge. What is the minimum width of the barge for stable equilibrium when the barge is floating 2 ft deep in the water?

2-56. In Problem 2-55 compute the minimum width of the barge when it is floating 3 ft deep in the water.

2-57. A circular log is 1 ft in diameter and 5 ft long. If the specific gravity of the log is 0.85, determine the equilibrium positions of the log when it floats on the surface of water. Which positions are stable?

2-58. A piece of log 1 ft in diameter and 1 in. thick floats on the surface of water. The specific gravity of the log is 0.80. Determine the stable equilibrium position of the piece of log.

2-59. Calculate the maximum length l of a log which has a diameter d such that the log will float in stable equilibrium on the surface of water with the length vertical. The specific gravity of the log is 0.80.

2-60. At what altitude would the pressure be 3 psia for an isothermal atmosphere? Consider the atmosphere as a perfect gas at 14.7 psia on the ground. The ground temperature is 70°F and the engineering gas constant is 53.3 ft/°F.

2-61. In Problem 2-60 at what altitude would the pressure be 3 psia for an isentropic atmosphere?

2-62. A polytropic atmosphere is one in which the relationship between p and ρ is

$$\frac{p}{\rho^n} = \text{constant}$$

when n is some constant. If in Problem 2-60 the altitude is 75,000 ft for a certain polytropic atmosphere, what is the value of n?

2-63. Salt Lake City is at an elevation of 4500 ft. What is the atmospheric pressure in Salt Lake City when the atmospheric pressure at sea level is 14.7 psia, the temperature at sea level is 70°F, and the engineering gas constant is 53.3 ft/°F? Assume an isentropic atmosphere.

2-64. In Problem 2-63 what would the atmospheric pressure be if the atmosphere were considered isothermal?

2-65. During a temperature inversion the temperature varied in the following manner

$$T = 530° + \frac{y}{400}$$

where T = temperature, in °R

$\quad\quad y$ = distance above the earth's surface, in ft

The atmospheric pressure is 14.7 psia at $y = 0$, and the engineering gas constant is 53.3 ft/°F.   Compute the pressure at 1500 ft elevation.

2-66. In Problem 2-65 compute the pressure at 2500 ft elevation.

2-67. During a temperature inversion the temperature varied in the following manner

$$T = 530e^{y/400,000}$$

where T = temperature, in °R

$\quad\quad y$ = distance above the earth's surface, in ft

The atmospheric pressure at $y = 0$ is 14.7 psia and the engineering gas constant is 53.3 ft/°F.   Compute the pressure at 800 ft.

2-68. In Problem 2-67 compute the pressure at elevation 4000 ft.

2-69. A rectangular tank 3 ft by 4 ft and 20 in. deep is filled with 8 in. of water.   When the tank is accelerated as shown in Fig. P.2-69, compute the depth of the water at the right end.   The acceleration a is 8 ft/sec².

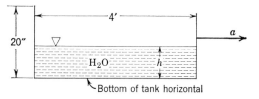

Fig. P.2-69

2-70. In Problem 2-69 compute the acceleration a necessary to reduce the depth of water at the right end of the tank to zero.

2-71. In Problem 2-69 calculate h so that the depth of water at the left end is 20 in.

2-72. In Fig. P.2-69, if $h = 13$ in., what is the maximum acceleration a possible without spilling any water?

2-73. The U tube shown in Fig. P.2-73 is placed in a car with the bottom of the tube horizontal and in the direction of motion of the car.   The maximum acceleration of the car is 12 ft/sec².   Calibrate the back leg of the U tube for each 2 ft/sec² of acceleration.   The liquid in the tube is oil with a specific gravity of 0.90.

2-74. In Problem 2-73 the back leg is sealed at the top so that with no acceleration the two liquid surfaces are level.   Assuming that the air in the back leg is compressed at a constant temperature, compute the elevation of the liquid surface in the back leg when the acceleration to the right is $\frac{1}{2}$ g.

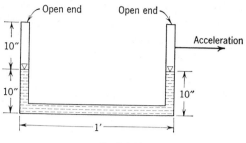

Fig. P.2-73

2-75. The observation airplane in Fig. P.2-75 is to be catapulted from a ship. When the fuel tank is full, what is the maximum acceleration possible without stopping the gravity feed of fuel to the carburetor?

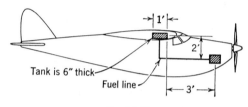

Fig. P.2-75

2-76. In the plane in Fig. P.2-75 a fuel pump is placed in the feed line between the fuel tank and the carburetor. The pump is at the same elevation as the carburetor and 1 ft behind it. What is the new maximum acceleration the plane can withstand without starving the fuel pump?

2-77. A U tube is filled with water as shown in Fig. P.2-77. The tube is rotated about the vertical center axis AA. What is the magnitude of the angular rotation ω when the pressure at the center is reduced to atmospheric pressure?

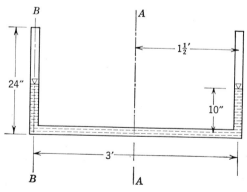

Fig. P.2-77

2-78. The U tube in Fig. P.2-77 is rotated about the axis BB at an angular rotation ω.   Compute ω when the height of the liquid at BB is 5 in.

2-79. In Problem 2-78 determine ω so that all the water is drained from one tube but the horizontal tube is full.

2-80. A 3 ft dia. drum which is 6 ft deep is filled to a depth of 4 ft with water.   The drum is rotated with an angular velocity ω about the vertical axis, such that the water is 6 ft deep on the edge.   Calculate ω.

2-81. The drum in Problem 2-80 is rotated at a different angular velocity ω such that the elevation of the water surface is zero at the center of the drum. Compute ω.

CONSERVATION
of MATTER
and EULER EQUATION

chapter **3**

19. Introduction

In Chapter 2 we dealt with fluids that were at rest, were moving with a uniform velocity, or were being accelerated as a solid body. In this chapter, we start working with fluid flow problems which have none of the above restrictions. We use two fundamental principles of science, conservation of matter and Newton's second law. From the principle of conservation of matter we derive the equation of continuity. From Newton's second law we derive the Euler equation and then the Bernoulli equation. But first we just define some pertinent terms.

There are two main approaches to the study of the motion of particles. The observer may travel with the particle being studied, or he may remain stationary and observe what happens at some particular point. The first case is similar to an observer riding downstream in a boat. In this case he is traveling with the particle, the boat, and he observes the motion of the water from the moving particle. Every motion is relative to the moving particle. In the second case the observer is on the shore and standing still. He watches the motion of the water as the boat travels past him.

In the first case, we may draw a reference axis with the observer as the origin and choose some arbitrary directions as axes. Then we can write equations of motion of the particles with respect to the moving axis system. This system has not proven itself a great assistance in fluid mechanics. The equations of motion are very difficult to solve, and the motion is hard to understand. Therefore, we shall use the second reference axis which is stationary with respect to the earth.

Newton's second law applied to this sytem leads to the Euler equations of motion.

When the properties of a fluid flow are independent of time, the flow is steady flow. This means that all quantities, such as velocity, acceleration, pressure, and temperature, to name just a few, are functions only of location and do not vary with time. When any one of the quantities varies with time, the flow is unsteady flow. Because this is an elementary textbook, we shall deal mainly with steady flow problems which are usually not as difficult as unsteady flow problems. We shall derive the fundamental equations for unsteady flow and simplify them for steady flow. We should then have the fundamental equations in their most complete forms so that, if it becomes necessary, we shall have the tools to solve unsteady flow problems as well as those of steady flow.

20. Definition of Terms

A streamline is a line drawn in a flow such that at any point on the line the tangent to the line is in the direction of the velocity of the fluid at that point. A series of streamlines gives a good picture, called the flow pattern, of a particular flow. For steady flow, the pattern is constant; for unsteady flow, it changes with time. Thus, when we draw a flow pattern for unsteady flow, we must give the time for the pattern. Because the velocity is everywhere tangent to a streamline, no velocity component is normal to the streamline, which indicates that fluid does not cross a streamline. In steady motion we must keep this in mind.

We choose a series of streamlines in steady flow so that they form a closed conduit. Because the fluid cannot cross any of them, the streamlines act as a solid boundary, and all the fluid must flow inside of them. This is called a stream tube. Figure 20 shows an example of a stream tube.

A path line is a line drawn in fluid flow to show the path traveled by a certain particle. Only in steady flow is a path line identical to a streamline. We should keep in mind that a group of path lines for a certain flow is not the flow pattern, unless the flow is steady. One of the essential differences between path lines and streamlines is that path lines may cross without any discontinuity. Streamlines crossing in a flow pattern whether the flow is steady or unsteady indicate that at the point of crossing the magnitude of the velocity must be either zero or infinite. When two streamlines cross, they will have a point in common. The tangent to the first streamline at this point will form an angle β with the tangent to the second streamline at this same point. This angle β will be different from zero. The velocity of the particle at this point would seem to have two directions, which is possible if the velocity is zero or infinite. Only for zero or infinite velocity is there no specified direction and can the velocity be in more than one direction.

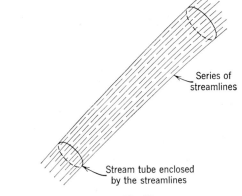

Series of streamlines

Stream tube enclosed by the streamlines

Fig. 20

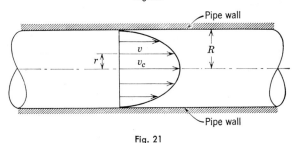

Pipe wall

Pipe wall

Fig. 21

Often in fluid problems it is necessary to draw or specify the variation of velocity in some direction normal to the velocity. This variation of velocity is called the velocity profile. In some problems in circular pipe flow the velocity of the fluid varies with the square of the distance from the pipe wall. The velocity profile (Fig. 21) then is written as

$$v = v_c \left[1 - \left(\frac{r}{R} \right)^2 \right]$$

where v = velocity a distance r from the center of the pipe

v_c = velocity at the center of the pipe

R = radius of the pipe

The velocity of the fluid at the pipe wall is the same as the velocity of the pipe wall, in this case zero. This is a characteristic of all real fluids unless the density becomes extremely low. In the future we shall assume the velocity of all real fluid at a surface to be the velocity of the surface. This is not true for a perfect fluid; the velocity at a surface may be any velocity tangent to the surface.

The velocity profile is not always a function of the distances squared as in the above example, but it can be almost any function of the distance normal to the flow. We should not confuse this specific example with the general case.

21. One- and Two-Dimensional Flow

When all quantities of a fluid flow depend upon only one length dimension, the flow is one-dimensional flow. We assume that the flow of a perfect fluid in a straight conduit which varies in cross-sectional area (Fig. 22a) has a velocity which varies along the conduit but is constant across it. The velocity varies along a pipe with the centerline as the x axis but is constant along the y and z axes, which are normal to each other and to the x axis. Thus, the velocity for steady flow is some function of x alone.

$$v = f(x)$$

For unsteady flow the velocity also is a function of time.

$$v = f(x, t)$$

In steady one-dimensional flow we sometimes consider the pressure to vary according to the hydrostatic equation:

$$dp = -\gamma \, dz$$

This is an unimportant factor in most one-dimensional problems, and we assume that the pressure varies only in the direction of motion.

In Fig. 22b we consider the parallel flow of a real incompressible fluid between two parallel plates that extend to infinity in the x and z directions. The velocity varies as the distance from either one of the plates but not as the distance along either. We take the x axis in the direction of flow, the y axis normal to both the flow and the plates, and the z axis normal to the flow but parallel to the plates. The velocity is a function of y alone for steady flow

$$v = f(y)$$

and a function of y and t for unsteady flow. Thus,

$$v = f(y, t)$$

The flow is called two dimensional when all quantities of the fluid flow vary in two directions in such a manner that the flow pattern in planes parallel to the two directions is the same. If we revise Fig. 22b as shown in Fig. 23a, the flow is two dimensional. In this case,

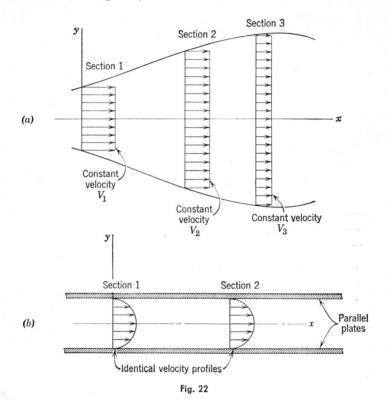

Fig. 22

the velocity varies in the x and y directions, and any plane parallel to the xy plane shows the same flow pattern. This is true of any two-dimensional flow where the quantities vary in the x and y directions.

Another example of two-dimensional flow (Fig. 23b) is a cylinder of infinite length placed in a stream that is uniform and parallel everywhere except near the cylinder. We see the x axis in the direction of the undisturbed flow, the z axis along the centerline of the cylinder, and the y axis perpendicular to both. Quantities such as velocity are independent of z and are functions of x and y alone, which means the flow pattern is exactly the same in every plane parallel to the xy plane. Of course, in two-dimensional flow the quantities may or may not be functions of time depending upon whether the flow is steady or unsteady because the variable "time" is not considered a dimension.

Three-dimensional flow, in which the quantities vary in all three dimensions, is the most general flow and also the most difficult to

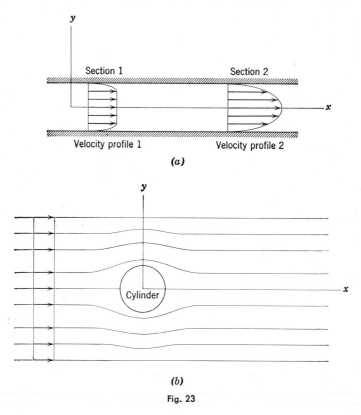

Fig. 23

handle. We usually simplify the flow from three dimensional whenever possible.

When a real fluid flows in a circular pipe, we may write the velocity profile as a function of the distance from the centerline and the distance along the pipe. Thus, the velocity is a function of only two dimensions. It is impossible, however, to pass two parallel planes that will have the same flow pattern. Therefore, this is not two-dimensional flow for it causes too many difficulties that do not appear in our definition of two-dimensional flow.

22. Control Volume Derivation of Continuity

One of the fundamental principles of science is that, in the absence of nuclear reaction, matter can be neither created nor destroyed. Since we do not take nuclear reaction into account in this book, for our purposes, matter can be neither created nor destroyed. This article puts the principle into a more usable form.

Figure 24a is a sketch of the volume completely occupied by a mass system, a defined system of matter, at time t. At time $t + \Delta t$ the mass

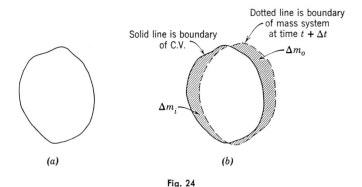

(a)   (b)

Fig. 24

system has moved into another location shown in dotted outline in Fig. 24b. The original space occupied by the mass at time t is the control volume, and the boundary of the control volume is the control surface. Fluid mass moves through the control surface into and out of the control volume, but the control surface of the control volume is fixed in space. We assume that the fluid is a continuum and that the whole control volume is filled with fluid. In time Δt the part of the mass system that has moved out of the control volume is Δm_o, and the new fluid mass that has moved into the control volume is Δm_i. The following notation appears in this chapter:

$$M_1 = \text{mass of the mass system at time } t$$
$$M_2 = \text{mass of the mass system at time } t + \Delta t$$
$$M_1' = \text{mass in the control volume at time } t$$
$$M_2' = \text{mass in the control volume at time } t + \Delta t$$

Since mass can be neither created nor destroyed and the quantity of the defined system of matter does not change,

$$M_1 = M_2 \tag{3-1}$$

At time t the mass system completely fills the control volume. Therefore, the mass in the control volume equals the mass of the mass system.

$$M_1 = M_1'$$ (3-2)

At time $t + \Delta t$ the mass in the mass system equals the mass in the control volume minus the new mass that has entered the control volume in time Δt plus the mass that has left the control volume in the same time. That is

$$M_2 = M_2' - \Delta m_i + \Delta m_o$$ (3-3)

We substitute Equations 3-2 and 3-3 in Equation 3-1 to get

$$M_1' = M_2' - \Delta m_i + \Delta m_o$$

rearrange to

$$0 = M_2' - M_1' + \Delta m_o - \Delta m_i$$

and divide by the time Δt

$$0 = \frac{M_2' - M_1'}{\Delta t} + \frac{\Delta m_o - \Delta m_i}{\Delta t}$$

We take the limit $\Delta t \to 0$ to get

$$0 = \lim_{\Delta t \to 0} \left(\frac{M_2' - M_1'}{\Delta t} + \frac{\Delta m_o - \Delta m_i}{\Delta t} \right)$$

$$0 = \frac{dM'}{dt} + \frac{dm_o - dm_i}{dt}$$ (3-4)

The term dM'/dt is the rate of accumulation of mass inside the control volume and $(dm_o - dm_i)/dt$ is the net rate of mass outflow through the control surface, a very general statement of the law of conservation of matter for fluid flow. To put this equation into more usable form, we consider the rate of outflow through the control surface.

A sketch (Fig. 25) of a small segment dA of the control surface, one edge shown in the figure and the other edge normal to the figure, shows an outward drawn normal N to the segment dA forming an angle θ with the velocity of the fluid through the segment. The amount of mass that flows out of the segment dA in time dt equals the product of the velocity component normal to the segment, the mass per unit volume, and the area dA of the segment. In time dt the outflow through dA is

$$\rho V \cos \theta \, dA \, dt$$

The total outflow through the control surface must be the sum of all the outflow through the control surface.   Thus,

$$dm_o - dm_i = \int_A \rho V \cos \theta \, dA \, dt$$

Here $\cos \theta$ is positive for fluid leaving the control volume and negative for fluid entering the control volume.   This automatically takes care of the minus sign in front of dm_i.   Since we take the integral over

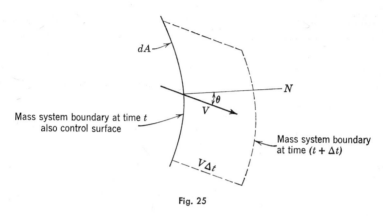

Fig. 25

the area of the control surface, the time dt is constant during the integration, and we may take it outside the integral sign.

$$dm_o - dm_i = dt \int_A \rho V \cos \theta \, dA$$

$$\frac{dm_o - dm_i}{dt} = \int_A \rho V \cos \theta \, dA$$

We substitute this in Equation 3-4 to get

$$0 = \frac{dM'}{dt} + \int_A \rho V \cos \theta \, dA \tag{3-4a}$$

The term dM'/dt is the rate of accumulation of mass inside the control volume.   The mass inside the control volume is

$$M' = \int_{\text{Vol.}} \rho \, dx \, dy \, dz$$

where $$\rho = f(x, y, z, t)$$

The rate of accumulation of mass is the derivative of the mass with respect to time. Therefore,

$$\frac{dM'}{dt} = \frac{d}{dt} \int_{\text{Vol.}} \rho \, dx \, dy \, dz$$

which we substitute in Equation 3-4a to obtain

$$\frac{d}{dt} \int_{\text{Vol.}} \rho \, dx \, dy \, dz + \int_A \rho V \cos \theta \, dA = 0 \tag{3-5}$$

which is the final form of the continuity equation. The only assumptions we make during this derivation are (1) no nuclear reaction is present and (2) the fluid is a continuum. Equation 3-5 applies equally well to both steady and unsteady motion.

For steady motion all properties of the fluid are independent of time. Thus,

$$\frac{d}{dt} \int_{\text{Vol.}} \rho \, dx \, dy \, dz = 0 \qquad \text{UNSTEADY}$$

For steady motion Equation 3-5 becomes

$$0 = \int_A \rho V \cos \theta \, dA \qquad \text{STEADY} \tag{3-6}$$

We shall use this form of the continuity equation most often. One other form of the general equation of continuity that appears frequently is for incompressible flow. Because the fluid is incompressible, the density ρ is constant. The volume of the control volume is constant by definition. Therefore,

$$\frac{d}{dt} \int_{\text{Vol.}} \rho \, dx \, dy \, dz = \rho \int_{\text{Vol.}} \frac{d}{dt} (\text{Vol.}) = 0$$

and Equation 3-5 becomes

$$0 = \int_A \rho V \cos \theta \, dA$$

Since ρ is constant, we may take it outside the integral sign. Then we divide both sides of the equation by ρ to get

$$0 = \int V \cos \theta \, dA \tag{3-7}$$

This is the general equation of continuity for steady and unsteady incompressible flow. Equations 3-5, 3-6, and 3-7 appear formidable, but a few illustrative problems demonstrate that they are not as difficult as they first appear. The amount per unit time of fluid that flows into or out of the control volume is called the flow rate. For steady flow or incompressible flow the amount per unit time of the fluid that flows into the control volume equals the amount per unit time of fluid that flows out because there is no accumulation of fluid within the control volume. We measure the flow rate as either a mass flow rate or as a volume flow rate.

The control surface chosen in pipe flow and channel flow usually includes two cross-sectional areas normal to flow. The flow rate, which is the mass per unit time of fluid flowing in the pipe or channel, in this case is the mass per unit time of fluid flowing through either of these two cross-sectional areas.

Illustrative Problems 1, 2, and 3 show the application of the principle of conservation of mass to some engineering problems. Illustrative Problem 1 concerns one-dimensional flow of a liquid in a branching pipe. Illustrative Problem 2 demonstrates the changes in analysis which are necessary when we consider the velocity profile of the flow as we must when the one-dimensional analysis is not accurate enough. Both illustrative problems are examples of pipe flow as found in water supply, fuel supply, irrigation, heating and ventilation, and refrigeration, to mention just a few engineering applications. Illustrative Problem 3 is an example of flow of liquid around a body submerged in a stream or a body moving through a stationary liquid.

▶Illustrative Problem 1. An incompressible fluid in a branching pipe flows with a velocity which may vary along the length of the pipe but is constant across the flow. The density of the fluid is 1.94 slugs/ft^3. The velocity at section 1 is 30 fps and at section 2 is 40 fps. Calculate the velocity at section 3.

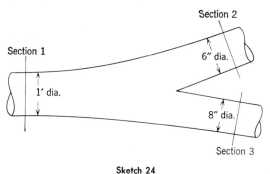

Sketch 24

Solution: First, select the control surface to simplify the solution of the problem as much as possible. Choose as the control surface the cross-sectional area normal to the flow at sections 1, 2, and 3 and the pipe wall between these sections.

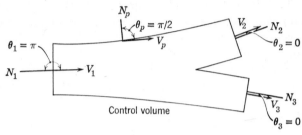

Sketch 25

The fluid is incompressible, and Equation 3-5 becomes

$$0 = \int_A V \cos \theta \, dA$$

This integral breaks down into four separate integrals

$$0 = \int_{A_1} V_1 \cos \theta_1 \, dA + \int_{A_2} V_2 \cos \theta_2 \, dA + \int_{A_3} V_3 \cos \theta_3 \, dA$$

$$+ \int_{A_p} V_p \cos \theta_p \, dA$$

The first integral is over the cross-sectional area at section 1, the second over the cross-sectional area at section 2, and the third over the cross-sectional area at section 3. Select these three areas because the velocities and the angle θ across them can be written as a function of the area. The fourth integral is over the remaining areas, the walls of the pipe, and is chosen as part of the control surface because the angle θ is equal to $\pi/2$ over the entire surface. The angle θ in the equation is the angle between the outward drawn normal and the velocity. For this fourth integral the $\cos \theta_p$ is $\cos \pi/2$ which is zero. Thus, the fourth integral is zero, and the equation becomes

$$0 = \int_{A_1} V_1 \cos \theta_1 \, dA + \int_{A_2} V_2 \cos \theta_2 \, dA + \int_{A_3} V_3 \cos \theta_3 \, dA$$

Since the velocity and the angle θ are constant across each cross section, you may take each of the velocities and the angles outside the integral sign. Thus,

$$0 = V_1 \cos \theta_1 \int_{A_1} dA + V_2 \cos \theta_2 \int_{A_2} dA + V_3 \cos \theta_3 \int_{A_3} dA$$

or $0 = V_1 \cos \theta_1 A_1 + V_2 \cos \theta_2 A_2 + V_3 \cos \theta_3 A_3$

From the control volume

$$\cos \theta_1 = \cos \pi = -1 \qquad A_1 = \frac{\pi d^2}{4} = \frac{\pi (1)^2}{4} = \frac{\pi}{4}$$

$$\cos \theta_2 = \cos 0 = 1$$

$$\cos \theta_3 = \cos 0 = 1 \qquad A_2 = \frac{\pi d^2}{4} = \frac{\pi \left(\frac{1}{2}\right)^2}{4} = \frac{\pi}{16}$$

$$V_1 = 30 \text{ fps}$$

$$V_2 = 40 \text{ fps} \qquad A_3 = \frac{\pi d^2}{4} = \frac{\pi \left(\frac{2}{3}\right)^2}{4} = \frac{\pi}{9}$$

Substitute these in the above equation.

$$0 = 30 \left(\frac{\pi}{4}\right)(-1) + 40 \left(\frac{\pi}{16}\right)(+1) + V_3 \left(\frac{\pi}{9}\right) \quad (1)$$

$$V_3 = 45 \text{ fps} \qquad \blacktriangleleft$$

▶**Illustrative Problem 2.**   A gas flows in a 4 ft dia. pipe.   Write the velocity profile as

$$v = 10 \left[1 - \left(\frac{r}{2}\right)^2 \right]$$

where r = the distance from the center, in ft
v = the velocity, in fps, at r

The density of the gas is assumed to be constant at 0.0238 slugs/ft^3 which would be approximately true for most low velocity flows.   Calculate the volume flow rate and the mass flow rate of the gas in the pipe.

Solution: In pipe flow the rate is the amount of fluid that flows through a cross-sectional area of the pipe per unit of time.   The velocity v is constant at a distance r from the center of the pipe.   Therefore, the amount of fluid that flows per second through the shaded area dA is the product of the velocity and the area.   The velocity v is normal to dA, and the flow dQ through dA is

Sketch 26

$$dQ = v \, dA = v 2\pi r \, dr$$

The total flow rate is

$$\int dQ = \int_0^2 v2\pi r\, dr = 2\pi \int_0^2 10\left[1 - \left(\frac{r}{2}\right)^2\right] r\, dr$$

$$Q = 20\pi \int_0^2 \left(r - \frac{r^3}{4}\right) dr$$

$$Q = 62.832 \text{ cfs}$$

This is volume flow rate.

The mass flow rate is the volume flow rate times the mass per unit volume. The mass flow rate M is

$$M = \rho Q = (0.0238)(62.832) = 1.495 \text{ slugs/sec} \quad \blacktriangleleft$$

▶**Illustrative Problem 3.** Consider an incompressible fluid which when undisturbed flows with a uniform velocity in the x direction. Place an infinite cylinder with the centerline perpendicular to the undisturbed stream of incompressible fluid and diameter d in this

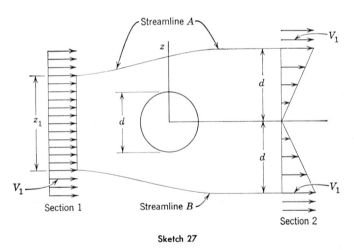

Sketch 27

stream and select the centerline as the y axis. The flow is two dimensional. Sketch 27 is a plane parallel to the xz plane. Determine the distance z_1 between the two streamlines shown in the above sketch.

Solution: Visualize the flow between two plates which are parallel to the xz plane and a distance l ft apart. Calculate the distance z_1 between the two streamlines in the undisturbed stream by use of the equation of continuity. Because fluid cannot flow into the control volume through the cylinder walls, choose the control volume as follows:

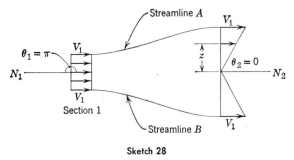

Sketch 28

For an incompressible flow the equation of continuity is

$$0 = \int_A V \cos \theta \, dA$$

Carry out the integration over three separate areas of the control surface for this control volume.

The three separate areas are the two cross-sectional areas A_1 and A_2 normal to the flow and all the remaining surfaces of the control volume. These surfaces are the two planes parallel to the xz axis and the streamlines which form stream surfaces normal to the xz plane.

$$0 = \int_{A_1} V_1 \cos \theta_1 \, dA + \int_{A_2} V_2 \cos \theta_2 \, dA + \int_{A_3} V_3 \cos \theta_3 \, dA \quad \text{(C)}$$

From the control volume you know that

$$\theta_1 = \pi, \qquad \theta_2 = 0, \qquad \theta_3 = \frac{\pi}{2}$$

The angle $\theta_3 = \pi/2$ because all the remaining surfaces are in the direction of the flow so that the normal to the surface is normal to the velocity. The velocity V_1 is constant over A_1. This reduces the Equation C to

$$0 = V_1 \cos \pi \int_{A_1} dA + \cos 0 \int_{A_2} V_2 \, dA + 0$$

$$0 = -V_1 \int_{A_1} dA + \int_{A_2} V_2 \, dA$$

But from control volume

$$\int_{A_1} dA = lz_1$$

Thus,

$$0 = -V_1 lz_1 + \int_{A_2} V_2 \, dA \qquad \text{(D)}$$

From the sketch of the control volume

$$v = V_1 \frac{z}{d}$$

You must choose the area dA so that the velocity is constant over dA. For this reason choose dA as a strip z above the xy plane, dz thick and the distance l between the two parallel planes.

$$dA = l \, dz$$

$$\int_{A_2} V_2 \, dA = 2 \int_0^d V_1 \frac{z}{d} l \, dz$$

$$= \frac{2V_1 l}{d} \frac{z^2}{2} \Big|_0^d = V_1 ld$$

Substitute this in Equation D.

$$0 = -V_1 lz_1 + V_1 ld$$

Therefore $$z_1 = d \qquad \blacktriangleleft$$

23. Derivation of Euler Equation

The next step is to study the motion of fluid particles under the action of external forces. The fundamental law of the relation between forces and motion is Newton's second law. In its original form, Newton's second law states that the rate of change of momentum of a mass system in any direction is proportional to the component in that direction of the external forces acting on the mass, written in the x direction as

$$\sum F_x = \frac{d(MV_x)}{dt}$$

This equation will be applied to a constant mass. Therefore, the mass M may be taken outside the differential. This leaves

$$\sum F_x = M \frac{dV_x}{dt} \qquad (3\text{-}8)$$

Equation 3-8 will be applied to the flow along a streamline. A free body diagram of a stream tube (Fig. 26) shows all the external forces with components in the s direction acting upon it. The shear forces on the side surfaces appear as a shear stress τ, the pressure forces on

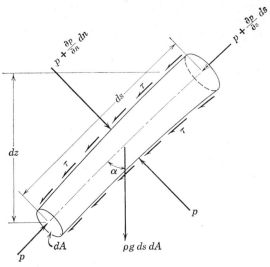

Fig. 26

the two ends as p and $p + (\partial p/\partial s)\, ds$, and the weight of the mass as $\rho g\, dA\, ds$, which makes an angle α with the streamline.

$$\sum F_s = p\, dA - \left(p + \frac{\partial p}{\partial s}\, ds\right) dA - \rho g\, dA\, ds \cos \alpha - \tau \text{ (outside area)}$$

The term $(dR\, ds)$ represents the outside area on which the shear stress acts. Thus,

$$\sum F_s = -\frac{\partial p}{\partial s}\, ds\, dA - \rho g\, dA\, ds \cos \alpha - \tau\, dR\, ds$$

Since the $\cos \alpha$ is (dz/ds)

$$\sum F_s = -\frac{\partial p}{\partial s}\, ds\, dA - \rho g\, dA\, ds\, \frac{dz}{ds} - \tau\, dR\, ds$$

$$\sum F_s = -\frac{\partial p}{\partial s}\, ds\, dA - \rho g\, dA\, dz - \tau\, dR\, ds$$

We can substitute this into Equation 3-8 to get

$$-\frac{\partial p}{\partial s}\, ds\, dA - \rho g\, dA\, dz - \tau\, dR\, ds = M\, \frac{dV_s}{dt} \qquad (3\text{-}9)$$

We must change the right-hand side to put Equation 3-9 in a workable form. The term dV_s/dt is the rate of change of velocity in the s direction, called the acceleration in the s direction. The velocity component normal to the streamline is zero by the definition of the streamline. Therefore, the velocity V_s is the total velocity V as V_s is in the direction of the streamline.

The velocity is a function of two variables, the distance s along the streamline and the time t. Thus,

$$V = f(s, t)$$

and from mathematics we know

$$dV = \frac{\partial V}{\partial s} ds + \frac{\partial V}{\partial t} dt$$

This expression can be visualized because the change dV in velocity equals two changes: (1) the change of velocity with respect to the change in the distance s times the distance ds and (2) the change of velocity with respect to the change of time multiplied by the change in time dt.

We divide by dt to get

$$\frac{dV}{dt} = \frac{\partial V}{\partial s} \frac{ds}{dt} + \frac{\partial V}{\partial t} \frac{dt}{dt}$$

but

$$\frac{ds}{dt} = V \quad \text{and} \quad \frac{dt}{dt} = 1$$

Therefore,

$$\frac{dV}{dt} = V \frac{\partial V}{\partial s} + \frac{\partial V}{\partial t} \tag{3-10}$$

The $V (\partial V/\partial s)$ term is caused by velocity changes which result from changes in cross-sectional area of the flow changes in density, or changes in both. Thus, this term is independent of whether the flow is steady or unsteady. The $\partial V/\partial t$ term is zero when the flow is steady because V then is independent of time.

The mass M of the particle is the volume $dA\,ds$ of the particle multiplied by the mass ρ per unit volume. Therefore, the mass is $\rho\,dA\,ds$. We substitute this term and Equation 3-10 into Equation 3-9

$$-\frac{\partial p}{\partial s} ds\,dA - \rho g\,dA\,dz - \tau\,dR\,ds = \rho\,dA\,ds \left(V \frac{\partial V}{\partial s} + \frac{\partial V}{\partial t} \right)$$

and divide by $\rho \, dA$

$$-\frac{1}{\rho}\frac{\partial p}{\partial s}\,ds - g\,dz - \frac{1}{\rho}\tau\frac{dR}{dA}\,ds = ds\left(V\frac{\partial V}{\partial s} + \frac{\partial V}{\partial t}\right)$$

We integrate this equation between two points on a stream tube to get Equation 3-11 which is the equilibrium equation for the fixed mass between the two points enclosed in the stream tube. We write this equilibrium equation in the direction of the streamline.

$$-\int_1^2 \frac{1}{\rho}\frac{\partial p}{\partial s}\,ds - g\int_{z_1}^{z_2} dz - \int_1^2 \frac{\tau}{\rho}\frac{dR}{dA}\,ds = \int_1^2\left(V\frac{\partial V}{\partial s} + \frac{\partial V}{\partial t}\right)ds$$

$$(3\text{-}11)$$

Equation 3-11 is good for a fixed mass system along a streamline for unsteady, compressible flow with friction. When we neglect friction and the flow is steady, we eliminate two terms. The term with the shear stress τ is zero for frictionless flow and changes Equation 3-11 to

$$-\int_1^2 \frac{1}{\rho}\frac{\partial p}{\partial s}\,ds - g\int_{z_1}^{z_2} dz = \int_1^2 V\frac{\partial V}{\partial s}\,ds + \int_1^2 \frac{\partial V}{\partial t}\,ds \quad (3\text{-}12a)$$

In this case, $(\partial V/\partial s)\,ds$ equals dV and $(\partial p/\partial s)\,ds$ equals dp. Thus the integral

$$\int_1^2 V\frac{\partial V}{\partial s}\,ds = \int_1^2 V\,dV = \int_{V_1}^{V_2} d\frac{V^2}{2}$$

and

$$\int_1^2 \frac{1}{\rho}\frac{\partial p}{\partial s}\,ds = \int_{p_1}^{p_2} \frac{1}{\rho}\,dp$$

We can now integrate all terms except one in Equation 3-12a and rearrange to get

$$\frac{V_2{}^2 - V_1{}^2}{2} + g(z_2 - z_1) + \int_{p_1}^{p_2} \frac{dp}{\rho} + \int_1^2 \frac{\partial V}{\partial t}\,ds = f(t) \quad (3\text{-}12b)$$

This equation is good for unsteady, frictionless, compressible flow. For steady flow the $\partial V/\partial t$ term is zero, and $f(t)$ is also zero. Equation 3-12b then becomes

$$\frac{V_2{}^2 - V_1{}^2}{2} + \int_{p_1}^{p_2} \frac{dp}{\rho} + g(z_2 - z_1) = 0 \quad (3\text{-}13)$$

For incompressible flow, the density ρ is a constant and may be taken outside the integral sign. This term then can be integrated to give

$$\frac{V_2{}^2 - V_1{}^2}{2} + g(z_2 - z_1) + \frac{p_2 - p_1}{\rho} = 0 \quad (3\text{-}14)$$

which is known as Bernoulli's equation, named for Daniel Bernoulli who first derived it. Bernoulli's equation is valid along a streamline for steady, frictionless, incompressible flow. It is one of the classic equations in fluid mechanics in spite of the number of restrictions placed upon it.

We can rearrange the Bernoulli equation to the form

$$\frac{V^2}{2} + \frac{p}{\rho} + gz = \frac{V_1{}^2}{2} + \frac{p_1}{\rho} + gz_1$$

We evaluate the left side of the equation at some point on the streamline and the right side of the equation at point 1 where we know all the terms. Thus, we can evaluate

$$\frac{V_1{}^2}{2} + \frac{p_1}{\rho} + gz_1 = \text{constant}$$

so that

$$\frac{V^2}{2} + \frac{p}{\rho} + gz = \text{constant} \qquad .$$

From this we say that the Bernoulli equation is constant along a streamline.

To derive Bernoulli's equation, we applied Newton's second law to the flow along a stream tube. If we had applied Newton's second law across a stream tube, we would get the same general terms except for the acceleration terms. This would give the differential equation

$$-\frac{1}{\rho}\frac{\partial p}{\partial n} - g\frac{\partial z}{\partial n} = a_n$$

The n indicates the direction normal to the stream tube. Two terms make up the acceleration normal to the flow. The first term $\partial V_n/\partial t$ is the change in the normal velocity with respect to time, and the second term V^2/R is the centrifugal acceleration. Thus,

$$-\frac{1}{\rho}\frac{\partial p}{\partial n} - g\frac{\partial z}{\partial n} = \frac{\partial V_n}{\partial t} + \frac{V^2}{R}$$

When the flow is steady and the streamlines are straight the acceleration is zero and the pressure across the flow is a function only of the height Z. Therefore, for parallel, uniform, horizontal, steady flow the normal direction is vertical and the above equation becomes

$$+\frac{1}{\rho}\frac{dp}{dZ} + \frac{\partial z}{\partial Z} = 0$$

This we integrate to give

$$\frac{p_2 - p_1}{\rho} + g(z_2 - z_1) = 0$$

or

$$\frac{p_2}{\rho} + gz_2 = \frac{p_1}{\rho} + gz_1$$

We can add $V^2/2$ to each side of the equation to get

$$\frac{p_1}{\rho} + gz_1 + \frac{V^2}{2} = \frac{p_2}{\rho} + gz_2 + \frac{V^2}{2}$$

For uniform flow $V_1 = V_2 = V$ and so we can change the subscript in the velocity terms to give

$$\frac{p_1}{\rho} + gz_1 + \frac{V_1{}^2}{2} = \frac{p_2}{\rho} + gz_2 + \frac{V_2{}^2}{2}$$

These are all the terms in the Bernoulli equation, which indicates that not only is the sum of all the terms constant along a streamline but for uniform flow the sum is the same constant for all streamlines. Thus, for steady, incompressible, frictionless flow, which is horizontal and uniform at one portion of the flow at least, the Bernoulli equation equals the same constant throughout the flow.

24. Applications of Bernoulli's Equation

The Bernoulli equation applies to the flow of a liquid through a small hole in the side of a large vessel (Fig. 27). A short distance

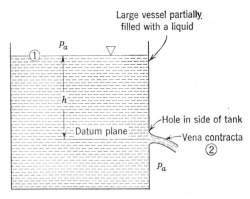

Fig. 27

from the hole the streamlines of the jet become parallel and straight momentarily. This section is called the vena contracta. The pressure all around the outside of the vena contracta is the pressure of the atmosphere p_a. Since the streamlines are straight and parallel, we know that this pressure exists all across the cross section. At any other section of the jet the streamlines are curving, and the pressure varies across the section. Thus, the only section of the jet where the pressure is completely known is the vena contracta.

We can apply the Bernoulli equation along a streamline. The streamline selected for this problem is one that starts at the surface of the liquid in the tank (point 1) and passes through the vena contracta (point 2).

The Bernoulli equation is valid for only steady, frictionless flow. We assume that the flow is steady and examine this assumption after the problem is solved. There will be a small amount of friction for a sharp-edged hole and a free jet, but we shall neglect this friction. A free jet is one that has no solid objects to restrict the flow or change it immediately after it has left the source, in this case the tank.

The Bernoulli equation written between points 1 and 2 as described above gives

$$\frac{p_2 - p_1}{\rho} + \frac{V_2{}^2 - V_1{}^2}{2} + g(z_2 - z_1) = 0$$

The pressure on the liquid surface at point 1 is atmospheric pressure p_a, and the distance from an arbitrary horizontal plane to the liquid surface is z_1 which equals h. Through the center of the vena contracta we select the datum plane. When we apply the continuity equation to the flow, we can compute quite easily the ratio of the velocities of the liquid surface and the liquid in the vena contracta. For a large vessel with a small hole this demonstrates that we **can** neglect the velocity of the liquid surface.

At point 2 in the vena contracta the velocity is unknown, $z_2 = 0$ as the datum plane goes through the vena contracta, and the pressure p_2 is atmospheric. We substitute these values at points 1 and 2 in the Bernoulli equation to get

$$\frac{p_a - p_a}{\rho} + \frac{V_2{}^2 - 0}{2} + g(0 - h) = 0$$

or
$$V_2{}^2 = 2gh$$

$$V_2 = \sqrt{2gh} \tag{3-15}$$

Thus, we compute the velocity of the jet at the vena contracta. We should keep in mind one of the assumptions we made in arriving at this conclusion, namely, that the pressure at the vena contracta is atmospheric pressure. Such is not necessarily true if some obstruction, such as a plate, is placed at the vena contracta or if the jet is not a free jet but is enclosed in a pipe. We also made the assumption that this was steady flow. However, the exit velocity of the liquid depends upon its depth. As liquid runs out of the side of the vessel, the depth changes unless liquid flows into the tank at some other point, the velocity changes, and the flow is unsteady. The acceleration term for unsteady flow is $V(\partial V/\partial s) + (\partial V/\partial t)$. For a large vessel and a small hole the $V(\partial V/\partial s)$ term will be large, and the $\partial V/\partial t$ term will be small because the changes in h will be very small. We should always check such terms in problems of this sort to see if assumptions are within reasonable limits.

Also, we should keep in mind that the liquid is accelerating and the equation of statics does not apply. Thus, the pressure in the vessel is difficult to compute, and we cannot compute it from the equations of statics.

We can, however, compute the amount of liquid that flows from the tank by using Equation 3-15. This is the velocity on any streamline at a vena contracta. The velocity at the vena contracta, therefore, is uniform, and the flow rate is this velocity multiplied by the cross-sectional area of the vena contracta.

$$Q = A_V \sqrt{2gh}$$

The area A_V at the vena contracta is not the same as the area of the hole. For circular holes the area of the vena contracta is about three-fifths the area of the hole. For holes of other shapes the factor varies and must be determined by experiment as done already for a number of common shapes.

There are several good hydraulics books in which we can locate these different factors. In this book, we refer to the area at the vena contracta as the effective area. We call the diameter of the vena contracta the effective diameter.

25. Pipe Flow

In pipe flow the diameter of the pipe is small compared with the pipe length. We consider the flow steady and the liquid incompres-

sible.   Thus, we can consider the pipe as a stream tube and use the
Bernoulli equation.   The pipe that branches into two different pipes
in Fig. 28a shows its known quantities, and the problem is to determine
the velocities at sections 2 and 3 and to determine the pressure p_3 at
section 3.

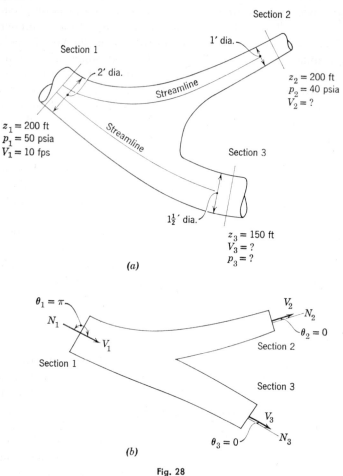

Section 2

1' dia.

Section 1

2' dia.

Streamline

$z_2 = 200$ ft
$p_2 = 40$ psia
$V_2 = ?$

$z_1 = 200$ ft
$p_1 = 50$ psia
$V_1 = 10$ fps

Streamline

Section 3

$1\frac{1}{2}'$ dia.

$z_3 = 150$ ft
$V_3 = ?$
$p_3 = ?$

(a)

$\theta_1 = \pi$

N_1

V_1

V_2

N_2

$\theta_2 = 0$

Section 2

Section 1

Section 3

V_3

$\theta_3 = 0$

N_3

(b)

Fig. 28

Since part of the flow is from section 1 to section 2, we can write the
Bernoulli equation along a streamline between these two sections.

$$\frac{p_2 - p_1}{\rho} + \frac{V_2{}^2 - V_1{}^2}{2} + g(z_2 - z_1) = 0$$

We take the datum plane as elevation zero and substitute the proper values into this equation, including the density $\rho = 2$ slugs/ft^3 of the liquid.

$$\frac{(40)(144) - (50)(144)}{2} + \frac{V_2{}^2 - (10)^2}{2} + 32.2(200 - 200) = 0$$

$$V_2{}^2 = 100 + 50(144) - 40(144) = 1540$$

$$V_2 = 39.28 \text{ fps}$$

The Bernoulli equation written between sections 1 and 3 gives

$$\frac{p_3 - (50)(144)}{2} + \frac{V_3{}^2 - (10)^2}{2} + g(150 - 200) = 0$$

The pressure p_3 and the velocity V_3 are both unknown. We must obtain another equation containing the two quantities and then solve the two equations simultaneously. Since we have not used the equation of continuity, we shall apply it to the problem. First, we must select a control volume. The pipe walls and the three cross-sectional areas at sections 1, 2, and 3 are the control surfaces. Figure 28b shows this control volume. For incompressible steady flow the equation of continuity is

$$\int_A V \cos \theta \, dA = 0$$

The value of this integral is zero over the area of the pipe wall because $\theta = \pi/2$ over this area and $\cos(\pi/2) = 0$. The rest of the integral is the sum of the integrals over the three cross sections.

$$\int_{A_1} V_1 \cos \theta_1 \, dA + \int_{A_2} V_2 \cos \theta_2 \, dA + \int_{A_3} V_3 \cos \theta_3 \, dA = 0$$

All the terms are constant over the area of integration and so they may be taken outside the integral sign. This gives

$$V_1(\cos \pi) A_1 + V_2(\cos 0) A_2 + V_3(\cos 0) A_3 = 0$$

$$-V_1 A_1 + V_2 A_2 + V_3 A_3 = 0 \qquad (E)$$

We substitute the values of the areas and the known velocities in Equation E to get

$$-(10)\frac{\pi(4)}{4} + (39.28)\frac{\pi(1)^2}{4} + V_3\frac{\pi(\frac{3}{2})^2}{4} = 0$$

$$V_3 = 0.32 \text{ fps}$$

This value of V_3 substituted into the Bernoulli equation results in

$$\frac{p_3 - (50)(144)}{2} + \frac{(0.32)^2 - (10)^2}{2} - 50g = 0$$

$$p_3 = 73 \text{ psia}$$

In problems of pipe flow it is important that the pressure in the pipe does not fall below the vapor pressure of the liquid. When the pressure in a siphon falls below the vapor pressure, the siphon breaks and the liquid ceases to flow. In regular pipe flow a pressure less than vapor pressure causes cavitation and must be avoided, for it can mean severe damage to the pipe walls. Many problems at the end of the chapter will have this limiting factor which must be taken into account.

26. Submerged Bodies

The Bernoulli equation is useful for solving problems in steady flow of an incompressible fluid around a submerged body. A streamlined body placed in an incompressible fluid that moves with a uniform velocity extends to infinity in both directions perpendicular to Fig. 29a. The flow is two dimensional, and all planes parallel to the plane

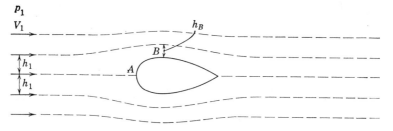

Dotted lines are streamlines

(a)

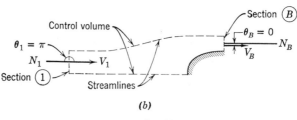

(b)

Fig. 29

of the page show exactly the same flow pattern.   Some distance from the body in the plane of Fig. 29a the velocity of the fluid is still uniform and parallel because the object causes only a local disturbance. A sketch of the flow pattern around the body also appears in the figure. The dotted lines are streamlines, and the pressure and the velocity of the undisturbed stream are p_1 and V_1.   We calculate the pressure at point A and an approximate value of the pressure and velocity at point B which is midway between the first streamline and the top of the body.   The equation of continuity for an incompressible fluid applies and is used to calculate the velocity at B.   The velocity between the streamline and the body at point B is assumed to be uniform and equal to V_B.   This is one assumption which makes the answers at B approximate.   The other main assumption, that the flow is frictionless, becomes important when we apply the Bernoulli equation.   We draw the control volume as shown in Fig. 29b.   The control surfaces appear as the two streamlines, two planes parallel to the page that are a distance L apart, and two cross-sectional areas at 1 and B.   The equation of continuity for an incompressible fluid is

$$\int_A V \cos \theta \, dA = 0$$

The angle θ is equal to $\pi/2$ everywhere except at sections 1 and B. Since $\cos (\pi/2) = 0$, the equation becomes

$$\int_{A_1} V_1 \cos \theta_1 \, dA + \int_{A_2} V_2 \cos \theta_2 \, dA = 0$$

We substitute the values shown in the control volume to get

$$-V_1 \int_{A_1} dA + V_B \int_{A_2} dA = 0 \tag{F}$$

The integrals are the areas of the cross section.   When we substitute these into Equation F, the equation becomes

$$V_1 h L + V_B h_B L = 0$$

$$V_B = \frac{h}{h_B} V_1$$

We write the Bernoulli equation between Sections 1 and B on the same streamline.

$$\frac{p_B - p_1}{\rho} + \frac{V_B{}^2 - V_1{}^2}{2} + g(z_B - z_1) = 0$$

The change in elevation is small so that $z_B - z_1 = 0$. We substitute this and the value of V_B into the equation to get

$$\frac{p_B - p_1}{\rho} + \frac{\left(\dfrac{h}{h_B} V_1\right)^2 - V_1^2}{2} = 0$$

$$p_B = \frac{\rho V_1^2}{2}\left[\left(\frac{h}{h_B}\right)^2 - 1\right] + p_1$$

To solve for the pressure at point A, it is necessary to know that this is the stagnation point. The stagnation point is the point on or near the nose of an object in a streamline of fluid where the velocity is zero. Thus, the velocity of the fluid at point A is zero. The change of elevation is zero between points 1 and A so the Bernoulli equation becomes

$$\frac{p_A - p_1}{\rho} + \frac{V_A^2 - V_1^2}{2} + 0 = 0$$

$$V_A = 0$$

We solve for p_A

$$p_A = p_1 + \frac{\rho V_1^2}{2}$$

The pressure at the point of zero velocity is known as the stagnation pressure. In this case we computed the stagnation pressure for only an incompressible flow.

Illustrative Problems 4 and 5 demonstrate further uses of the Bernoulli equation and some of the notation used in the problems at the end of the chapter.

Illustrative Problem 4 is an example of a method for measuring the flow rate in a pipe of constant cross-sectional area.

Illustrative Problem 5 demonstrates how to compute the time needed to drain by gravity a circular tank of changing cross section. The method applies in many engineering problems where we use gravity feed of a liquid, such as fuel and water used in irrigation.

▶**Illustrative Problem 4.**   Water flows in a horizontal pipe of constant diameter (Fig. 30). Assume that the water is frictionless and that the velocity is constant across and along the pipe. A tube connected to the side of the pipe bends into a U shape and returns to the inside of the pipe. The right end of the tube bends with the open end of the tube facing upstream. The U part of the tube is filled partially with mercury. The part of the tube connected to a hole in the side of the pipe at point B measures the pressure of the liquid at that point. The velocity at B is undisturbed and equals the uniform velocity of the water. The other end of the tube is a stagnation point and so it

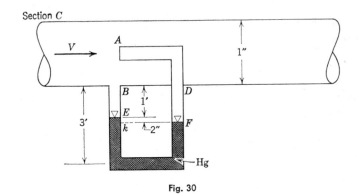

Fig. 30

measures the stagnation pressure. The tube is filled with water except for the part filled with mercury. Compute the average velocity of the water.

Solution: The Bernoulli equation can be applied to a pipe where the pipe is considered a stream tube. Since this pipe is a stream tube, the streamline that goes through point B and the streamline that goes through point A must come from streamlines that go past section C, which is far enough upstream to have uniform velocity and pressure. Write the Bernoulli equation between A and C along the streamline that goes through A.

$$\frac{p_A - p_C}{\rho} + \frac{V_A{}^2 - V_C{}^2}{2} = 0$$

or

$$\frac{p_A}{\rho} + \frac{V_A{}^2}{2} = \frac{p_C}{\rho} + \frac{V_C{}^2}{2}$$

Do the same for the streamline through point B

$$\frac{p_B - p_C}{\rho} + \frac{V_B{}^2 - V_C{}^2}{2} = 0$$

or

$$\frac{p_B}{\rho} + \frac{V_B{}^2}{2} = \frac{p_C}{\rho} + \frac{V_C{}^2}{2}$$

From this see that

$$\frac{p_A}{\rho} + \frac{V_A^2}{2} = \frac{p_C}{\rho} + \frac{V_C^2}{2} = \frac{p_B}{\rho} + \frac{V_B^2}{2}$$

$$\frac{p_A}{\rho} + \frac{V_A^2}{2} = \frac{p_B}{\rho} + \frac{V_B^2}{2}$$

Since point A is a stagnation point, $V_A = 0$ and from the above expression

$$V_B = \left[\frac{2(p_A - p_B)}{\rho} \right]^{\frac{1}{2}}$$

The velocity V_B equals the uniform velocity of the water in the pipe. Determine the difference in pressure between A and B to calculate V_B.

The pressure at point E can be computed from fluid statics because the water in the tube is stationary.

$$p_E = p_B + \gamma_{H_2O}(1)$$

The radius of the pipe is small; therefore assume that the pressure p_D at point D inside the tube equals p_A.

$$p_D = p_A$$

Compute the pressure p_F at the surface of the mercury from fluid statics.

$$p_F = p_D + \gamma_{H_2O}(1\tfrac{2}{12}) = p_A + \gamma_{H_2O}(1\tfrac{2}{12})$$

The pressure in the other side of the tube at point k equals p_F, because points F and k are at the same elevation in a continuum. The pressure at k is

$$p_k = p_E + (\tfrac{2}{12})\gamma_{Hg}$$

but

$$p_k = p_F$$

and so

$$p_B + (\tfrac{2}{12})\gamma_{Hg} = p_A + \gamma_{H_2O}(1\tfrac{2}{12})$$

but

$$p_E = p_B + \gamma_{H_2O}(1)$$

Therefore, $p_B + \gamma_{H_2O}(1) + (\tfrac{2}{12})\gamma_{Hg} = p_A + \gamma_{H_2O}(1\tfrac{2}{12})$

$$p_A - p_B = (1)\gamma_{H_2O} + \tfrac{1}{6}\gamma_{Hg} - 1\tfrac{1}{6}\gamma_{H_2O}$$

$$= \tfrac{1}{6}(\gamma_{Hg} - \gamma_{H_2O}) = 130.4 \text{ lb/ft}^2$$

Substitute this result into the equation for V_B

$$V_B = \left[\frac{2(p_A - p_B)}{\rho} \right]^{\frac{1}{2}} = \left[\frac{2(130.4)}{1.94} \right]^{\frac{1}{2}} = 11.5 \text{ fps}$$ ◀

▶Illustrative Problem 5. A tank (Fig. 31) is partially filled with water which drains out a 1 in. dia. hole in the side. The x axis is horizontal through the center of the hole and perpendicular to the tank's center-line which is the y axis positive upward. The inside surface of the tank is a surface of revolution. The y axis is the axis of revolution.

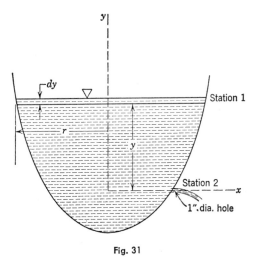

Fig. 31

The radius r of the inside surface is a function of the distance y above the hole. This function is

$$y = r^2 - 1$$

How long does it take the water level in the tank to fall from 6 ft above the hole to 4 ft above the hole?

Solution: As the water drains out the hole in the tank, the water level in the tank drops, which changes the velocity of the water as it leaves the tank. This makes the flow unsteady, and the $\partial V / \partial t$ term is not zero. Assume that, although this $\partial V / \partial t$ term is not zero, you can neglect it. The accuracy of this assumption will be checked later. With this term neglected you can use the Bernoulli equation.

When the water surface (station 1) is a distance y above the hole, you can compute the velocity of the water at the vena contracta (station 2). Writing the Bernoulli equation between these two stations gives

$$\frac{V_2{}^2 - V_1{}^2}{2} + \frac{p_2 - p_1}{\rho} + g(z_2 - z_1) = 0$$

The pressure at the water surface and at the vena contracta is atmospheric pressure p_a.   The velocity V_1 of the water is small compared with V_2 and may be neglected.   Use the xz plane as the datum plane, which reduces the Bernoulli equation to

$$\frac{V_2{}^2}{2} + g(-y) = 0$$

$$V_2 = \sqrt{2gy}$$

In time dt the level of the water surface will fall a distance dy.   Also in time dt an amount of water equal to $Q\,dt$ will have flowed out of the hole.   This amount of water $Q\,dt$ must equal the change in volume in the tank.   The change in volume of the tank is the cross-sectional area of the tank at the water surface times the distance the water drops.

$$Q\,dt = \pi r^2\,(-dy) = -\pi r^2\,dy \qquad\qquad\text{(G)}$$

The term dy is negative because the surface drops.

The flow rate Q is the velocity multiplied by the cross-sectional area. The effective area is three-fifths of the area of the hole.

$$Q = V_2\,\frac{\pi\left(\tfrac{1}{12}\right)^2}{4}\,(\tfrac{3}{5}) = \tfrac{3}{5}\,\sqrt{2gy}\,\frac{\pi}{576}$$

Substitute this into Equation G.

$$Q\,dt = \tfrac{3}{5}\,\sqrt{2gy}\,\frac{\pi}{576}\,dt = -\pi r^2\,dy$$

Given

$$y = r^2 - 1$$

or

$$r = \sqrt{y+1}$$

Therefore,

$$\frac{\pi}{576}\,(\tfrac{3}{5})\,\sqrt{2g}\,\sqrt{y}\,dt = -\pi(\sqrt{y+1})^2\,dy$$

$$\int_0^t dt = -\frac{5}{3}\,\frac{576}{\sqrt{2g}}\int_6^4 \frac{y+1}{\sqrt{y}}\,dy$$

$$t = 542\ \text{sec}$$

To check and get an idea of the error introduced by omitting the $\partial V/\partial t$ term, make some rough approximation.   The true acceleration dV/dt is

$$\frac{dV}{dt} = V\frac{\partial V}{\partial s} + \frac{\partial V}{\partial t}$$

Change this to a finite form

$$\frac{\Delta V}{\Delta t} = V\left(\frac{\Delta V}{\Delta s}\right)_{t=\text{constant}} + \left(\frac{\Delta V}{\Delta t}\right)_{s=\text{constant}}$$

$$\left(\frac{\Delta V}{\Delta t}\right)_{s=\text{constant}} = \frac{V_{y=6} - V_{y=4}}{\Delta t}$$

$$= \frac{\sqrt{2g6} - \sqrt{2g4}}{542} = \frac{(8.08)(0.453)}{542} = \frac{1}{100}$$

From the water surface to the vena contracta there is a change in velocity equal to the velocity of the water at the vena contracta. Assume the distance Δs traveled is $2y$. The 2 is introduced as a factor to put the result on the conservative side. Thus,

$$V\frac{\Delta V}{\Delta s} = \sqrt{2gy}\,\frac{\sqrt{2gy} - 0}{2y} = g$$

Therefore,

$$\frac{\Delta V}{\Delta t} = g + \tfrac{1}{100} = 32.2 + \tfrac{1}{100}$$

The $\tfrac{1}{100}$ is obviously too small to be considered. This is certainly a rough estimate, but it does give some idea of the order of magnitude of the error. Even if this calculation of error is off by a factor of 100, the error is only 3 per cent and still can be neglected.   ◀

27. Compressible Flow

Up to this point, we have considered only incompressible flow problems. When the fluid is compressible, the Bernoulli equation does not apply, and we must return to the modified Euler equation which is Equation 3-13.

$$\frac{V_2{}^2 - V_1{}^2}{2} + g(z_2 - z_1) + \int_{p_1}^{p_2} \frac{dp}{\rho} = 0 \qquad (3\text{-}13)$$

The Bernoulli equation was derived from this equation for incompressible fluids or flow when we could neglect the compressibility effects.

All the terms in the equation are simple and straightforward except the term that includes the integral sign. To carry out this integration, we must know the relation between p and ρ. We assume that this relation is known and can be written as

$$\rho = f(p)$$

where f is a known function. This function is then substituted for ρ in Equation 3-13 to get

$$\frac{V_2^2 - V_1^2}{2} + g(z_2 - z_1) + \int_{p_1}^{p_2} \frac{dp}{f(p)} = 0 \qquad (3\text{-}16)$$

Now we can carry out the integration and use the equation for compressible flow in the same way the Bernoulli equation is used for incompressible flow. Equation 3-16 has limitations as follows: the flow must be along a streamline, it must be steady and frictionless, and the relation between ρ and p must be written $\rho = f(p)$.

The insentropic flow of a fluid takes into account the compressibility effects but not the effect of friction. A comparison of isentropic flow and incompressible flow gives a true picture of the effects of the compressibility of the fluid. We write the Bernoulli equation for incompressible flow along a streamline and Equation 3-13 for an isentropic flow along the same streamline. To cancel out the gravitational effects, the streamline will be taken as horizontal. The velocity of the fluid along the streamline will vary from $V_2 = 0$ to V_1. The pressure at point 1 will be the same for both cases. The comparison will be made between the pressures p_2 at point 2. For incompressible flow the Bernoulli equation is

$$\frac{p_2}{\rho} + \frac{V_2^2}{2} + gz_2 = \frac{p_1}{\rho} + \frac{V_1^2}{2} + gz_1$$

When the above assumptions are substituted into the Bernoulli equation, it becomes

$$\frac{p_2}{\rho} = \frac{p_1}{\rho} + \frac{V_1^2}{2}$$

$$p_2 = p_1 + \frac{\rho V_1^2}{2} \qquad (3\text{-}17)$$

By substituting the isentropic relationship $p/\rho^k = K$ into Equation 3-13, we can solve for p_2 in the isentropic case. We make this substitution and the other substitutions of this problem, that is, $z_2 = z_1$, $V_2 = 0$, changing Equation 3-13 to

$$K_1^{1/k} \int_{p_1}^{p_2} \frac{dp}{p^{1/k}} = \frac{V_1^2}{2}$$

We carry out the integration and substitute

$$K_1 = \frac{p_1}{\rho_1{}^k}$$

into the result to obtain

$$\frac{1}{\rho_1}\, p_1{}^{1/k}\, \frac{k}{k-1}\, (p_2^{(k-1)/k} - p_1^{(k-1)/k}) = \frac{V_1{}^2}{2}$$

We rearrange this equation to the following form.

$$\left(\frac{p_2}{p_1}\right)^{(k-1)/k} = \frac{V_1{}^2 \rho_1^{(k-1)}}{2kp_1} + 1$$

For isentropic flow we show in appendix A that the acoustic velocity c equals $\sqrt{kp/\rho}$. We substitute c_1 for $\sqrt{kp_1/\rho_1}$ and solve for p_2.

$$p_2 = p_1 \left(1 + \frac{k-1}{2}\frac{V_1{}^2}{c_1{}^2}\right)^{k/(k-1)}$$

We expand this by the binomial theorem to get for the first few terms

$$p_2 = p_1 \left[1 + \frac{k}{2}\left(\frac{V_1}{c_1}\right)^2 + \frac{k}{8}\left(\frac{V_1}{c_1}\right)^4 + \frac{k(2-k)}{48}\left(\frac{V_1}{c_1}\right)^6 + \cdots\right]$$

or $\quad p_2 = p_1 + \tfrac{1}{2}\rho V_1{}^2 \left[1 + \frac{1}{4}\left(\frac{V_1}{c_1}\right)^2 + \frac{2-k}{24}\left(\frac{V_1}{c_1}\right)^4 + \cdots\right]$ (3-18)

Equation 3-17 for incompressible flow and Equation 3-18 for isentropic flow are the same except for the bracketed terms which may be considered as the correction term for the compressibility effects. This correction is a function of k, which is nearly constant for the fluid, and the ratio V_1/c_1 which is called the Mach number. Thus, for any fluid we can measure the compressibility effects if we can compute the Mach number. When the velocity is one-half of the acoustic velocity, the correction term will make a change of about 7 per cent in the $\tfrac{1}{2}\rho_1 V_1{}^2$ terms. For this reason, air with velocities of less than 300 mph can be considered incompressible.

In Illustrative Problem 6 we compute the pressure on the nose of a blunt body under varying assumptions. As far as the analysis of the problem is concerned, the body such as an airplane or missile may be moving in still air, or the body such as a chimney, sign, or other structure in a strong wind may be stationary with the fluid flowing around the body.

▶**Illustrative Problem 6.** A blunt-nosed object is traveling through standard air at a velocity of 400 mph. Compute the pressure on the nose of the object for each of the following assumptions: (*a*) the fluid is incompressible; (*b*) the fluid is a perfect gas and the process is isothermal; (*c*) the process is isentropic. The density of standard air is 0.00238 slug/ft³, and the pressure is 14.7 psia. There is no friction in the flow in front of the body.

Solution: The easiest way to solve this problem is to consider the object as stationary and the air as flowing at a uniform velocity of 400 mph well upstream of the object. At first glance this would appear to be an entirely different problem, but it is really the same problem as an observer on the object would see it. The pressures will not change just because the flow is seen from a different point. Another way to look at this is to add a velocity of 400 mph in the opposite direction to the velocity of the body. The 400 mph velocity is added to all the particles of the flow. This will give the same flow pattern as shown in Fig. 32, but because the velocity is constant, the

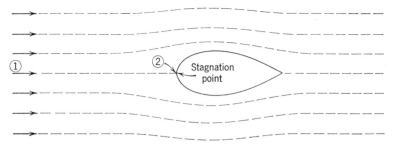

Fig. 32

pressures will not change. Consider the undisturbed stream of air (Fig. 32) at standard pressure and temperature. The dotted lines are streamlines. The center streamline which hits the nose of the object has a 400 mph velocity at the undisturbed point 1 and a zero velocity at the nose which is point 2.

(*a*) For an incompressible fluid

$$\rho = \text{constant}$$

Write the modified Euler equation between points 1 and 2.

$$\frac{V_2{}^2 - V_1{}^2}{2} + g(z_2 - z_1) + \int_1^2 \frac{dp}{\rho} = 0$$

Since ρ is a constant, take it outside the integral sign. Then integrate to get

$$\frac{V_2{}^2 - V_1{}^2}{2} + g(z_2 - z_1) + \frac{p_2 - p_1}{\rho} = 0 \qquad \text{(H)}$$

Points 1 and 2 are at the same elevation; therefore, $z_2 = z_1$. Substitute the given values of $V_1 = 400$ mph, $V_2 = 0$, $p_1 = 14.7$ psia into Equation H.

$$0 - \frac{1}{2}\left(\frac{(400)(5280)}{3600}\right)^2 + 0 + \frac{p_2(144) - (14.7)(144)}{0.00238} = 0$$

$$-172,600 + \frac{p_2(144) - (14.7)(144)}{0.00238} = 0$$

$$p_2 = 14.7 + \frac{(172,600)(0.00238)}{144} = 17.55 \text{ psia}$$

(b) For a perfect gas and an isothermal process

$$\frac{p}{\rho} = g_c R T$$

where $T = $ constant

$$\frac{p}{\rho} = \text{constant}$$

Again write Equation 3-16 between points 1 and 2.

$$\frac{V_2{}^2 - V_1{}^2}{2} + g(z_2 - z_1) + \int_1^2 \frac{dp}{f(p)} = 0$$

Given

$$V_2 = 0, \qquad V_1 = \frac{(400)(5280)}{3600} = 588 \text{ fps}$$

$$z_1 = z_2$$

which when substituted in the equation between points 1 and 2 gives

$$0 - \frac{(588)^2}{2} + 0 + \int_{p_1}^{p_2} \frac{dp}{\rho} = 0 \qquad \text{(I)}$$

$$\frac{p}{\rho} = \frac{p_1}{\rho_1} \qquad \text{as } \frac{p}{\rho} = \text{constant}$$

therefore

$$\frac{1}{\rho} = \frac{p_1}{\rho_1 p}$$

which you substitute in equation I.

$$-172,600 + \frac{p_1}{\rho_1} \int_{p_1}^{p_2} \frac{dp}{p} = 0$$

$$-172,600 + \frac{(14.7)(144)}{0.00238} \log_e p \Big|_{p_1}^{p_2} = 0$$

$$-172,600 + 890,000 \log_e \frac{p_2}{p_1} = 0$$

$$\log_e \frac{p_2}{p_1} = \frac{172,600}{890,000}$$

but $p_1 = (14.7)(144)$

therefore,

$$\log_e \left[\frac{p_2(144)}{(14.7)(144)} \right] = 0.194$$

and

$$p_2 = (14.7)e^{0.194} = (14.7)(1.214) = 17.85 \text{ psia}$$

During the pressure increase, the fluid temperature probably will increase and so this result is not the true case.

(c) For an isentropic process

$$\frac{p}{\rho^k} = \text{constant}$$

where $k = 1.4$ for air.

Substitute the appropriate values into Equation 3-16 to obtain

$$-172,600 + \int_{p_1}^{p_2} \frac{dp}{\rho} = 0 \qquad \text{(J)}$$

Now,

$$\frac{p}{\rho^{1.4}} = \frac{p_1}{\rho_1^{1.4}} = \frac{p_2}{\rho_2^{1.4}}$$

Rearrange this to

$$\frac{1}{\rho} = \left(\frac{p_1}{p} \right)^{1/1.4} \frac{1}{\rho_1}$$

and substitute it into Equation J.

$$-172,600 + \frac{p_1^{1/1.4}}{\rho_1} \int_{p_1}^{p_2} \frac{dp}{p^{1/1.4}} = 0$$

$$-172,600 + \frac{p_1^{1/1.4}}{\rho_1} \frac{p^{1-1/1.4}}{1 - \frac{1}{1.4}} \Big|_{p_1}^{p_2} = 0$$

$$-172,600 + \frac{p_1^{5/7}}{\rho_1} \frac{7}{2} (p_2^{2/7} - p_1^{2/7}) = 0$$

Substitute

$$p_1 = (14.7)(144) \text{ psia}$$

and

$$\rho_1 = 0.00238 \text{ slug/ft}^3$$

Thus, $\quad -172{,}600 + \dfrac{[(14.7)(144)]^{5\!\!/\!7}}{0.00238} \left(\dfrac{7}{2}\right) \left\{ p_2^{2\!\!/\!7} - [(14.7)(144)]^{2\!\!/\!7} \right\} = 0$

$$-172{,}600 + \frac{236}{0.00238}\frac{7}{2} p_2^{2\!\!/\!7} - \frac{7}{2}\frac{(14.7)(144)}{0.00238} = 0$$

$$347{,}000 p_2^{2\!\!/\!7} = 172{,}600 + \frac{(14.7)(144)(\tfrac{7}{2})}{0.00238}$$

$$p_2^{2\!\!/\!7} 347{,}000 = 3{,}287{,}100$$

$$p_2 = \left(\frac{3{,}287{,}100}{347{,}000}\right)^{7\!\!/\!2} = 2600 \text{ psfa}$$

$$= \tfrac{2600}{144} = 18.05 \text{ psia} \qquad \blacktriangleleft$$

28. Summary

The statement concerning conservation of matter for a mass system is the basis upon which we develop the continuity equation for control volume.

$$0 = \frac{dM'}{dt} + \int_A \rho V \cos\theta \, dA \qquad (3\text{-}4)$$

The only limitations on this equation are those of a fixed control volume and the absence of nuclear reaction.

We apply Newton's second law to a mass system and derive a modified Euler equation.

$$\frac{V_2{}^2 - V_1{}^2}{2} + g(z_2 - z_1) + \int_{p_1}^{p_2} \frac{dp}{\rho} = 0 \qquad (3\text{-}13)$$

Equation 3-13 applies to steady, frictionless flow along a streamline. The modified Euler equation becomes the Bernoulli equation when the fluid is incompressible.

$$\frac{V_2{}^2 - V_1{}^2}{2} + g(z_2 - z_1) + \frac{p_2 - p_1}{\rho} = 0 \qquad (3\text{-}14)$$

The Bernoulli equation is valid along a streamline for steady, incompressible, frictionless flow.

We must always keep in mind the limitations on both the Bernoulli and the modified Euler equations.   We can find approximations for the friction effects which increase the uses for the two equations.

Chapter 6 explains one of these approximations, and more advanced textbooks as well as less theoretical ones discuss the others.

PROBLEMS

3-1. An incompressible fluid is flowing with an average velocity V_1 of 40 fps in an 8 in. dia. pipe.   The pipe branches into two pipes, one of 4 in. diameter and the other one of 6 in. diameter, as shown in Fig. P.3-1.   The average velocity V_2 in the 4 in. dia. pipe is 50 fps.   Calculate the average velocity V_3 in the 6 in. dia. pipe.

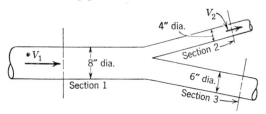

Fig. P.3-1

3-2. Work Problem 3-1 for a compressible fluid which has a density $\rho_1 = 0.023$ slug/ft^3, $\rho_2 = 0.021$ slugs/ft^3, and $\rho_3 = 0.015$ slug/ft^3.

3-3. In Fig. P.3-1 an incompressible fluid is flowing.   The average velocity at section 1 is 49 fps.   At section 2 the velocity profile is

$$v = V_c \left[1 - \left(\frac{r}{R} \right)^2 \right]$$

where v = velocity a distance r in inches from the centerline
  V_c = centerline velocity = 30 fps
  R = radius of pipe = 2 in.

Compute the average velocity at section 3.

3-4. In Problem 3-1 change the velocity profile at section 3 to

$$v = V_c \left(\frac{y}{R} \right)^{1/7}$$

where v = velocity a distance y from the wall of the pipe
  R = radius of pipe = 3 in.
  V_c = centerline velocity, in fps

Calculate the centerline velocity V_c.

3-5. Figure P.3-5 is a sketch of a flat plate with an incompressible fluid flowing past it.   At section 2, 4 ft downstream from the front edge of the

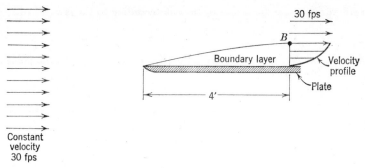

Fig. P.3-5

plate, the velocity profile inside the boundary layer is

$$v = V(y/\delta)^2$$

where v = velocity a distance y in feet from the plate
  V = free stream velocity = 30 fps
  δ = thickness of boundary layer, in ft

Calculate the distance d at the front edge of the plate from the plate to the streamline that goes through point B.

3-6. Compute the distance in Problem 3-5 when the velocity profile at B is

$$v = V(y/\delta)$$

3-7. Figure P.3-7 is a sketch of a manifold pipe.   The pipe is 8 in. in diameter and has three holes drilled in the side at A, B, and C.   The average velocity of the fluid as it leaves the pipe at A is 30 fps, at B is 40 fps, and at C is

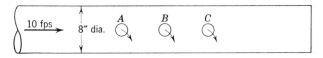

Fig. P.3-7

50 fps.   One-third of the fluid flow rate flows out each hole.   Calculate the diameter of each hole.

3-8. In Problem 3-7 the holes at A, B, and C are the same size.   Compute the diameter of these holes.   The velocity of the fluid at each hole is the same as in Problem 3-7.

3-9. A manifold closed-end pipe has a slit along one side as shown in Fig.

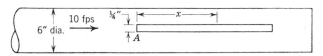

Fig. P.3-9

P.3-9.   The velocity of the incompressible liquid as it leaves the pipe through

the slit varies along the length of the slit according to the law

$$v = 10 + x$$

where v = velocity of liquid leaving the pipe a distance x feet from point A at the beginning of the slit

What is the length of the slit for steady flow?

3-10. In Fig. P.3-9 the velocity of the liquid leaving the slit varies according to

$$v = 10e^{x/10}$$

where x is in feet. Compute the length of the slit for steady flow.

3-11. Calculate the shape of the slit in Problem 3-9 so that the flow rate per unit length of the slit is a constant. The thickness of the slit at A is $\frac{1}{4}$ in.

3-12. Fluid flows from a large reservoir through a bell mouth into a long horizontal pipe of constant diameter. The velocity is constant across the pipe at section 1. As the fluid flows down the pipe, the wall causes the growth

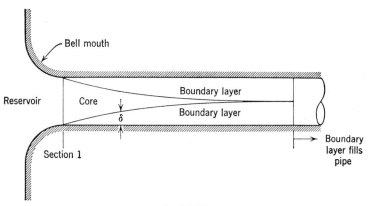

Fig. P.3-12

of a boundary layer. The velocity of the fluid inside the boundary layer varies according to the law

$$v = V_c(y/\delta)^{1/7}$$

where v = velocity a distance y from the wall
V_c = core velocity
δ = thickness of boundary layer

When the diameter of the pipe is 6 in. and the flow rate is 2 cfs, compute the core velocity when the boundary layer is 1 in. thick. Figure P.3-12 is a sketch of the pipe. Assume that the velocity is constant across the core but will vary along the core.

3-13. In Problem 3-12 compute the velocity of the core when the boundary layer is 2 in. thick.

3-14. In Problem 3-12 calculate the velocity of the core when the boundary layer is 3 in. thick.

3-15. Determine the thickness of the boundary layer in Problem 3-12 when the core velocity is 15 fps.

3-16. In the pipe in Problem 3-12 the flow rate is reduced to 0.006 cfs, which changes the velocity profile to

$$v = V_c \left(\frac{y}{\delta}\right)\left(2 - \frac{y}{\delta}\right)$$

where v = velocity a distance y from the wall
V_c = core velocity
δ = boundary layer thickness

Compute the core velocity when the boundary layer thickness is $\delta = 1\frac{1}{2}$ in.

3-17. A compressible gas with gas constant $R = 50$ ft/°F discharges, as shown in Fig. P.3-17, from a 12 in. dia. duct through a 4 in. nozzle into the

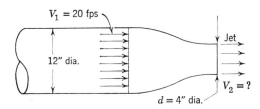

Fig. P.3-17

atmosphere. Pressure in the duct is 5 psig, whereas in the jet it is 15 psia. Temperature in the duct is 150°F, in the jet 100°F. Assume steady flow, uniform over each section, and calculate the jet velocity V_2.

3-18. The transition between two pipes of diameter 2 ft and 1 ft is 16 in. long as shown in Fig. P.3-18. The flow rate of water is steady at 10 cfs.

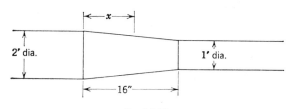

Fig. P.3-18

Compute the acceleration at $x = 8$ in. Assume that the velocity is uniform across each section perpendicular to the flow.

3-19. In Problem 3-18 compute the acceleration when the flow rate is increasing at the rate of 0.5 ft³/sec².

3-20. In Fig. P.3-18 the fluid is flowing at the rate of 3 cfs. Compute the acceleration at any point x in the transition length.

3-21. Figure P.3-21 is a sketch of two streamlines A_1A_2 and B_1B_2. Assum-

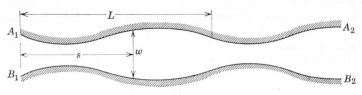

Fig. P.3-21

ing one-dimensional flow in the s direction, compute the acceleration when the distance w between the streamlines varies as

$$w = 2 - \sin\left(\frac{s}{L}\right)\pi$$

where s = unknown distance along the pipe, in ft
L = some fixed distance along the pipe, in ft

The flow rate is Q cfs per foot of width of incompressible fluid.

3-22. In Fig. P.3-21 compute the acceleration at $x = L/2$ when the flow rate is $Q = 2e^{-t}$ cfs per foot of width, where t is time in seconds.

3-23. Water is flowing from a tank through a hole in the side as shown in Fig. P.3-23a. From experience it is known that the jet of water converges so

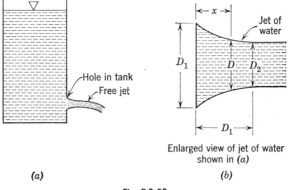

Enlarged view of jet of water
shown in (a)

(a)   (b)

Fig. P.3-23

that its diameter changes from the diameter D_1 of the hole to a diameter D_2 of approximately $0.8D_1$. Assume that the change takes place in a length of D_1 and that the diameter D between D_1 and D_2 varies as the length x along the jet according to

$$D = \left(D_1 - \frac{x}{5}\right) \quad \text{for } 0 \le x \le D_1$$

Compute the acceleration at $x = 0$ and $x = D_1/2$. The jet is shown in Fig. P.3-23b and the flow rate is constant at Q cfs.

3-24. Assume that the diameter of the jet in Problem 3-23 varies as

$$D = D_1 \left[1 - \frac{1}{5} \left(\frac{x}{D_1} \right)^2 \right]$$

Calculate the acceleration at $x/D_1 = \frac{1}{2}$.

3-25. In Problem 3-23 assume that the flow rate is

$$Q = Q_o e^{-t/50}$$

where t = time, in sec

Determine the acceleration at $x/D_1 = \frac{1}{3}$

3-26. In Problem 3-23 assume that the flow rate is

$$Q = Q_o \left(1 - \frac{t}{100} \right)$$

where t = time, in sec

Compute the acceleration at $x/D_1 = \frac{3}{4}$

3-27. In Problem 3-1 the pressure at section 1 is 75 psia. Calculate the pressure at section 2 and at section 3. Neglect the changes in elevation. Here $\rho = 2.00$ slugs/ft³.

3-28. In Problem 3-7 the pressure in the pipe upstream of the holes is 5 psig. Determine the pressure in the pipe between the holes A and B, B and C, and the hole C and the end of the pipe. Here $\rho = 2.00$ slugs/ft³.

3-29. In Problem 3-8 the pressure in the pipe upstream of the holes is 10 psig. Determine the pressure in the pipe between the holes A and B, B and C, and the hole C and the end of the pipe. Here $\rho = 2.00$ slugs/ft³.

3-30. Determine the velocity of the fluid leaving the nozzle shown in Fig. P.3-30. Calculate the flow rate for this nozzle. Here $\rho = 1.94$ slugs/ft³.

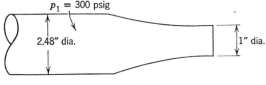

Fig. P.3-30

3-31. Calculate the velocity of the water as it leaves the pipe at A as shown in Fig. P.3-31. The elevation of A is 300 ft.

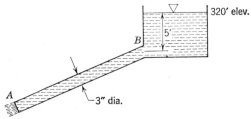

Fig. P.3-31

3-32. In Fig. P.3-31 determine the minimum elevation of point A if there is no cavitation. The vapor pressure of the water is 4 psia, and the atmospheric pressure is 14.7 psia.

3-33. The tank shown in Fig. P.3-33 has a nozzle at A. The water leaves the tank at A perpendicular to the surface AB. The tank is filled with water to a height h. Calculate d. Neglect all friction. Here $\alpha = 60°$ and $\beta = 30°$.

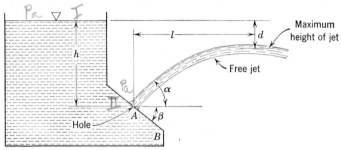

Fig. P.3-33

3-34. Repeat Problem 3-33 for $\alpha = 30°$ and $\beta = 60°$.

3-35. In Problem 3-33 compute l.

3-36. In Fig. P.3-36 compute the largest value of h for which flow can be maintained. The vapor pressure is 1.7 psia, and the surface tension is 4.98 $(10)^{-3}$ lb/ft.

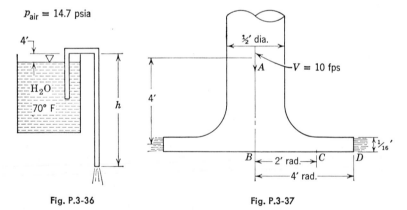

Fig. P.3-36   Fig. P.3-37

3-37. Water is flowing through the vertical pipe shown in Fig. P.3-37 out of the flange at D. The flow in the pipe is of uniform velocity, and the flow out the flange is radial away from the centerline of the pipe. Compute the pressure and velocity at A, B, C, and D.

3-38. A Venturi Meter is a common means of measuring the flow rate of an incompressible fluid in a pipe. Figure P.3-38 is a sketch of a Venturi Meter placed in a pipe of uniform 6 in. diameter. For the reading on the manometer shown, compute the flow rate in cubic feet per second.

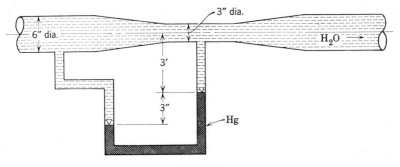

Fig. P.3-38

3-39. Water, with a uniform velocity of 10 fps, leaves a vertical pipe at point A. Assuming the fluid falls as a continuum, calculate the cross-sectional area at B.

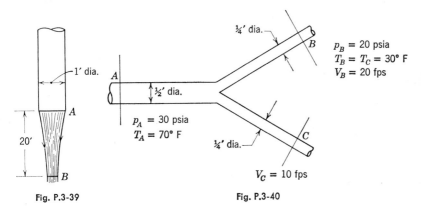

Fig. P.3-39   Fig. P.3-40

3-40. Consider all properties as constant across each cross section of the pipes in Fig. P.3-40. A perfect gas flows from left to right. The engineering gas constant is 50 ft/°F abs. Calculate the pressure at C. $V_A = 6$ fps.

3-41. In Fig. P.3-41 calculate h for maximum Q. Water vapor pressure is 3.7 psia. The pipe is constant diameter.

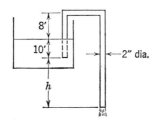

Fig. P.3-41

3-42. Water is flowing in the pipe constriction shown in Fig. P.3-42.   Determine the flow rate.

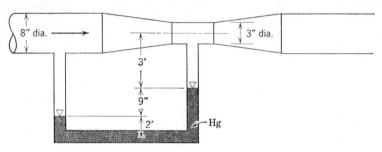

Fig. P.3-42

3-43. Calculate the steady flow rate in the problem shown in Fig. P.3-43. Atmospheric pressure is 15 psia; water vapor is 2.0 psia.

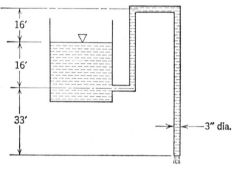

Fig. P.3-43

3-44. Determine the area A for the maximum flow rate of water.   Neglect friction; vapor pressure is 4.7 psia, and atmospheric pressure is 14.7 psia.

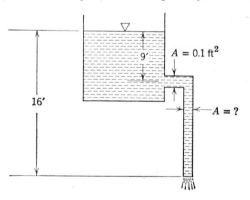

Fig. P.3-44

3-45. Water is flowing as shown in Fig. P.3-45. Calculate the flow rate. Here $\rho = 1.94$ slugs/ft^3.

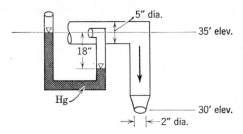

Fig. P.3-45

3-46. Calculate the velocity of water at section 1. The water flows steadily in the horizontal pipe shown in Fig. P.3-46. Neglect all friction.

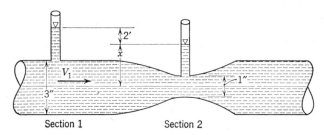

Fig. P.3-46

3-47. A vertical 3 in. dia. pipe shoots a jet of water 100 ft straight up above the end of the pipe. Compute the velocity of the jet at the end of the pipe.

3-48. Sixteen cubic feet per second of water flows in the pipe in Fig. P.3-48. Calculate the diameter of the vena contracta. State any assumptions used.

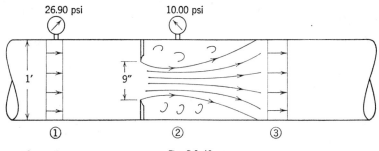

Fig. P.3-48

3-49. A farmer siphons water from a large lake over a hill and into a well. The elevation of the lake is 300 ft, the elevation of the highest point in the siphon is 315 ft, and the elevation of the water surface in the well is 275 ft. The pipe used in the siphon has a cross-sectional area of 0.3 ft^2. Calculate the flow rate for vapor pressure of 3.7 psia and atmospheric pressure of 14.7 psia.

3-50. The tank in Fig. P.3-50 is filled to a depth of h ft of water.   Drill a hole in the side so that the distance a from the tank to where the water hits the ground is a maximum.

Fig. P.3-50   **Fig. P.3-51**

3-51. Determine the length of time it takes the water level to fall from 6 ft to 4 ft in a cylindrical tank that has a 2 in. effective diameter hole drilled in the bottom.   The tank as shown in Fig. P.3-51 is 4 ft in diameter.

3-52. In Fig. P.3-52 the tank is 8 ft high.   The diameter varies as a straight line from 4 ft at the top to 2 ft at the bottom.   Compute the time for the water level in the tank to drop from 8 ft to 2 ft.

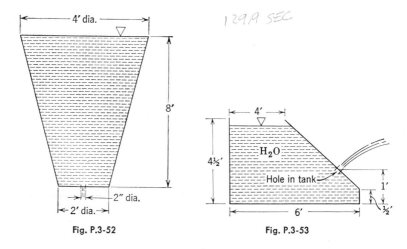

Fig. P.3-52   **Fig. P.3-53**

3-53. Figure P.3-53 is a side view of a tank that is 2 ft wide.   Calculate the time for the water level in the tank to drop from 3 ft to 2 ft above the bottom of the tank.   The effective diameter of the hole in the tank is 3 in.

3-54. Air flows in a horizontal pipe that is 6 in. in diameter at section 1. The velocity of the air at section 1 is 30 fps.   The velocity at section 2 is 200 fps.   The pressure at section 1 is 30 psia, and the temperature is 530°R. For an isothermal expansion compute the pressure, diameter, and the density at section 2.

3-55. Rework Problem 3-54 for an isentropic expansion instead of an isothermal one.

3-56. A plane is flying 500 mph relative to the still air. The atmospheric pressure is 10 psia. For an isentropic expansion compute the pressure on the nose of the plane. The air temperature is 485°R.

3-57. In Problem 3-56 the average velocity of the air relative to the wing is 550 mph on the top of the wing and 450 mph on the bottom of the wing. What must the wing area be to support a 15,000 lb airplane? Assume isentropic expansion.

3-58. A cylinder 2 ft in diameter and 20 ft long is rotating in a stream of fluid which flows with a uniform steady velocity V when undisturbed. The

2160 .145 FSFA

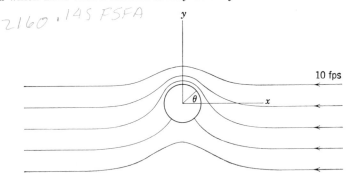

Fig. P.3-58

flow around the cylinder is approximated by the streamlines shown in Fig. P.3-58. The velocity u of the fluid at the surface of the cylinder can be approximated by the equation

$$u = (20 \sin \theta + 10) \text{ fps}$$

The pressure in the undisturbed stream where the velocity is 10 fps is 15 psia. Locate points on the cylinder where pressure is a maximum. Compute the pressure at these points for an incompressible fluid of density $\rho = 0.0029$ slug/ft³.

3-59. Calculate the pressure force in the x direction on the cylinder in Problem 3-58.

3-60. Compute the pressure force in the y direction on the cylinder in Problem 3-58.

3-61. The temperature and density of the undisturbed stream in Problem 3-58 is 70°F and 0.0029 slug/ft³. For an isentropic expansion, compute the pressure at the stagnation points.

3-62. In Problem 3-61 compute the resultant pressure force on the cylinder.

3-63. Assume the straight line in Fig. P.3-63 to be the profile of a wing with the velocity distribution of u_t on the upper surface and u_L on the lower surface.

$$u_t = V(x)(x - 10)$$

$$u_L = \frac{V}{2}(x)(x - 10)$$

The velocities u_t, u_L, and V, the velocity of the undisturbed stream, are all in feet per second. The distance x is in feet. Compute the pressure on the front edge of the profile when $V = 200$ fps and the pressure, the density, and the temperature of the undisturbed stream are $p = 15$ psia, $\rho = 0.0024$ slug/ft^3 and $T = 70°F$ respectively. State assumptions. Note that the profile is at an angle α with the direction of the undisturbed stream.

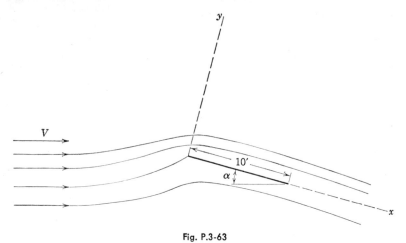

Fig. P.3-63

3-64. Compute the pressure force per unit width normal to the xy plane on the wing profile in Problem 3-63.

3-65. When the velocity V is 400 fps, compute the pressure at the front edge of the wing profile in Problem 3-63. Is the assumption of incompressible fluid valid?

3-66. In Problem 3-65 compute the pressure force per unit wing in the x and y directions.

3-67. The force of the fluid on the wing in the direction of the velocity V is called the drag force, and the force normal to the direction of V is called the lift. Compute the lift and drag in Problem 3-63, assuming no friction and a 60 ft wing.

3-68. Defining lift and drag as in Problem 3-67, compute the lift and drag in Problem 3-66, assuming no friction and a 60 ft wing.

MOMENTUM
and ANGULAR MOMENTUM

chapter **4**

29. Introduction to Momentum Analysis

In the preceding chapter, we used Newton's second law to derive the Bernoulli equation which is valid for steady, incompressible, frictionless flow along a streamline. In this chapter we use Newton's second law to derive the momentum equations which have many advantages over the Bernoulli equation. In the derivation of the momentum equation we assume only that Newton's second law applies. The flow may be compressible or incompressible, with friction or frictionless, steady or unsteady, and the equation need not be applied along a streamline. This lack of restriction is the main value of the momentum equation.

In the next chapter, we shall apply the energy principle to fluid flow problems. We shall find that we must compute the energy losses inside a control volume in order to solve many of the problems, a difficulty that is not encountered in the momentum analysis.

30. Derivation of Momentum Equation

Newton's second law may be written in the form

$$\sum F_x = \frac{d(MV_x)}{dt} \tag{4-1}$$

Therefore, the sum of external forces in the x direction equals the rate of change of momentum in the x direction. The symbol for the momentum MV will be $\mathbf{M}$. A mass system occupies a certain space at some time t and moves into a new space at time $t + \Delta t$ (Fig. 33a and b).

$\mathbf{M}_{x_1}$ = momentum in x direction of mass system at time t

$\mathbf{M}_{x_2}$ = momentum in x direction of mass system at time $t + \Delta t$

$\mathbf{M}_{x_1}'$ = momentum in x direction of mass in control volume at time t

$\mathbf{M}_{x_2}'$ = momentum in x direction of mass in control volume at time $t + \Delta t$

$\Delta \mathbf{M}_{x_o}$ = momentum in x direction of the mass that has left the control volume in time Δt

$\Delta \mathbf{M}_{x_i}$ = momentum in x direction of the mass that has entered the control volume in time Δt

The momentum in the x direction of the mass system equals the momentum of the mass in the control volume at time t because the same mass is involved in both cases.

$$\mathbf{M}_{x_1} = \mathbf{M}_{x_1}'$$

At time $(t + \Delta t)$ the momentum in the x direction of the mass system equals the momentum in the x direction of the mass in the

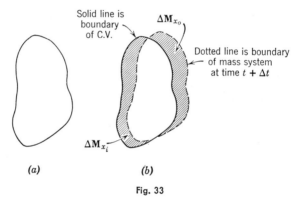

Solid line is boundary of C.V.

$\Delta \mathbf{M}_{x_o}$

Dotted line is boundary of mass system at time $t + \Delta t$

$\Delta \mathbf{M}_{x_i}$

(a)   (b)

Fig. 33

control volume, plus the momentum in the x direction of the mass that has flowed out of the control volume, minus the momentum in the x direction of the mass that has flowed into the control volume in time Δt.

$$\mathbf{M}_{x_2} = \mathbf{M}_{x_2}' + \Delta \mathbf{M}_{x_o} - \Delta \mathbf{M}_{x_i}$$

The change of momentum in the x direction of the mass system is $(\mathbf{M}_{x_2} - \mathbf{M}_{x_1})$. As this takes place in time Δt, the change is $\Delta \mathbf{M}_x$. Thus,

$$\Delta \mathbf{M}_x = \mathbf{M}_{x_2} - \mathbf{M}_{x_1}$$

We substitute the above values of $\mathbf{M}_{x_2}$ and $\mathbf{M}_{x_1}$ to get

$$\Delta \mathbf{M}_x = \mathbf{M}_{x_2}' - \mathbf{M}_{x_1}' + \Delta \mathbf{M}_{x_o} - \Delta \mathbf{M}_{x_i}$$

and divide by Δt to form

$$\frac{\Delta \mathbf{M}_x}{\Delta t} = \frac{\Delta (MV_x)}{\Delta t} = \frac{\mathbf{M}_{x_2}' - \mathbf{M}_{x_1}'}{\Delta t} + \frac{\Delta \mathbf{M}_{x_o} - \Delta \mathbf{M}_{x_i}}{\Delta t}$$

The limit of $\Delta \mathbf{M}_x / \Delta t$ as $\Delta t \to 0$ is

$$\lim_{\Delta t \to 0} \frac{\Delta \mathbf{M}_x}{\Delta t} = \frac{d \mathbf{M}_x}{dt} = \frac{d(MV)}{dt} = \frac{\mathbf{M}_{x_2}' - \mathbf{M}_{x_1}'}{dt} + \frac{d \mathbf{M}_{x_o} - d \mathbf{M}_{x_i}}{dt} \quad (4\text{-}2)$$

By substituting Equation 4-2 into Equation 4-1, we get the momentum equation for a control volume, the most general form of the momentum equation.

$$\sum F_x = \frac{\mathbf{M}_{x_2}' - \mathbf{M}_{x_1}'}{dt} + \frac{d \mathbf{M}_{x_o} - d \mathbf{M}_{x_i}}{dt} \quad (4\text{-}3)$$

The only restrictions are those that apply to Newton's second law. The $(\mathbf{M}_{x_2}' - \mathbf{M}_{x_1}')/dt$ is the rate of accumulation of momentum in the x direction inside the control volume. The second term

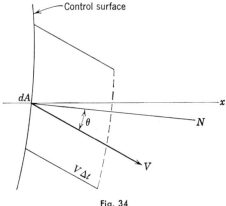

Fig. 34

$(d \mathbf{M}_{x_o} - d \mathbf{M}_{x_i})/dt$ is the rate of outflow of momentum in the x direction through the control surfaces.

To put Equation 4-3 in more usable form, we examine the outflow of momentum in the x direction through an increment of the area dA on the control surface. One side of this area appears in Fig. 34; the other dimension is normal to the figure. The momentum in the x direction of the fluid that leaves the control volume through the area dA is the mass that leaves the area times the velocity in the x direction of this mass. All this is in time dt. The mass outflow in time dt is $\rho V \cos \theta \, dA \, dt$. The velocity component in the x direction is $\bar{V}_x$.

The bar over the V_x is to show that this is a vector quantity which can be either negative or positive. The outflow of momentum in the x direction through all of the area is the total outflow of momentum in the x direction. Thus,

$$dM_{x_o} - dM_{x_i} = \int_A \bar{V}_x \rho V \cos \theta \, dA \, dt$$

Since the $\int_A$ signifies the integration over the entire surface area of the control volume at some specific time, the dt term is constant during the integration and may be taken outside the integral sign. We then divide by dt to get

$$\frac{dM_{x_o} - dM_{x_i}}{dt} = \int_A \bar{V}_x \rho V \cos \theta \, dA \qquad (4\text{-}4)$$

and combine Equations 4-3 and 4-4.

$$\sum F_x = \frac{M_{x_2}' - M_{x_1}'}{dt} + \int_A \bar{V}_x \rho V \cos \theta \, dA \qquad (4\text{-}5)$$

Equation 4-5 is the momentum equation in the x direction. Just as the sum of the forces in statics is set equal to zero in three different directions normal to each other, so the momentum equation applies in three different directions. In a three-dimensional flow problem, then, there are three independent momentum equations. The equations in the y and z directions are derived in the same manner as the equation in the x direction.

$$\left. \begin{aligned} \sum F_x &= \frac{M_{x_2}' - M_{x_1}'}{dt} + \int_A \bar{V}_x \rho V \cos \theta \, dA \\[2mm] \sum F_y &= \frac{M_{y_2}' - M_{y_1}'}{dt} + \int_A \bar{V}_y \rho V \cos \theta \, dA \\[2mm] \sum F_z &= \frac{M_{z_2}' - M_{z_1}'}{dt} + \int_A \bar{V}_z \rho V \cos \theta \, dA \end{aligned} \right\} \qquad (4\text{-}6)$$

The final form of the general momentum equations, Equations 4-6, is a very powerful tool in fluid mechanics. One of the limitations of Newton's second law concerns velocity and acceleration terms which must be measured from an axis system at rest or traveling with a constant velocity of translation. Thus, it is possible to compute external forces in the general momentum equation by using an axis system that is not stationary.

It should be repeated that $\bar{V}_x$, $\bar{V}_y$, and $\bar{V}_z$ are vector components of the velocity in the x, y, and z directions. The vector components can be either negative or positive. Whichever sense is positive in summing the external forces must be positive for the velocity vector. It is also necessary to be on the alert for the sign of the $\cos \theta$ term.

Illustrative Problems 1 through 5 demonstrate the use of the momentum equations.

In Illustrative Problem 1 we use the momentum equations to solve for the forces necessary to hold a pipe bend in place. This type of problem is encountered in the construction of pipe networks, water systems, hydraulic lines, and other pipe work.

In Illustrative Problem 2 we use the momentum equations to solve for the thrust developed by a stationary jet engine. If the jet engine were moving with a constant velocity V of translation and the intake and exit conditions remained unchanged, the solution would be the same. We would write all terms with respect to a moving axis system which is attached to the engine. The intake and exit conditions varying with changing V, however, are the main difficulties with this approach. Also questioned often is the assumption of uniform velocity at the exit.

We use the momentum equations to determine the vane forces in Illustrative Problem 3. We encounter this general type of problem in water scoops on locomotives and in stopping the rocket sleds used in high acceleration testing on land.

In Illustrative Problem 4 we use the momentum equations to calculate the force on a flat plate being towed through water. This problem demonstrates that with no knowledge of shear stresses on the plate we can calculate the resultant forces of the shear stresses by the momentum equations and by knowing how friction changes the velocity. This ideal problem does not take into account some turbulent effects which we are not yet ready to discuss. Now is an excellent time to point out that we can solve many problems by the use of these fundamental equations, but in many cases a complete understanding of the flow of a real fluid is necessary before we can determine the entrance and exit conditions.

In Illustrative Problem 5 we use the momentum equations to compute the maximum velocity of a type of sled used by the United States Air Force in acceleration tests on human beings.

▶**Illustrative Problem 1.** Water flows steadily in a 4 in. dia. horizontal pipe. The pipe bends and reduces in size at the same time. A top view (Fig. 35a) shows the vertical-axis and the horizontal x and y

axes.   Calculate the forces in the x and y directions necessary to hold the pipe bend in place.   The pressure at section 1 is 50 psia, the atmospheric pressure is 15 psia, and the velocity of the water at section 1 is 10 fps.   Assume that the water is a perfect fluid with a density of 1.94 slugs/ft^3.

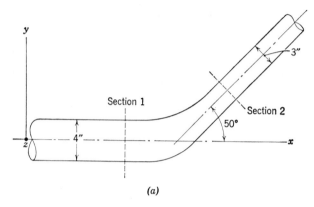

(a)

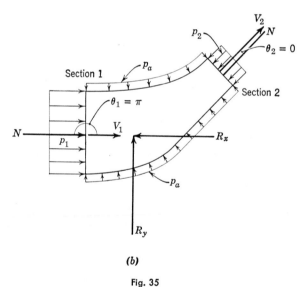

(b)

Fig. 35

Solution: Figure 35b is a sketch of the control volume that includes the pipe between sections 1 and 2 and all the water inside the pipe between the two sections.   The forces R_x and R_y are the resultant forces on the pipe bend due to the stresses in the pipe wall cut at sections 1 and 2.

Atmospheric pressure acts upon all external surfaces of the pipe. The pressure of the surrounding fluid must replace any fluid that is cut. Then the fluid pressure at sections 1 and 2 acts on the control volume at those surfaces.

Use Equations 4-6 to compute the forces R_x and R_y. The two equations in the x and y directions will be the only two needed. They are

$$\sum F_x = \frac{\mathbf{M}_{x2}' - \mathbf{M}_{x1}'}{dt} + \int_A \bar{V}_x \rho V \cos \theta \, dA$$

$$\sum F_y = \frac{\mathbf{M}_{y2}' - \mathbf{M}_{y1}'}{dt} + \int_A \bar{V}_y \rho V \cos \theta \, dA$$

Because the flow is steady, the momentum of the fluid inside the control volume is constant. Thus

$$\mathbf{M}_{x2}' = \mathbf{M}_{x1}', \ \mathbf{M}_{y2}' = \mathbf{M}_{y1}'$$

The sum of the external forces in the x direction is

$$\overset{+}{\rightarrow} \quad \Sigma F_x = (p_1 - p_a) A_1 - (p_2 - p_a) A_2 \cos 50 - R_x$$

Assume that the atmospheric pressure acts on every surface of the control volume. Neglect the difference in elevation, and the body will be in equilibrium. Therefore, if you subtract atmospheric pressure from every surface of the control volume, there is no change in the resultant forces on the control volume, because for every pressure times area in the x direction subtracted, an equal product of pressure and area has been subtracted in the negative x direction. This leaves as the only pressure forces $(p_1 - p_a) A_1$ and $(p_2 - p_a) A_2$ which are the only ones you need to consider.

The sum of these external forces must equal $\int_A \bar{V}_x \rho V \cos \theta \, dA$. Here $\cos \theta$ is zero everywhere except on the surfaces at sections 1 and 2. Thus,

$$\int_A \bar{V}_x \rho V \cos \theta \, dA = \int_{A_1} \bar{V}_{x1} \rho_1 V_1 \cos \theta_1 \, dA$$

$$+ \int_{A_2} \bar{V}_{x2} \rho_2 V_2 \cos \theta_2 \, dA \quad \text{(K)}$$

where $\rho_1 = \rho_2 = 1.94$ slugs/ft^3

$\theta_1 = \pi$

$\theta_2 = 0$

$V_1 = 10$ fps

and where V_2 is constant over A_2 and $\bar{V}_{x_2}$ is constant over A_2. Substitute these values into Equation K and carry out the integration.

$$\int_A \bar{V}_{x}\rho V \cos\theta\, dA = (1.94)(10)(-1)(+10)\,\frac{\pi\left(\frac{1}{3}\right)^2}{4}$$

$$+ (1.94)V_2\bar{V}_{x_2}(+1)\,\frac{\pi\left(\frac{1}{4}\right)^2}{4}$$

When all of these are combined in the momentum equation, there results

$$(p_1 - p_a)A_1 - (p_2 - p_a)A_2 \cos 50 - R_x$$

$$= 0 + (1.94)(10)(-1)(+10)\,\frac{\pi}{36} + 1.94(V_2)(\bar{V}_{x_2})(+1)\,\frac{\pi}{64}$$

Given $p_1 = 50$ psia and $p_a = 15$ psia.

$$(144)\,\frac{\pi}{36}\,(50 - 15) - (144)\,\frac{\pi}{64}\,(p_2 - 15)\cos 50 - R_x$$

$$= -(194)\,\frac{\pi}{36} + 1.94(V_2)(\bar{V}_{x_2})\,\frac{\pi}{64}$$

Here $\bar{V}_{x_2}$ is the x component of V. Therefore,

$$\bar{V}_{x_2} = +V_2 \cos 50$$

$$(144)\,\frac{(\pi)}{36}\,35 - (144)\,\frac{\pi}{64}\,(p_2 - 15)\cos 50 - R_x$$

$$= -\frac{194\pi}{36} + (1.94)(V_2)^2 \cos 50 \left(\frac{\pi}{64}\right) \quad (L)$$

To solve for R_x, you must obtain values for V_2 and p_2. To use the other momentum equations will only add R_y and R_z unknowns and will not help obtain values for V_2 and p_2. Try the continuity and the Bernoulli equations. Using the same control volume, write the continuity equation for an incompressible fluid.

$$\int_A V \cos\theta\, dA = 0$$

$$V_1(-1)\,\frac{\pi\left(\frac{1}{3}\right)^2}{4} + V_2(+1)\,\frac{\pi\left(\frac{1}{4}\right)^2}{4} = 0$$

$$V_2 = \tfrac{10}{9}\,16 = \tfrac{160}{9} = 17.8 \text{ fps}$$

Because this is an incompressible perfect fluid that flows steadily, apply the Bernoulli equation along the centerline of the pipe bend which is a streamline.

$$\frac{p_2 - p_1}{\rho} + \frac{V_2{}^2 - V_1{}^2}{2} + g(z_2 - z_1) = 0$$

$$\frac{(p_2 - 50)(144)}{1.94} + \frac{(17.8)^2 - (10)^2}{2} + 32.2(0 - 0) = 0$$

$$p_2 = 50 - \frac{1.94}{144}\left[\frac{(17.8)^2 - (10)^2}{2}\right] = 50 - \frac{(1.94)(216.5)}{(2)(144)}$$

$$p_2 = 50 - 1.45 = 48.55 \text{ psia}$$

In the Bernoulli equation this time, you used absolute pressure, but it makes no difference whether you use absolute or gage pressure just as long as you use the same one throughout the equation.

Substitute the values of V_2 and p_2 into the momentum equation L to get

$$(144)\frac{35\pi}{36} - (144)\frac{\pi}{64}(48.55 - 15)\cos 50 - R_x = -194\frac{\pi}{36}$$

$$+ (1.94)(17.8)^2 \cos 50\left(\frac{\pi}{64}\right)$$

$$R_x = 221.3 \text{ lb}$$

The plus sign means the assumed direction was correct.   Now compute R_y by using the momentum equation in the y direction.

$$\sum F_y = \frac{\mathbf{M}_{y2}{}' - \mathbf{M}_{y1}{}'}{dt} + \int_A \bar{V}_y \rho V \cos \theta \, dA$$

The sum of the external forces in the y direction is

$$+\uparrow \sum F_y = R_y - (p_2 - p_a)A_2 \sin 50$$

$$\sum F_y = R_y - (48.55 - 15)\frac{\pi(\frac{1}{4})^2}{4}(144)\sin 50$$

$$= (R_y - 182) \text{ lb}$$

The momentum of the water inside the control volume does not change. Therefore, $(\mathbf{M}_{y2}{}' - \mathbf{M}_{y1}{}')/dt = 0$ and

$$\sum F_y = \int_A \bar{V}_y \rho V \cos \theta \, dA$$

$$R_y - 182 = \int_{A_1} \bar{V}_{y_1} \rho_1 V_1 \cos \theta_1 \, dA + \int_{A_2} \bar{V}_{y_2} \rho_2 V_2 \cos \theta_2 \, dA$$

but $\qquad \bar{V}_{y_1} = 0$

therefore $\qquad R_y - 182 = 0 + \rho_2 V_2 \cos \theta_2 \, \bar{V}_{y_2} \dfrac{\pi (\frac{1}{4})^2}{4}$

Since $\bar{V}_{y_2}$ is the y component of V_2, $\bar{V}_{y_2} = V_2 \sin 50$. Thus,

$$R_y - 182 = (1.94)(17.8)(+1)(17.8) \sin 50 \, \frac{\pi}{64}$$

$$R_y = 182 + (1.94)(17.8)^2 \, \frac{\pi}{64} \sin 50 = 205 \text{ lb}$$

Again the plus sign signifies that R_y was selected in the proper sense. ◀

▶**Illustrative Problem 2.**   The air intake duct of a jet engine being tested on a stationary stand takes in air at an average velocity of 600 fps.   Air enters the intake duct, and exhaust gases exit the tail pipe at atmospheric pressure.   Fuel enters the top of the engine at the rate of 1 slug of fuel to 50 slugs of intake air.   The intake duct area is 2 ft^2.   The exit velocity of the exhaust gases is 4000 fps.   The density of the entering air is 0.00238 slug/ft^3.   What force is necessary to hold the engine?

Solution: Sketch a schematic control volume of the engine.   Write the momentum equation for the x direction.

$$\sum F_x = \frac{\mathbf{M}_{x_2}{}' - \mathbf{M}_{x_1}{}'}{dt} + \int_A \bar{V}_x \rho V \cos \theta \, dA$$

Section 1
$V_1 = 600$ fps
$\rho_1 = 0.00238$ slug/ft^3

Section 2
$V_2 = 4000$ fps

Sketch 29

This is steady flow; therefore, $(\mathbf{M}_{x_2}' - \mathbf{M}_{x_1}')/dt = 0$

The forces due to the external pressures must be zero because the pressure is constant on all external surfaces of the control volume. Thus, the external forces ΣF_x are

$$\Sigma F_x = F_x$$

and the momentum equation becomes

$$F_x = \int_A \bar{V}_x \rho V \cos \theta \, dA \qquad \text{(M)}$$

Since $\theta = \pi/2$ at all control volume surfaces except the intake duct, the fuel injection opening, and the tail pipe, the value of the integral is zero except at these three surfaces. The fuel has no component V_{x_3} in the x direction so that the above integral in Equation M over this opening is zero, which reduces the equation to

$$F_x = \int_{A_1} \bar{V}_{x_1} \rho_1 V_1 \cos \theta_1 \, dA + \int_{A_2} \bar{V}_{x_2} \rho_2 V_2 \cos \theta_2 \, dA$$

Because all quantities are constant over the areas of integration, take them outside the integral sign.

$$F_x = \rho_1 V_1(-1)\bar{V}_{x_1} \int_{A_1} dA + \rho_2 V_2(+1)\bar{V}_{x_2} \int_{A_2} dA$$

where $\bar{V}_{x_1}$ is the x component of V_1 and $\bar{V}_{x_2}$ is the x component of V_2. Therefore,

$$\bar{V}_{x_1} = V_1 \qquad \text{and} \qquad \bar{V}_{x_2} = V_2$$

Thus,

$$F_x = -\rho_1 A_1 V_1^2 + \rho_2 A_2 V_2^2$$

To find the values of ρ_2 and A_2, try the continuity equation. For steady flow it is

$$0 = \int_A \rho V \cos \theta \, dA$$

Since $\theta = \pi/2$ at all control surfaces except the three mentioned above, the equation becomes

$$0 = \int_{A_1} \rho_1 V_1 \cos \theta_1 \, dA + \int_{A_2} \rho_2 V_2 \cos \theta_2 \, dA + \int_{A_3} \rho_3 V_3 \cos \theta_3 \, dA$$

Again these are constant over the integration area and so take them outside the integral sign and carry out the integration.

$$0 = \rho_1 V_1 A_1 \cos \theta_1 + \rho_2 V_2 A_2 \cos \theta_2 + \rho_3 V_3 A_3 \cos \theta_3$$

Substitute the values of θ taken from the sketch of the control volume.

$$0 = -\rho_1 A_1 V_1 + \rho_2 A_2 V_2 - \rho_3 A_3 V_3 \qquad \text{(N)}$$

The term $\rho_1 A_1 V_1$ is the mass intake of air, and the term $\rho_3 A_3 V_3$ is the mass intake of fuel. The problem states that 50 slugs of air are used for every slug of fuel. Therefore,

$$\rho_1 A_1 V_1 = 50\rho_3 A_3 V_3$$

which, when substituted into the continuity equation N, becomes

$$0 = -\rho_1 A_1 V_1 + \rho_2 A_2 V_2 - \tfrac{1}{50}\rho_1 A_1 V_1$$

or

$$\tfrac{51}{50}\rho_1 A_1 V_1 = \rho_2 A_2 V_2$$

Rearrange the momentum equation for F_x from

$$F_x = -\rho_1 A_1 V_1{}^2 + \rho_2 A_2 V_2{}^2$$

to

$$F_x = (-\rho_1 A_1 V_1)V_1 + (\rho_2 A_2 V_2)V_2$$

Substitute the above for $\rho_2 A_2 V_2$ to obtain

$$F_x = (-\rho_1 A_1 V_1)V_1 + \tfrac{51}{50}(\rho_1 A_1 V_1)V_2$$
$$F_x = \rho_1 A_1 V_1(\tfrac{51}{50}V_2 - V_1)$$

By using the values given in the problem, calculate F_x as

$$F_x = (0.00238)(2)(600)\left(\frac{51}{50}\,4000 - 600\right)$$

$$= 9940 \text{ lb}$$

If this force is required to hold the engine in place, the engine develops 9940 lb of thrust under the conditions indicated. ◀

▶**Illustrative Problem 3.** A jet of water, 1.94 slugs/ft^3 density, is directed against a vane (Fig. 36a), which could be a blade in a turbine or in any other piece of hydraulic machinery. The jet of water, in the x direction before striking, enters the vane with a velocity of 30 fps tangent to the surface at A. The inside surface of the vane at B makes an angle of 150° with the x direction. Compute the forces F_x and F_y for the following two cases: (a) when the vane is stationary and (b) when the vane is moving with a constant velocity of 20 fps in the negative x direction. Calculate the power input to the vane for both cases, neglecting changes in elevation.

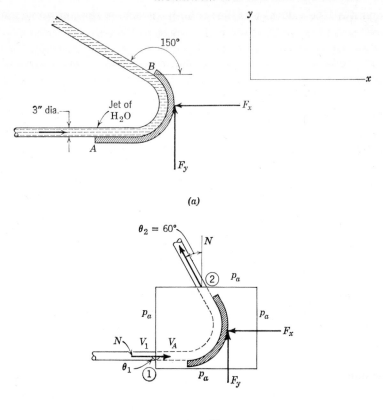

Fig. 36

Solution: (a) First, select a control volume that is stationary (Fig. 36b). The pressure on all external surfaces of the control volume is atmospheric pressure. Therefore, the resultant external force on the control volume due to the pressure is zero, and the sum of the external forces is

$$\overset{+}{\rightarrow} \quad \Sigma F_x = -F_x$$

$$+\uparrow \quad \Sigma F_y = F_y$$

The main assumption in vane problems supposes that the fluid leaves the vane with the same relative velocity to the wetted surface at the exit as the fluid had at the entrance. In this problem the rela- tive velocity of the fluid to the wetted surface at A is 30 fps to the right. Thus, the relative velocity to point B of the fluid at point B

is 30 fps. Sketch 30 shows this with all velocities indicated as the relative velocity of the fluid with respect to the adjacent surface.

Consider the control volume to be stationary. The entering velocity V_1 is 30 fps, and the leaving velocity V_2 is 30 fps. The momentum equations for steady flow are

$$\sum F_x = \int_A \bar{V}_x \rho V \cos \theta \, dA$$

$$\sum F_y = \int_A \bar{V}_y \rho V \cos \theta \, dA$$

Substitute the appropriate values in the momentum equation in the

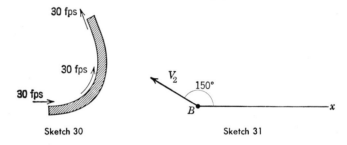

Sketch 30   Sketch 31

x direction and note that the integral is zero everywhere except where the fluid enters the control volume at section 1 and leaves at section 2.

$$-F_x = \int_{A_1} \bar{V}_{x_1} \rho_1 V_1 \cos \theta_1 \, dA + \int_{A_2} \bar{V}_{x_2} \rho_2 V_2 \cos \theta_2 \, dA$$

$$-F_x = (\bar{V}_{x_1}) \rho_1 V_1 \int_{A_1} dA + (\bar{V}_{x_2}) \rho_2 V_2 (\cos 60) \int_{A_2} dA$$

$$-F_x = -\rho_1 A_1 V_1{}^2 + \rho_2 A_2 V_2 (\cos 60) \bar{V}_{x_2}$$

Here $\bar{V}_{x_2}$ is the component of V_2 in the x direction. The velocity V_2 is 30 fps relative to B as shown in Fig. 36b. The vane is stationary and so V_2 is the absolute velocity of the fluid. The assumption of relative velocity at B demands that the fluid leaves the vane parallel to the vane. Therefore, at point B as shown in Sketch 31

$$\bar{V}_{x_2} = V_2 \cos 150 = -V_2 \cos 30 = (-0.866) V_2$$

Thus,

$$-F_x = -\rho_1 A_1 V_1{}^2 + \rho_2 A_2 V_2 (-0.866) V_2 (\cos 60)$$

$$= -\rho_1 A_1 V_1{}^2 - \rho_2 A_2 V_2{}^2 (0.866)(\cos 60)$$

Apply the equation of continuity to the control volume to try to eliminate the unknown area A_2. For steady flow the continuity equation is

$$0 = \int_A \rho V \cos \theta \, dA$$

$$0 = \rho_1 A_1 V_1(-1) + \rho_2 A_2 V_2 \cos 60$$

or $\qquad \rho_1 A_1 V_1 = \rho_2 A_2 V_2 \cos 60 = \tfrac{1}{2}\rho_2 A_2 V_2$

The momentum equation can be written as

$$-F_x = -\rho_1 A_1 V_1{}^2 - \frac{\rho_2 A_2 V_2}{2}(0.866 V_2)$$

By substituting $\rho_1 A_1 V_1$ for $\rho_2 A_2 V_2/2$, you get

$$-F_x = -\rho_1 A_1 V_1{}^2 - \rho_1 A_1 V_1(0.866 V_2)$$

$$+F_x = (1.94)\left[\frac{\pi\left(\frac{1}{4}\right)^2}{4}\right](30)^2 + 1.94\left[\frac{\pi\left(\frac{1}{4}\right)^2}{4}\right](30)(0.866)(30)$$

$$F_x = (1.94)\frac{\pi}{64}30[30 + 0.866(30)] = 160 \text{ lb}$$

To calculate the component in the vertical direction, use the other momentum equation.

$$F_y = \int_{A_1} \bar{V}_{y_1}\rho_1 V_1 \cos \theta_1 \, dA + \int_{A_2} \bar{V}_{y_2}\rho_2 V_2 \cos \theta_2 \, dA$$

Substitute the appropriate values into this equation to get

$$F_y = \rho_1 A_1 V_1(-1)(\bar{V}_{y_1}) + \rho_2 A_2 V_2(+1)\left(\tfrac{1}{2}\right)\bar{V}_{y_2}$$

Here $\bar{V}_{y_1}$ is the y component of V_1 and is zero because V_1 is in the x direction.

$$\bar{V}_{y_1} = 0$$

Here too, $\bar{V}_{y_2}$ is the y component of V_2; therefore,

$$\bar{V}_{y_2} = V_2 \sin 150 = V_2 \sin 30 = \frac{V_2}{2}$$

Thus,

$$F_y = 0 + \frac{\rho_2 A_2 V_2}{2}\frac{V_2}{2} = (\rho_1 A_1 V_1)\frac{V_2}{2}$$

$$F_y = (1.94)\frac{\pi}{64}(30)\frac{(30)}{2} = 42.8 \text{ lb}$$

Power input would be the force times the distance moved in the direction of the force divided by the time taken to move the distance.

This is actually force multiplied by the velocity in the direction of the force.   Since the vane is stationary, the velocity is zero.   Therefore, the power input is zero.

(b) The vane is moving to the left with a constant velocity of 20 fps. Select the axis system as though attached to the vane with the x axis

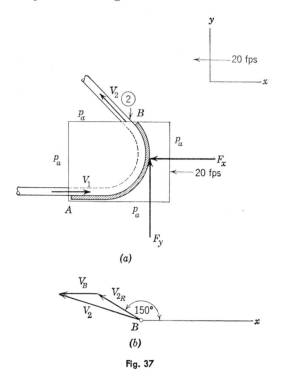

(a)

(b)

Fig. 37

in the direction of motion.   Thus, the control volume (Fig. 37a) will look the same except that it is moving with the vane at a velocity of 20 fps in the negative x direction.   Compute all of the velocities relative to this new axis system.   The flow is steady, and the pressure forces on the control volume cancel each other.   Thus, the only external forces on the control surfaces are the forces F_x and F_y which move the vanes.

The momentum equations reduce to

$$\overset{+}{\rightarrow} \quad -F_x = \int_A \bar{V}_x \rho V \cos \theta \, dA$$

$$+\uparrow \quad F_y = \int_A \bar{V}_y \rho V \cos \theta \, dA$$

Figure 37b shows the velocity of the water at section 2 as made up of two components. The first is the velocity V_{2R} of the water relative to point B, and the second is V_B, the velocity of point B. In the derivation of the momentum equation, the velocities were those relative to the control volume. Thus, in these momentum equations the velocities used must be relative to the control volume. Because the vane, control volume, and axis system move together, the velocities relative to the vane are relative to the control volume and the axis system, and you can substitute them directly into the momentum equations. At section 2 the velocity used should be V_{2R} which is the velocity relative to the axis system. At point A the absolute velocity of the water is 30 fps to the right. The velocity of the axis system is 20 fps to the left. Thus, the velocity of the water relative to the axis system is the sum of these two or 50 fps. The velocity V_R of water relative to the vane is 50 fps, and, because this does not change, the velocity relative to point B is also 50 fps and at an angle of 150° to the positive x axis. Substitute these values of velocity relative to the moving axis system into the momentum equations.

$$-F_x = \int_{A_1} \bar{V}_{x_1}\rho_1 V_1 \cos \theta_1 \, dA + \int_{A_2} \bar{V}_{x_2}\rho_2 V_2 \cos \theta_2 \, dA$$

$$F_y = \int_{A_1} \bar{V}_{y_1}\rho_1 V_1 \cos \theta_1 \, dA + \int_{A_2} \bar{V}_{y_2}\rho_2 V_2 \cos \theta_2 \, dA$$

All quantities inside the integral are constant over the area of integration and, therefore, are taken outside. Complete the integration to change the momentum equation to

$$-F_x = \rho_1 A_1 V_{1R}(\cos \theta_1)\bar{V}_{x_{1R}} + \rho_2 A_2 V_{2R}(\cos \theta_2)\bar{V}_{x_{2R}}$$

Now

$$\bar{V}_{x_{2R}} = V_{2R} \cos 150 = (-0.866) V_{2R}$$

$\qquad = x$ component of velocity relative to moving axis system at exit.

$\bar{V}_{x_{1R}} = x$ component relative to moving axis system at entrance $= V_{1R}$

Therefore,

$$-F_x = \rho_1 A_1 V_{1R}(-1) V_{1R} + \rho_2 A_2 V_{2R}(\cos 60)(V_{2R})(-0.866)$$

$$= -\rho_1 A_1 V_{1R}{}^2 - \rho_2 A_2 V_{2R}(\tfrac{1}{2})(0.866) V_{2R}$$

By continuity $\rho_1 A_1 V_{1R} = \rho_2 A_2 V_{2R}/2$

and so $\qquad -F_x = -\rho_1 A_1 V_{1R}(V_{1R} + 0.866 V_{2R})$

$$F_x = +(1.94)\frac{\pi}{64}50[50 + 0.866(50)]$$

$$= 444 \text{ lb}$$

The momentum equation in the y direction, after you carry out the integration, is

$$F_y = \int_{A_1} \bar{V}_{y_1}\rho_1 V_1 \cos\theta_1 \, dA + \int_{A_2} \bar{V}_{y_2}\rho_2 V_2 \cos\theta_2 \, dA$$

where $\bar{V}_{y_1} = y$ component of V_1.   Therefore,

$$\bar{V}_{y_1} = 0$$

All the quantities within the integral sign are constant.   Therefore,

$$F_2 = \rho_2 A_2 V_{2R} \cos\theta_2 \, \bar{V}_{y_{2R}}$$

$$= \frac{\rho_2 A_2 V_{2R}}{2} \bar{V}_{y_{2R}}$$

By continuity $\qquad \rho_1 A_1 V_{1R} = \dfrac{\rho_2 A_2 V_{2R}}{2}$

and so $\qquad \bar{V}_{y_{2R}} = V_{2R}\cos\theta = \dfrac{V_{2R}}{2}$

Therefore,

$$F_y = \rho_1 A_1 V_{1R}\frac{V_{2R}}{2} = (1.94)\frac{\pi}{64}\frac{(50)(50)}{2}$$

$$F_y = 119.2 \text{ lb}$$

As shown before, the power input is the velocity multiplied by the force in the direction of this velocity.   Thus, the power input P is

$$P = F_x V_x = (444)(20) = 8880 \text{ ft-lb/sec}$$

$$= \tfrac{8880}{550}$$

$$P = 16.1 \text{ hp} \qquad\qquad \blacktriangleleft$$

▶Illustrative Problem 4.   When a flat plate is towed through water with the surface of the plate parallel to the direction of the velocity, friction affects only a thin layer of fluid adjacent to the surface.   The zero thickness of this layer at the leading edge of the plate grows

larger in the downstream direction.   The fluid outside this layer is
not affected by it or the friction.   Figure 38a demonstrates all of
these circumstances with one exception: the figure shows the flow
as seen by an observer traveling with the plate.   This is tantamount

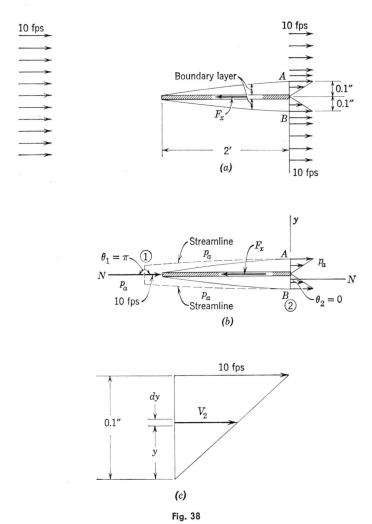

Fig. 38

to measuring all velocities with respect to an axis system rigidly
attached to the plate.   The plate is 2 ft square and has a velocity of
10 fps.   Compute the force necessary to drag the plate through the
water.

Solution: In the Figure, the line of demarcation between the boundary layer and the rest of the liquid is not a streamline.   Fluid is crossing this line continually.

First, select a control volume as shown in Fig. 38b with the control volume in a dotted outline.   Neglect the end effects of the side edges and assume that the flow is two dimensional.   The control volume is the two streamlines that pass through the points A and B, two planes perpendicular to flow at sections 1 and 2, and two planes normal to the plate and parallel to the stream.   The area at section 1 is unknown. The momentum equation for steady flow is

$$\sum F_x = \int_A \bar{V}_x \rho V \cos \theta \, dA$$

The pressure is assumed to vary hydrostatically.   Thus, at each elevation the pressure on the control volume is constant which means the sum of the pressure forces must be zero.   Therefore,

$$\xleftarrow{+} \quad \Sigma F_x = F_x$$

The only surfaces of the control volume where $\cos \theta$ differs from zero are at sections 1 and 2.   This makes the momentum equation

$$F_x = \int_{A_1} \bar{V}_{1x} \rho_1 V_1 \cos \theta_1 \, dA + \int_{A_2} \bar{V}_{2x} \rho_2 V_2 \cos \theta_2 \, dA$$

All quantities inside the integral sign are constant over the area of integration except the velocity at section 2.   When you substitute the values in the above equation, it reduces to the following:

$$F_x = \rho_1 V_1 (-1) \bar{V}_{1x} A_1 + \rho_2 (+1) \int_{A_2} \bar{V}_{2x} V_2 \, dA$$

However

$$\bar{V}_{1x} = -V_1 \text{ because } V_1 \text{ is in the minus } x \text{ direction}$$

$$\bar{V}_{2x} = -V_2 \text{ because } V_2 \text{ is in the minus } x \text{ direction}$$

Thus,

$$F_x = -\rho_1 V_1 (-V_1) A_1 + \rho_2 \int_{A_2} V_2 (-V_2) \, dA$$

$$= \rho_1 A_1 V_1{}^2 - \rho_2 \int_{A_2} V_2{}^2 \, dA$$

You must next evaluate the integral $\int_{A_2} V_2{}^2 \, dA$ which you can do easily by dividing it into two equal integrals: one covering the flow above the plate, and the other the flow below the plate. Since both flows are identical, the total integral will be twice the integral for the area above the plate.

Figure 38c is a drawing of the velocity profile above the plate. The increment of area for section 2 is dy by 2 ft, where dy is the width of the area and 2 ft is the length. This is a strip a constant distance y above the x axis. Thus, the velocity is constant over the area dA. The integral becomes

$$\rho_2 \int_{A_2} V_2{}^2\, dA = 2\rho_2 \int_0^{0.1/12} V_2{}^2\, 2\, dy = 4\rho_2 \int_0^{0.1/12} V_2{}^2\, dy \quad (O)$$

From Fig. 38c calculate the relation between V_2 and y by similar triangles.

$$\frac{V_2}{y} = \frac{10}{0.1/12} \quad \text{or} \quad V_2 = \frac{120}{0.1}\, y = 1200y$$

Substitute this into Equation O to get

$$\rho_2 \int_{A_2} V_2{}^2\, dA = 4\rho_2 \int_0^{0.1/12} (1200y)^2\, dy = \frac{10\rho_2}{9}$$

or

$$F_x = \rho_1 A_1 V_1{}^2 - \frac{10\rho_2}{9} = \rho(100) A_1 - \frac{10\rho}{9}$$

Since $\rho_1 = \rho_2 = \rho = 1.94$ slugs/ft^3

$$F_x = (1.94)(100) A_1 - \frac{(10)(1.94)}{9} = 194 A_1 - \frac{19.4}{9}$$

You must solve for A_1. Use the continuity equation for an incompressible flow.

$$\int_A V \cos\theta\, dA = 0$$

Here it becomes

$$V_1(-1) A_1 + \int_{A_2} V_2\, dA = 0$$

Substitute into this equation the above values of dA and V_2.

$$-V_1 A_1 + 2 \int_0^{0.1/12} 1200y\, dy = 0$$

$$-10 A_1 + \tfrac{1}{6} = 0$$

$$A_1 = \tfrac{1}{60}\ \text{ft}^2$$

Then substitute $\frac{1}{60}$ into the equation for F_x.

$$F_x = (194)\frac{1}{60} - \frac{19.4}{9} = \frac{194}{180} = 1.08 \text{ lb} \qquad \blacktriangleleft$$

▶**Illustrative Problem 5.**   A rocket sled weighs 4 tons including 1 ton of fuel.   The motion resistance in the track on which the sled rides and in the air equals KV, where K is 100 lb/fps and V is the velocity of the sled in feet per second.   Compute the maximum possible velocity of the sled when the exit velocity u of the rocket exhaust gas relative to the rocket is 10,000 fps and the rocket burns fuel at the rate of 200 lb/sec.

Solution: Consider the axis system as attached to the earth, and measure all velocities relative to the axis system.   You cannot consider the axis system as attached to the rocket because the rocket is

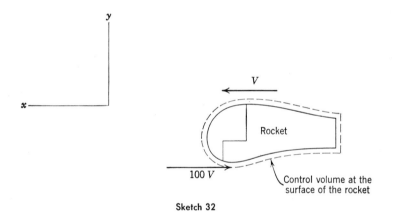

Sketch 32

accelerating and an accelerating axis system is in violation of the restrictions on Newton's second law.   Draw a control volume around the rocket which moves with the rocket.   (See Sketch 32.)

$$F_x = \frac{\mathbf{M}_{x_2}{}' - \mathbf{M}_{x_1}{}'}{dt} + \int_A \bar{V}_x \rho V \cos \theta \, dA$$

The resistance term $100V$ includes all external forces acting on the rocket.   Except at the exhaust area, the integration term around the control volume is zero everywhere.   Measure the vector velocity $\bar{V}_x$ relative to the axis system, $\bar{V}_x = V - u$.   This is constant over the exhaust area and, therefore, may be taken outside the integration. Thus, you get

$$-100V = \frac{\mathbf{M}_{x_2}{}' - \mathbf{M}_{x_1}{}'}{dt} + (V - u) \int_{\substack{\text{exhaust} \\ \text{area}}} \rho V \cos \theta \, dA$$

Over the exhaust area, $\theta = 0$. Therefore, $\cos \theta = 1$. The $\int \rho V \, dA$ is the mass flow rate of fuel leaving the rocket, $200/32.2$ slugs/sec. Now the momentum equation is

$$-100V = \frac{\mathbf{M}_{x_2}{}' - \mathbf{M}_{x_1}{}'}{dt} + \left(\frac{200}{32.2}\right)(V - u)$$

The only term left to consider is the $(\mathbf{M}_{x_2}{}' - \mathbf{M}_{x_1}{}')/dt$ term. Take the general case at time t when the rocket and remaining fuel have a total mass M and are traveling at a velocity V in the positive x direction. The momentum of the mass in the control volume, MV, is the momentum of the rocket and remaining fuel. At time $t + dt$ the mass in the control volume is $M - dM$ and the velocity is $V + dV$. Therefore, the momentum $\mathbf{M}_{x_2}{}'$ of the mass in the control volume at time $t + dt$ is $(M - dM)(V + dV)$. Substitute these values into $(\mathbf{M}_{x_2}{}' - \mathbf{M}_{x_1}{}')/dt$ to get

$$\frac{\mathbf{M}_{x_2}{}' - \mathbf{M}_{x_1}{}'}{dt} = \frac{(M - dM)(V + dV) - MV}{dt}$$

$$= \frac{M \, dV - V \, dM - dM \, dV}{dt}$$

Neglect the $dM \, dV$ term because it is small compared to the other terms. Thus

$$\frac{\mathbf{M}_{x_2}{}' - \mathbf{M}_{x_1}{}'}{dt} = \frac{M \, dV - V \, dM}{dt} = M \frac{dV}{dt} - V \frac{dM}{dt}$$

where dM/dt is the rate of change of mass in the control volume. The rate of change equals the mass rate at which fuel burns, or $dM/dt = 200/32.2$ slugs/sec. Therefore, the momentum equation becomes

$$-100V = M \frac{dV}{dt} - \frac{200}{32.2} V + \frac{200}{32.2}(V - u)$$

or

$$-100V = M \frac{dV}{dt} - \frac{200}{32.2} u = M \frac{dV}{dt} - \frac{(200)(10,000)}{32.2}$$

You must remember that M is the mass of the rocket and remaining fuel at time t and, therefore, is a function of t. Take the time $t = 0$ as the time when the rocket first ignites.   Then $M = [4(2000) - (200)t]/$ 32.2 which is the original mass minus the mass burned in time t. Reduce the momentum equation now to the form

$$-100V = \left(\frac{8000 - 200t}{32.2}\right)\frac{dV}{dt} - \frac{(200)(10,000)}{32.2}$$

Solve this differential equation by separating the variables and integrating

$$\int_0^t \frac{(32.2)\, dt}{8000 - 200t} = \int_0^V \frac{dV}{\left[\frac{(2)(10)^6}{32.2} - 100V\right]}$$

$$\frac{32.2}{200}\ln\frac{8000 - 200t}{8000} = \frac{1}{100}\ln\left(\frac{\frac{2(10)^6}{32.2} - 100V}{\frac{2(10)^6}{32.2}}\right)$$

$$\left(\frac{8000 - 200t}{8000}\right)^{16.1} = \frac{2(10)^6 - 3220V}{2(10)^6}$$

$$-V = \left[(2)(10)^6\left(1 - \frac{200t}{8000}\right)^{16.1} - 2(10)^6\right]\frac{1}{3220}$$

$$V = \frac{2(10)^6}{3220}\left[1 - \left(1 - \frac{t}{40}\right)^{16.1}\right]$$

The rocket attains maximum velocity at the instant that the fuel burns out completely.   One ton of fuel burns at the rate of 200 lb/sec; the fuel, then, will burn for 10 sec.   Substitute $t = 10$ sec and solve for V.

$$V = 622\left[1 - (1 - \tfrac{10}{40})^{16.1}\right]$$

$$= 615 \text{ fps} \qquad \blacktriangleleft$$

31. Derivation of Angular Momentum

Just as in dynamics of solids a special method handles rotation of matter about an axis, so in fluid mechanics a method takes care of rotation about an axis.   Momentum of a particle is a vector quantity, and we can compute the moment of the vector around any axis.   This moment of the momentum we call the angular momentum.   The sum of the angular momenta of all the particles in a system of matter is the angular momentum of the system. The relation between the moment T of the external forces that act on the mass system and the angular momentum H when we take both about the same axis is

$$\sum T_x = \frac{dH_x}{dt}$$

The subscript x denotes that we take the moments about the x axis. The same is true concerning the y and z axes.

Thus, there are three independent equations of angular momentum

$$\left. \begin{aligned} \sum T_x &= \frac{dH_x}{dt} \\[2mm] \sum T_y &= \frac{dH_y}{dt} \\[2mm] \sum T_z &= \frac{dH_z}{dt} \end{aligned} \right\} \tag{4-7}$$

The angular momentum equations are not very useful in this form. They apply to a mass system, and we must convert them to a control volume system in the same way we did in Art. 30. Figure 39a is a sketch of a mass system at time t. In Fig. 39b the mass system has moved to a new location at time $t + \Delta t$ where it appears as a solid line and where the space occupied by the mass system at time t, called the control volume, is shown by dotted lines. The angular momentum about the x axis of the portion of the mass system that has moved out of the control volume in time Δt is ΔH_{ox}. The angular momentum about the x axis of the mass that has entered the control volume in time Δt is ΔH_{ix}. We use the following notation:

H_{x1} = angular momentum about x axis of mass system at time t
H_{x2} = angular momentum about x axis of mass system at time $t + \Delta t$
H_{x1}' = angular momentum about x axis of the mass in the control volume at time t
H_{x2}' = angular momentum about x axis of the mass in the control volume at time $t + \Delta t$

At time t the angular momentum H_{x1} of the mass system equals the angular momentum of the mass in the control volume because it is the same mass.

$$H_{x1} = H_{x1}'$$

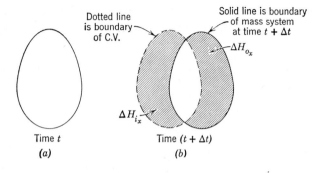

Time t
(a)

Time $(t + \Delta t)$
(b)

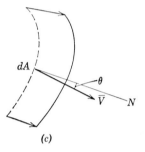

(c)

Fig. 39

At time $t + \Delta t$ the angular momentum H_{x_2} of the mass system equals the angular momentum H_{x_2}' of the mass in the control volume, plus the angular momentum ΔH_{o_x} of the mass system that has moved out of the control volume in time Δt, minus the angular momentum ΔH_{i_x} of the mass that has moved into the control volume in time Δt.   Thus,

$$H_{x_2} = H_{x_2}' + \Delta H_{o_x} - \Delta H_{i_x}$$

The change in angular momentum about the x axis of the mass system in time Δt is ΔH_x.   This change is also $H_{x_2} - H_{x_1}$.   Therefore,

$$\Delta H_x = H_{x_2} - H_{x_1}$$

We substitute the terms for H_{x_2} and H_{x_1} here, which results in

$$\Delta H_x = H_{x_2}' + \Delta H_{o_x} - \Delta H_{i_x} - H_{x_1}'$$

and divide by Δt

$$\frac{\Delta H_x}{\Delta t} = \frac{H_{x_2}' - H_{x_1}'}{\Delta t} + \frac{\Delta H_{o_x} - \Delta H_{i_x}}{\Delta t}$$

The limit of $\Delta H_x/\Delta t$ as $\Delta t \rightarrow 0$ is

$$\lim_{\Delta t \rightarrow 0} \frac{\Delta H_x}{\Delta t} = \frac{dH_x}{dt}$$

In a similar manner we take the limit on the other terms to get

$$\frac{dH_x}{dt} = \frac{H_{x2}' - H_{x1}'}{dt} - \frac{dH_{ox} - dH_{ix}}{dt}$$

This we substitute in the angular momentum equation to get

$$\sum T_x = \frac{H_{x2}' - H_{x1}'}{dt} + \frac{dH_{ox} - dH_{ix}}{dt}$$

We can apply the same method to the other axes to obtain the three equations of angular momentum for a control volume.

$$\left.\begin{cases} \sum T_x = \dfrac{H_{x2}' - H_{x1}'}{dt} + \dfrac{dH_{ox} - dH_{ix}}{dt} \\[3mm] \sum T_y = \dfrac{H_{y2}' - H_{y1}'}{dt} + \dfrac{dH_{oy} - dH_{iy}}{dt} \\[3mm] \sum T_z = \dfrac{H_{z2}' - H_{z1}'}{dt} + \dfrac{dH_{oz} - dH_{iz}}{dt} \end{cases}\right\} \qquad (4\text{-}8)$$

To make these equations useful in solving problems, we must put them into a different form. We consider an increment of area dA on the control surface. Figure 39c shows the side view of area dA, with the dotted line showing one dimension; the other dimension is normal to the figure. The angular momentum about the x axis of the fluid moving out of the area dA in time dt is the momentum of the fluid times the distance R_x from the x axis to the momentum vector.

Thus, the angular momentum is $\rho V \cos \theta \, (dA) \, dt \, \bar{V} R_x$ where $\rho V \cos \theta \, (dA) \, dt$ is the mass flowing out of the area dA in time dt, $\bar{V}$ is the velocity vector of the fluid leaving the area dA, and R_x is the perpendicular distance from the x axis to $\bar{V}$. The total angular momentum about the x axis of the fluid leaving the control volume is the integral over the entire surface of the control volume.

$$\int_A \bar{V} R_x \rho V \cos \theta \, (dA) \, dt$$

The total angular momentum about the x axis of the fluid leaving the control volume in time dt is the definition of $dH_{ox} - dH_{ix}$.

Therefore,

$$dH_{o_x} - dH_{i_x} = \int_A \bar{V} R_x \rho V \cos \theta \, (dA) \, dt$$

Because dt is constant during the integration over the area dA, we may take it outside the integral sign. We then can divide both sides of the equation by dt to give

$$\frac{dH_{o_x} - dH_{i_x}}{dt} = \int_A \bar{V} R_x \rho V \cos \theta \, dA$$

We can do this derivation just as well for the y and z axes and substitute the result into Equations 4-8 to give

$$\left.\begin{aligned}
\sum T_x &= \frac{H_{x_2}' - H_{x_1}'}{dt} + \int_A \bar{V} R_x \rho V \cos \theta \, dA \\
\sum T_y &= \frac{H_{y_2}' - H_{y_1}'}{dt} + \int_A \bar{V} R_y \rho V \cos \theta \, dA \\
\sum T_z &= \frac{H_{z_2}' - H_{z_1}'}{dt} + \int_A \bar{V} R_z \rho V \cos \theta \, dA
\end{aligned}\right\} \qquad (4\text{-}9)$$

For steady flow the angular momentum of the mass in the control volume does not change. Therefore,

$$H_{x_2}' = H_{x_1}', \quad H_{y_2}' = H_{y_1}', \quad H_{z_2}' = H_{z_1}'$$

This reduces the angular momentum equations for steady flow to

$$\left.\begin{aligned}
\sum T_x &= \int_A \bar{V} R_x \rho V \cos \theta \, dA \\
\sum T_y &= \int_A \bar{V} R_y \rho V \cos \theta \, dA \\
\sum T_z &= \int_A \bar{V} R_z \rho V \cos \theta \, dA
\end{aligned}\right\} \qquad (4\text{-}10)$$

We derived these equations with only two limitations, steady flow and the restrictions of Newton's second law. The equations may appear complex and difficult to use, but Illustrative Problems 6 and 7 should clarify them.

In Illustrative Problems 6 and 7 we use the angular momentum equation to determine the torque and the horsepower developed and used by a turbine and a pump. In this analysis we make many assumptions. The two most important ones are (1) the flow is steady (2) there is no external torque on the control volume.

To examine the first assumption, we look at the flow immediately outside the control volume of the pump. The velocity of the flow at any point is certainly going to change as the blade tips go by. The velocity, then, is not constant but varies with time. In cases such as this, where the quantities vary periodically with time, it is possible to take an average value of the quantity and assume that the flow is steady.

Actually, the shear stresses that act on the control surfaces apply an external torque to the control volume. The liquid between the solid control surfaces and the casing of the pump or turbine produces these shear stresses which may be very large and cause appreciable torque that is impossible to neglect. To completely solve the problem, we must be able to calculate or estimate the external torques. Since we are not far enough advanced, we must neglect them until we have studied stresses further. Frictional effects, which we have not taken into account, change the velocity profile also. Thus, answers here are only first approximations.

▶**Illustrative Problem 6.** Figure 40 is the drawing of a turbine. The arrows in the cross-sectional view in Fig. 40a show the direction of flow. Fluid flowing through the blade exerts a torque on the shaft which starts the shaft rotating at 600 rpm to deliver power to machinery at the other end. The fluid is water and enters the blade radially with a velocity of 165 fps. Calculate the horsepower developed by the turbine.

Solution: The flow is symmetrical about the axis and so compute the velocities at any point to determine the velocity at every point that distance from the x axis. In problems dealing with this type of turbine the main assumption is that the space between the blades is always completely filled with fluid flowing with a relative velocity parallel to the blade. Thus, the fluid leaves the outer ring with a relative velocity V_{2R} parallel to the blade at the point of exit. From the above assumptions the relative velocity V_{2R} leaves the turbine at an angle of 155° (Fig. 40b).

The torque applied to the blades by the liquid multiplied by the rotational velocity of the blade is the power output of rotating machinery. Because the flow is steady, compute the torque about the rotating shaft from the angular momentum equations, Equations 4-10. The equation for this case is

$$\sum T_x = \int_A \bar{V} R_{xp} V \cos \theta \, dA$$

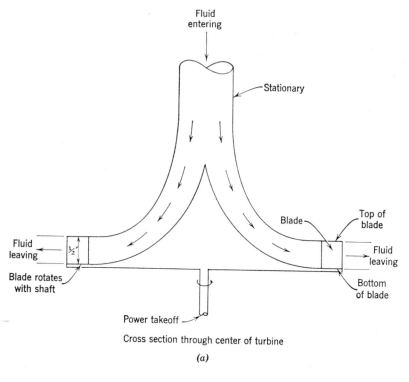

Cross section through center of turbine

(a)

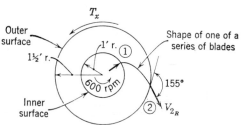

Reduced size top view of rotating sector

(b)

Fig. 40

where the centerline of the shaft is the x axis. To apply this equation, first choose the control volume, selecting the space that is swept by one blade making one complete revolution about the x axis. Solid rings cover the top and bottom of the blades so that the water cannot flow in the x direction while passing through the control volume.

The top view of the rotating section (Fig. 40b) is also the top view of the control volume. Figure 41a shows an enlarged view of section 1 and section 2. The velocity of water normal to the surface of the control volume at section 2 is V_{2N}, the tangential component of V_{2R} is V_{2RT}, and the velocity of the blade tip is V_{2B}.

The only external torque applied to the control volume would have to be the one applied through the shaft. It acts upon the control volume through the solid metal which connects the blades to the shaft. Thus,

$$\sum T_x = T_x = \int_A \bar{V} R_x \rho V \cos \theta \, dA$$

The angle θ is $\pi/2$ for the control surface at the top and bottom of the blades. At the inner surface Fig. 41a demonstrates that θ equals π, and at the outer surface Fig. 41b shows that θ equals some constant θ_2. Thus, the integration breaks down into two separate integrations, the first over the inner surface area, and the second over the outer surface area. All integrals over other surfaces of the control volume are zero, because $\cos(\pi/2) = 0$. Therefore, the angular momentum equation becomes

$$T_x = \int_{A_1} \bar{V}_1 R_{x_1} \rho_1 V_1 (-1) \, dA + \int_{A_2} \bar{V}_2 R_{x_2} \rho_2 V_2 \cos \theta_2 \, dA$$

The $\bar{V} R_x$ term which appears in both integrals is the moment of the velocity vector about the x axis. A simple way to calculate the product is to break the velocity vector $\bar{V}$ into two components at the control surfaces. One component goes through the x axis, and the other is normal to the first. Then $\bar{V} R_x$ is the second component times the distance from the control surface to the x axis. Over the inner control surfaces the normal velocity component goes through the x axis, and the other component is the tangential component of velocity. The same is true over the outer surface of the control volume. Thus, the values of $\bar{V} R_x$ are

$$(\bar{V} R_x)_1 = (0)(1) = 0$$

$$(\bar{V} R_x)_2 = V_{2t}(\tfrac{3}{2}) = \tfrac{3}{2} V_{2t}$$

Select the control volume with all quantities constant over the areas of integration. When these values are substituted into the angular momentum equation and all quantities that are constant over the areas of integration are taken outside the integral sign, the angular momentum equation becomes

$$T_x = \rho_2 V_2 \cos \theta_2 \tfrac{3}{2} V_{2t} \int_{A_2} dA$$

$$T_x = \rho_2 V_2 \cos \theta_2 (\tfrac{3}{2}) V_{2t} (2\pi)(\tfrac{3}{2})(\tfrac{1}{2})$$

$$= (1.94)\tfrac{9}{4}\pi V_2 \cos \theta_2 \, V_{2t} = 13.74 V_2 (\cos \theta_2) V_{2t}$$

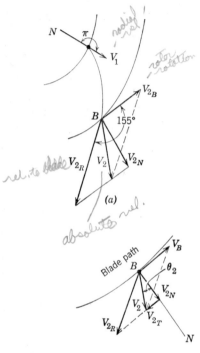

You must use some other means to compute V_2, θ_2, and V_{2t}. The continuity equation and geometry give the needed information. The continuity equation for incompressible flow is

$$0 = \int_A V \cos\theta \, dA$$

Apply it to the control volume to get

$$0 = \int_{A_1} V_1 \cos \theta_1 \, dA + \int_{A_2} V_2 \cos \theta_2 \, dA$$

$$0 = V_1(-1)2\pi R_1(\tfrac{1}{2}) + V_2(\cos \theta_2)2\pi R_2(\tfrac{1}{2})$$

Substitute the given values of V_1, R_1, and R_2 into this equation.

$$0 = -(165)\pi + V_2(\cos \theta_2)\pi\tfrac{3}{2}$$

$$V_2 \cos \theta_2 = \tfrac{2}{3} 165 = 110 \text{ fps}$$

Figure 41b shows that $V_2 \cos \theta_2$ is the normal velocity component of V_2. Therefore,

$$V_{2n} = V_2 \cos \theta_2 = 110 \text{ fps}$$

(a)

(b)

Fig. 41

From Fig. 41a notice that this is the normal velocity component of V_{2R}. Thus,

$$V_{2R} \cos(155 - 90) = V_{2n} = 110 \text{ fps}$$

Also from Fig. 41a

$$V_{2Rt} = V_{2R} \sin (155 - 90) = V_{2R} \sin 65$$

Solve for V_{2Rt} in terms of V_{2n}.

$$V_{2Rt} = V_{2n} \tan 65 = 110 \tan 65 = 236 \text{ fps}$$

This is the tangential component of the velocity relative to the blade at section 2. You must add the tangential component of the blade itself at section 2 to V_{2Rt} to get the tangential component of the absolute velocity V_2. The tangential component of the blade tip and the velocity of the blade are equal.

$$V_{2B} = \frac{2\pi N}{60} R_2 = \frac{2\pi(600)}{60} \frac{3}{2}$$

$$V_{2B} = 30\pi \text{ fps}$$

$$V_{2t} = V_{2Rt} + V_{2B} = -236 + 94.2 = -141.8 \text{ fps}$$

The negative direction of the velocity calls for a minus sign.
Substitute these values into the torque equation.

$$T_x = 13.74 V_2 \cos \theta_2 \, V_{2t} = (13.74)(110)(-141.8)$$

$$T_x = -214,000 \text{ ft-lb}$$

The minus here means torque opposing motion.

$$\text{Power} = T_x \omega_x = (-214,000) \frac{2\pi(600)}{60} = -13,460,000 \text{ lb-ft/sec}$$

$$\text{Horsepower} = \frac{\text{power (ft-lb/sec)}}{550} = \frac{-13,460,000}{550} = 24,500 \text{ hp}$$

The minus sign denotes that the water turns the blades against the torque and that the water gives up power. ◀

▶**Illustrative Problem 7.** The centrifugal pump (Fig. 42) pumps water at a steady rate of 1.1 cfs. The rotor's outside diameter is 8 in. and inside diameter is 6 in., and the blade's height is $\frac{3}{4}$ in. Calculate

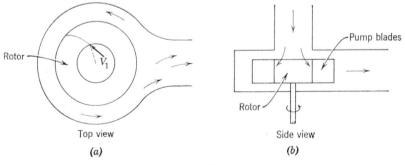

Top view
(a)

Side view
(b)

Fig. 42

the power input to the rotor which revolves counterclockwise at 1200 rpm.

Solution: As in Illustrative Problem 6 the power input is the product of the torque and the angular velocity. You know the angular velocity and can compute the torque from the angular momentum equation for steady flow, which is

$$\sum T_x = \int_A \bar{V} R_x \rho V \cos \theta \, dA$$

where the axis of revolution of the rotor is the x axis.

First, select the control volume, which in this case is the rotor, as in Fig. 43.

The external torques can come only from the pressure on the control surface and the torque applied to the rotor through the shaft. Neglect the torque due to shear stresses transmitted by the fluid. It is not a valid assumption, necessarily, to neglect it; but, until your knowledge of fluid shear stresses is more complete, it is an assumption you must make.

The pressure must be normal to the surface. Because the inner and the outer surfaces are surfaces of revolution about the x axis, the pressure acting on them passes through the x axis. The moment of these pressure forces, therefore, is zero. Thus, the only external torque is the torque of the shaft which is in the direction of rotation because it causes the rotation. The sum of all external torques is

$$+ \quad \Sigma T_x = +T_x$$

As in the preceding problem, the angle θ equals $\pi/2$ everywhere except at the inner and the outer surfaces. Thus, write the integral as the sum of two different integrals, one over the inner surface and the other over the outer surface. The angular momentum equation is now

$$T_x = \int_{A_1} \bar{V}_1 R_{x_1} \rho_1 V_1 \cos \theta_1 \, dA + \int_{A_2} \bar{V}_2 R_{x_2} \rho_2 V_2 \cos \theta_2 \, dA$$

Since all terms inside the integral signs are constant over that area of integration, you may take them outside to arrive at

$$T_x = \rho_1 V_1 (\cos \theta_1) \bar{V}_1 R_{x_1} \int_{A_1} dA + \rho_2 V_2 (\cos \theta_2) \bar{V}_2 R_{x_2} \int_{A_2} dA$$

$$T_x = \rho_1 V_1 (\cos \theta_1) \bar{V}_1 R_{x_1} A_1 + \rho_2 V_2 (\cos \theta_2) \bar{V}_2 R_{x_2} A_2$$

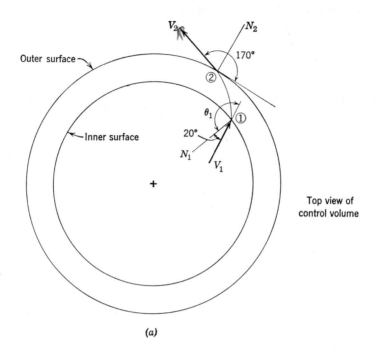

Outer surface

Inner surface

170°

θ_1

20°

N_1

V_1

V_2

N_2

Top view of
control volume

(a)

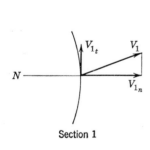

V_{1_t}

V_1

N

V_{1_n}

Section 1

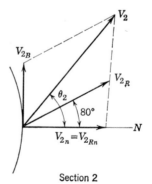

V_2

V_{2_B}

V_{2_R}

θ_2

80°

$V_{2_n} = V_{2_{Rn}}$

N

Section 2

(b)

Fig. 43

From Fig. 43 $\qquad \theta_1 = 160°$

$$A_1 = 2\pi R_1(\tfrac{3}{4})(\tfrac{1}{12}) = \pi/32 \text{ ft}^2$$

$$A_2 = 2\pi R_2(\tfrac{3}{4})(\tfrac{1}{12}) = \pi/24 \text{ ft}^2$$

$$\rho_1 = \rho_2 = 1.94 \text{ slugs/ft}^3$$

$$\cos \theta_1 = \cos 160 = -\cos 20$$

Therefore,

$$T_x = (1.94)(V_1)(-\cos 20)\,\bar{V}_1 R_{x_1}\,\frac{\pi}{32} + (1.94)V_2 \cos \theta_2\,\bar{V}_2 R_{x_2}\,\frac{\pi}{24}$$

Compute the values of the quantities not known from the continuity consideration and geometry.   When you apply the equation of continuity to this control volume, the following equation results:

$$0 = \int_A V \cos \theta \, dA = \int_{A_1} V_1 \cos \theta_1 \, dA + \int_{A_2} V_2 \cos \theta_2 \, dA$$

$$0 = V_1(-\cos 20)A_1 + V_2(\cos \theta_2)A_2$$

Therefore, $V_2 \cos \theta_2 = \dfrac{A_1}{A_2} V_1 \cos 20 = \dfrac{\pi}{32}\dfrac{V_1}{\pi/24} \cos 20 = \tfrac{3}{4}V_1 \cos 20$

By definition the flow rate Q is the total outflow of the control volume.   This is

$$Q = \int_A V_1 \cos \theta_1 \, dA = V_1(-\cos 20)A_1 = -V_1(\cos 20)\,\frac{\pi}{32}$$

Neglect the minus sign for it only indicates that the flow is into the control volume.   The flow rate is 1.1 cfs.   Therefore,

$$1.1 = V_1(\cos 20)\,\frac{\pi}{32}$$

$$V_1 = \frac{35.2}{\pi \cos 20} = 11.97 \text{ fps}$$

As in Illustrative Problem 6 break down the entrance velocity V_1 and the exit velocity V_2 into two components, one tangent to the control surface and the other normal to the control surface.   Thus,

$$\bar{V}_1 = \bar{V}_{1_n} \nleftrightarrow \bar{V}_{1_t}; \quad \bar{V}_2 = \bar{V}_{2_n} \nleftrightarrow \bar{V}_{2_t}$$

$$\bar{V}_1 R_{x_1} = \bar{V}_{1_n}(o) \nleftrightarrow \bar{V}_{1_t}(R_1) = \bar{V}_{1_t}R_1$$

$$\bar{V}_2 R_{x_2} = \bar{V}_{2_n}(o) \nleftrightarrow \bar{V}_{2_t}(R_2) = \bar{V}_{2_t}R_2$$

From Fig. 43b the tangential velocity V_{1_t} equals

$$V_{1_t} = V_1 \sin 20 = (11.97) \sin 20 = +4.1 \text{ fps}$$

The absolute velocity of water as it leaves the blade is the vector sum of the velocity relative to the blade and the velocity of the blade tip.

$$\bar{V}_2 = \bar{V}_{2R} + \bar{V}_{2B}$$

The component V_{2B} of the blade tip is tangential and has no normal component. Thus, the normal component $\bar{V}_{2_n}$ of the absolute velocity at point 2 equals the normal component of $\bar{V}_{2R}$ (Fig. 43b). From it you can deduce the following:

$$V_{2_n} = V_2 \cos \theta_2 = V_{2R} \cos 80$$

From the continuity equation you know that

$$V_2 \cos \theta_2 = \tfrac{3}{4} V_1 \cos 20 = \tfrac{3}{4}(11.97) \cos 20 = 8.44 \text{ fps}$$

$$V_{2R} \cos 80 = 8.44 \text{ fps}$$

$$V_{2R} = 48.66 \text{ fps}$$

From Fig. 43b note that the tangential component $\bar{V}_{2_t}$ of $\bar{V}_2$ is the sum of the tangential components of $\bar{V}_{2B}$ and $\bar{V}_{2R}$. The tangential velocity $\bar{V}_{2R_t}$ of $\bar{V}_{2R}$ is

$$\bar{V}_{2R_t} = \bar{V}_{2R} \sin 80 = 47.8 \text{ fps}$$

Thus, $\bar{V}_{2_t}$ is

$$\bar{V}_{2_t} = \bar{V}_{2B} + \bar{V}_{2R_t} = 2\pi R_2 N_1 + 47.8$$

because $\bar{V}_{2B}$ is tangential. Therefore,

$$\bar{V}_{2_t} = 2\pi(\tfrac{1}{3})(\tfrac{1200}{60}) + 47.8 = 88.6 \text{ fps}$$

Substitute all of the above values into the equation for torque T_x to get

$$T_x = (1.94)(11.\overset{7}{9}\overset{}{9})(-\cos 20)(4.1)(\tfrac{1}{4})\left(\frac{\pi}{32}\right) + (1.94)(7.5)(88.6)(\tfrac{1}{3})\left(\frac{\pi}{24}\right)$$

$$T_x = 54.0 \text{ ft lb}$$

The power input, therefore, is

$$P = (54.0)\,\frac{2\pi N}{60} = (54.0)\,\frac{2\pi(1200)}{60}$$

$$P = 6800 \text{ ft-lb/sec}$$

$$P = \tfrac{6800}{550} = 12.35 \text{ hp}$$

◄

32. Summary

We derived two fundamental momentum equations from Newton's second law in this chapter. In Chapter 3 we derived the Euler equation from Newton's second law. Only one difference exists between the momentum equation and the Euler equation: we write the Euler equation for a mass system and the momentum equation for a control volume system. We must keep in mind this very important difference.

In a very general manner we derive the linear momentum equations

$$
\left.
\begin{aligned}
\sum F_x &= \frac{\mathbf{M}_{x2}{}' - \mathbf{M}_{x1}{}'}{dt} + \int_A \bar{V}_x \rho V \cos\theta\, dA \\[2ex]
\sum F_y &= \frac{\mathbf{M}_{y2}{}' - \mathbf{M}_{y1}{}'}{dt} + \int_A \bar{V}_y \rho V \cos\theta\, dA \\[2ex]
\sum F_z &= \frac{\mathbf{M}_{z2}{}' - \mathbf{M}_{z1}{}'}{dt} + \int_A \bar{V}_z \rho V \cos\theta\, dA
\end{aligned}
\right\} \qquad (4\text{-}6)
$$

with their only limitations, Newton's second law and the control volume.

Also we derived the angular momentum equations in a very general form and added to the limitations of the linear momentum equation the limitations that the axis system and the axis about which the angular momentum is taken must be stationary. These angular momentum equations are

$$
\left.
\begin{aligned}
\sum T_x &= \frac{H_{x2}{}' - H_{x1}{}'}{dt} + \int \bar{V} R_x \rho V \cos\theta\, dA \\[2ex]
\sum T_y &= \frac{H_{y2}{}' - H_{y1}{}'}{dt} + \int \bar{V} R_y \rho V \cos\theta\, dA \\[2ex]
\sum T_z &= \frac{H_{z2}{}' - H_{z1}{}'}{dt} + \int \bar{V} R_z \rho V \cos\theta\, dA
\end{aligned}
\right\} \qquad (4\text{-}10)
$$

It would seem that powerful and general equations would make the solution of fluid mechanics problems rather routine. This is not true because the determination of the external forces and torques depends upon the kind of fluid and fluid motion involved. In many cases we must use an approximate solution, as we did in the illustrative problems, by neglecting frictional and other effects. Friction not only effects the external forces and torques but also changes the velocity profile. This change in velocity profile very definitely effects the momentum and, consequently, the solution to any fluid problem solved by momentum analysis. We can solve many problems by using empirical data to account for the frictional effects. We discuss some of these in Chapter 6. True understanding comes, however, only by studying the more advanced books on flow of a real fluid.

PROBLEMS

4-1. Water is flowing in a 6 in. dia. pipe with a uniform velocity of 16 fps. Where the pipe bends through 90°, compute the force necessary to hold the bend in place. The pressure inside the pipe is 20 psia and the atmospheric pressure is 15 psia.

4-2. A fluid of density ρ is flowing with a uniform velocity V_1 in a pipe of diameter D_1. The pipe suddenly enlarges to a new diameter D_2. Neglecting friction, determine the force necessary to hold the enlargement in place.

4-3. Water is flowing in a 4 in. dia. pipe. At section 1 the velocity is uniform and equal to 20 fps. At section 2, well downstream from section 1, the velocity profile has just become fully developed and is

$$v = 40 \left[1 - \left(\frac{r}{R_1} \right)^2 \right] = 40(1 - 36r^2)$$

where v = velocity at section 2 a distance r in feet from the centerline

Write the Bernoulli equation along the centerline to determine the pressure difference. Calculate the force necessary to hold the pipe between section 1 and section 2 in place. The pressure at section 1 is 20 psia.

4-4. Compute the force of the jet on the vane shown in Fig. P.4-4. The vane is stationary. *98.2# @55° BELOW HORIZONTAL TO RIGHT*

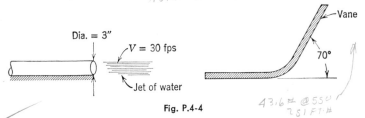

Dia. = 3″
V = 30 fps
Vane
70°
Jet of water

Fig. P.4-4

43.6# @55°
251 FT-#

4-5. The vane shown in Fig. P.4-4 is moving with a velocity of 10 fps to the right. Calculate the force of the water on the vane. Determine the work done per second by the water.

4-6. Calculate the force necessary to hold in place the rack of vanes shown in Fig. P.4-6. Assume the flow is frictionless. The flow rate is 1 cfs and the liquid is water.

4-7. Calculate the velocity of the vane shown in Fig. P.4-7 so that the horsepower developed is a maximum. The area of the jet is A; the velocity of the water leaving the jet is 6 fps.

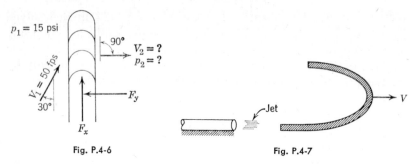

Fig. P.4-6   Fig. P.4-7

4-8. A cylinder of infinite length is placed in a uniform parallel stream as shown in Fig. P.4-8. The cylinder has a diameter d. Calculate the force per unit length on the cylinder assuming constant pressure and density.

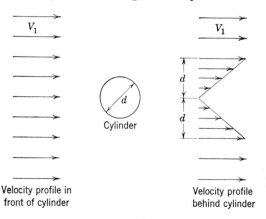

Velocity profile in   Velocity profile
front of cylinder   behind cylinder

Fig. P.4-8

4-9. Calculate the thrust of a stationary rocket which consumes $1\frac{1}{2}$ lb/sec of fuel and oxygen. The velocity of the jet is 6000 fps, and the exit pressure at the nozzle is atmospheric.

4-10. A water jet with a constant velocity V_1 to the right strikes a vane as shown in Fig. P.4-10. Neglecting friction and gravity, determine the power input necessary to move the vane with a constant velocity U to the left.

Here $V_1 = 40$ fps, $U = 30$ fps, $A_1 = \pi/144$ ft^2, and $\theta = 20°$

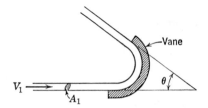

Fig. P.4-10

4-11. A jet of water of cross-sectional area $\frac{1}{194}$ ft² impinges on a vane mounted on a solid block and is deflected as shown in Fig. P.4-11. Determine the jet velocity V required to push the block up the incline at a constant

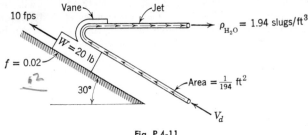

Fig. P.4-11

velocity of 10 fps. Neglect any gravity effects on the jet, and assume that the coefficient of friction between the block and the plane is $f = 0.2$.

4-12. The jet engine shown in Fig. P.4-12 burns 900 slugs of fuel per hour. The fuel enters the engine vertically. The density of the air at the intake of the engine is 2.3×10^{-3} slug/ft³, the entering velocity is 300 fps, and the intake

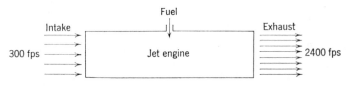

Fig. P.4-12

cross-sectional area is 4 ft². The mixture leaving the exhaust of the jet has a density of 0.0088 slug/ft³ and a velocity of 2400 fps. Determine the horizontal thrust developed by the engine.

4-13. A large tank is filled 8 ft deep with water. A hole is drilled in the side of the tank such that the jet of water issuing from the hole has a diameter of 4 in. at the vena contracta. The tank is on wheels as shown in Fig. P.4-13. Neglecting friction and assuming that the water level in the tank is constant, calculate the force F necessary to hold the tank in position.

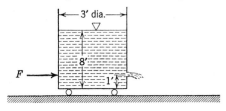

Fig. P.4-13

4-14. The friction in the wheels of the tank shown in Fig. P.4-13 is such that the friction will oppose motion of the tank. The friction force F_f is

$$F_f = \frac{W}{100}$$

where W is the combined weight of the tank and the water. The tank weighs 150 lb. Determine the minimum size hole for which motion of the tank will impend. Assume that $F = 0$ in Fig. P.4-13.

4-15. A tank 1 ft in diameter is filled to a depth of 8 ft with water. A $\frac{1}{10}$ ft^2 hole is located in the side. The water flows steadily out this hole. Determine the maximum height above the floor that the hole can be located for motion of the tank to impend. The coefficient of friction between the floor and the tank is $\mu = 0.20$. Neglect momentum change in the vertical direction and the weight of the tank. The tank rests on the floor.

4-16. The pump in the boat shown in Fig. P.4-16 pumps 2 cfs of water. The inlet at the bow of the boat has a $\frac{1}{4}$ ft^2 cross-sectional area. The outlet at the rear is $\frac{1}{10}$ ft^2 in cross-sectional area. Calculate the force carried by the rope that holds the boat to the dock.

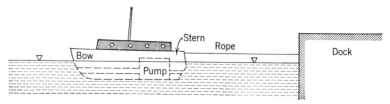

Fig. P.4-16

4-17. Air flows steadily through the rectangular bend shown in Fig. P.4-17. The bend has a width of 1 ft normal to the paper. Compute the magnitude of the force F_x and F_y. State assumptions.

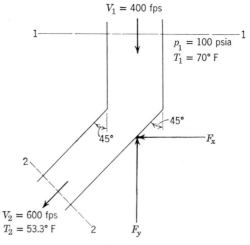

Fig. P.4-17

4-18. Two tanks A and B have identical holes in the sides opposite each other as shown in Fig. P.4-18. A block C covers the hole in tank B and diverts the jet of water from the hole in tank A. Calculate the minimum h that will hold the block C in place. The fluid in tank B is water.

4-19. Compute h in Fig. P.4-18 if the fluid in tank B is carbon tetrachloride.

4-20. Compute h in Fig. P.4-18 if tank B is sealed so that pressure of 5 psig acts on the surface of the water in tank B.

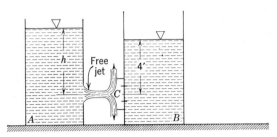

Fig. P.4-18

4-21. Tank A and tank C are filled with water as shown in Fig. P.4-21. The water in tank A flows out of the 4 in. dia. hole in the side and strikes block B. The block B diverts the water jet through an angle of 90° as shown. Neglecting the weight of the block B, compute the minimum pressure p_1 in tank A that will hold the block in place. There is a 3 in. $\times$ 3 in. square hole behind block B in tank C.

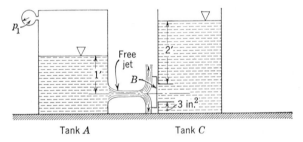

Fig. P.4-21

4-22. The tank shown in Fig. P.4-22 is 3 ft in diameter and 8 ft high. The tank is filled to a depth of 6 ft with water. The top of the tank is sealed

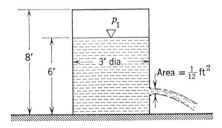

Fig. P.4-22

closed with air at a pressure p_1 psig inside the tank. A hole with an effective area of $\frac{1}{12}$ ft^2 is drilled in the side of the tank 1 ft from the bottom of the tank.

The tank empty weighs 150 lb, and the coefficient of friction between the bottom of the tank and the surface is 0.015. Calculate the pressure p_1 for motion of the tank to impend.

4-23. The jet engine shown in Fig. P.4-23 burns 1000 slugs of fuel per hour. The fuel enters the engine vertically. The density of the air at the intake is 0.002 slug/ft³. The entering velocity is 500 fps, and the intake cross-sectional area is 3 ft². The mixture leaving the exhaust has a density of 0.004 slug/ft³.

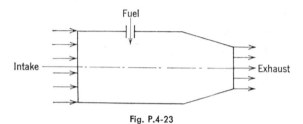

Fuel

Intake

Exhaust

Fig. P.4-23

The exhaust cross-sectional area is 1 ft in diameter. Determine the ratio of the thrusts T_A/T_B when (a) the exit velocity is constant across the diameter and (b) the exit velocity varies according to the equation

$$v = V_c(1 - 2r)$$

where V_c = velocity at the centerline of the exhaust area
v = velocity at a distance r ft from the centerline

Assume that the intake velocity is uniform and the intake and exhaust pressures are atmospheric.

4-24. In the jet engine in Problem P.4-23 compute the ratio of the thrusts T_A/T_B when (a) the exit velocity is constant across a 1 ft diameter and (b) the exit velocity is constant across a $\frac{1}{2}$ ft diameter.

4-25. A stationary rocket has a tail pipe with an exhaust cross section 1 ft in diameter. The steady average velocity of the exhaust gas is 8000 fps, and the density of the exhaust gas is 0.001 slug/ft³. Compute the ratio of the thrust assuming a uniform velocity profile at the exhaust to the thrust assuming that the velocity v at the exhaust varies as follows:

$$v = 16,000(1 - 4y^2)$$

where y = distance from the center to the point where v is computed, in ft.

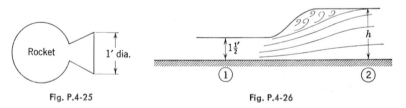

Rocket

1′ dia.

Fig. P.4-25

Fig. P.4-26

4-26. Water is flowing at a depth of $1\frac{1}{2}$ ft in a channel of rectangular cross section. The channel is 10 ft wide and 8 ft deep. A hydraulic jump occurs between section 1 and section 2 as shown in Fig. P.4-26. There is a considerable energy loss due to turbulence of the fluid so that the Bernoulli equation cannot be used. Assuming that the friction on the bottom and sides of the channel is small and that at sections 1 and 2 the pressure varies according to the hydrostatic equation, compute the new depth h of the water at section 2. The flow rate is steady at 120 cfs.

4-27. In Problem 4-26 compute h if the depth of water at section 1 is 1 ft.

4-28. A large tank is filled with water and has a pipe in one side as shown in Fig. P.4-28. Calculate the diameter of the vena contracta of the exit stream in terms of the diameter D of the pipe. *Hint:* The resultant force due to the horizontal pressure on the tank walls must be equal to the rate of change momentum of the water.

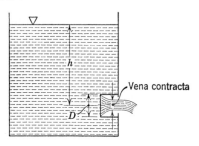

Fig. P.4-28

4-29. A large tank has a 8 in. dia. horizontal pipe attached to a hole in the side as shown in Fig. P.4-29. The pipe is supported so that there is no stress in the pipe due to the weight of the pipe or the weight of the water. Assume that the flow is steady and frictionless. Determine whether the pipe walls are in tension or compression when the exit diameter of the nozzle is 2 in.

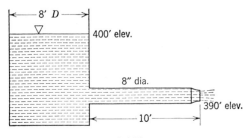

Fig. P.4-29

4-30. In Problem 4-29 determine whether the pipe is in tension or compression when the elevation of the water surface is increased to 405 ft. The tank and nozzle are not moved or changed.

4-31. In Problem 4-29 determine whether the pipe walls are in tension or compression when the nozzle is changed to 6 in. diameter.

4-32. In Problem 4-29 calculate the diameter or diameters of the nozzle for which the stress in the pipe is zero.

4-33. A rocket sled and empty rockets weigh 8000 lb. The fuel for the rockets weighs 4000 lb and will burn at a steady rate for 20 sec. The cross-sectional area of the exit nozzle of the rockets is a 15 in. dia. circle. The exit velocity of the exhaust gases is 5000 fps. Calculate the velocity of the sled 10 sec after firing of the rockets. Assume that the sled starts at zero and that there is no resistance to motion.

4-34. In Problem 4-33 compute the maximum velocity attained by the sled.

4-35. In Problem 4-33 assume that there is a constant force of 2000 lb that resists the motion. Compute the maximum velocity attained by the sled.

4-36. A small rocket is attached to a boat. The rocket and fuel weigh 300 lb, and the boat and passengers weigh 500 lb. The exhaust gases leave the rocket with a velocity of 7000 fps, and the fuel burns for 30 sec at a steady rate. The fuel weighs 250 lb, and the resistance to motion is kV^2, where $k = 2$ lb sec^2/ft^2. Compute the maximum velocity of the boat.

4-37. Figure P.4-37 is the sketch of a scoop on a locomotive tender. When the velocity of the tender is 10 mph, calculate the force $(-F)$ of the scoop on the tender. Neglect changes in elevation. The water ahead of the scoop is stationary.

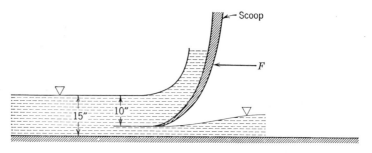

Fig. P.4-37

4-38. Figure P.4-38 is the side view of a sluice gate. For the conditions shown, calculate the force of the water on the gate.

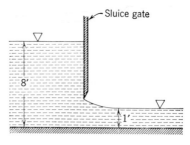

Fig. P.4-38

4-39. A rocket sled is halted by a scoop which picks the water out of a trough and throws the water out in front of the sled as shown in Fig. P.4-39.

The sled weighs 6000 lb throughout the deceleration, and at the time $t = 0$, when the scoop which is 1 ft wide first hits the water, the sled is traveling 600 fps. Calculate h so the maximum deceleration of the sled will be 10 g, and calculate the velocity of the sled 10 sec after the scoop hits the water.

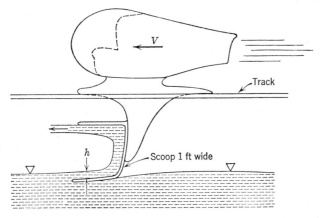

Fig. P.4-39

4-40. In Problem 4-39 calculate the distance traveled in the 10 sec after the scoop hits the water.

4-41. The sled in Problem 4-39 can accelerate to only 300 mph. Compute h so that the maximum deceleration is 5 g. Calculate the velocity after 5 sec.

4-42. In Problem 4-40 compute the distance required to reduce the speed to 10 mph.

4-43. A sled similar to the one in Fig. 4-39 is traveling at a velocity V_i when the scoop hits the water. The mass of the sled is M. Derive an expression for the velocity V at any time t in terms V_i, M, ρ, and h.

4-44. Suggest a simple method that will help make the deceleration of the rocket sled in Fig. P.4-39 more constant.

4-45. A boy builds a rocket which weighs 20 lb when fully loaded with fuel. The fuel weighs 10 lb and burns at the rate of $\frac{1}{2}$ lb/sec. The velocity of the exhaust gas is 1,600 fps. When the rocket is fired vertically, calculate the velocity and height 20 sec after firing. Assume that g is constant.

4-46. A rocket sled and fuel weigh M_o initially. The velocity of the exhaust gases is constant V_e, and the density is ρ. The area of the tail pipe is A. Derive an expression for the velocity V of the sled at time t. The resistance to motion is constant F.

4-47. In Problem 4-46 derive an expression for the velocity V of the rocket if the resistance to motion is kV when k is a constant.

4-48. In Problem 4-46 derive an expression for the velocity V of the rocket if the resistance to motion is kV^2 where k is a constant.

4-49. The bucket on the impulse turbine shown in Fig. P.4-49 has an angle of 150°. What is the maximum horsepower that can be developed by this

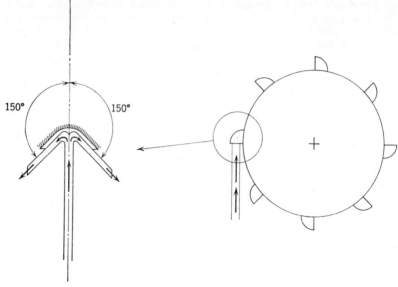

Fig. P.4-49

turbine when a 2 in. dia. jet with a velocity of 200 fps strikes the blades as shown?   The diameter across the bucket centers is 3 ft.

4-50. The turbine shown in Fig. P.4-50 is running free.   The only external torque is due to friction in the bearings which is 0.1 ft-lb.   Calculate the

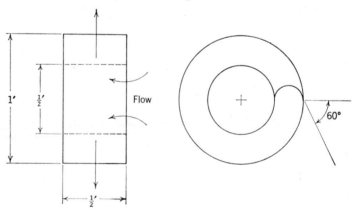

Fig. P.4-50

revolutions per minute of the turbine.   The flow rate is 4 cfs, and the flow enters radially.

4-51. In Fig. P.4-51 water enters the outside of the turbine with a velocity V and flows inward.   Calculate the revolutions per minute of the turbine for the power output to be a maximum.

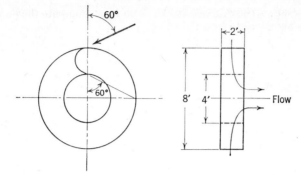

Fig. P.4-51

4-52. The bucket on the impulse turbine shown in Fig. P.4-52 has an angle of 135° as shown. Determine the torque on the turbine when the turbine is stationary.

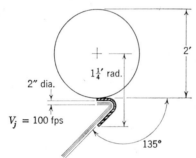

Fig. P.4-52

4-53. Calculate the torque necessary to drive the pump shown in Fig. P.4-53 at 120 rpm and to deliver 75 cfs of water. Here V_1 is the entering velocity at 20° to the normal.

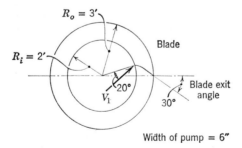

Width of pump = 6″

Fig. P.4-53

4-54. The centrifugal pump shown in Fig. P.4-54 is rotating at 1500 rpm in the clockwise direction. The water enters the center radially and leaves at an angle of 60°. The exit velocity V_e = 90 fps. Compute the flow rate and the torque necessary to turn the pump.

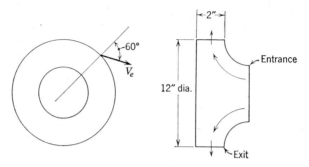

Fig. P.4-54

4-55. Water flows through the turbine shown in Fig. P.4-55 at the rate of 300 cfs. The water enters the turbine blades radially and leaves tangent to the blades. Compute the angular velocity of the turbine for maximum horsepower to be developed.

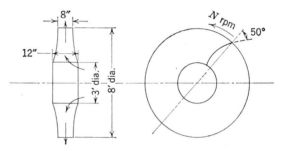

Fig. P.4-55

4-56. Figure P.4-56 is a top view of a sprinkler which rotates about axis c. Water leaves the sprinkler at a velocity of 20 fps relative to the tip A in the horizontal plane in which the arms would rotate. Compute the force F necessary to hold the arms in place. The nozzle at A is $\frac{1}{2}$ in. in radius.

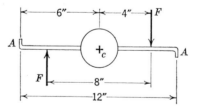

Fig. P.4-56

4-57. When the nozzles at A in Problem 4-56 are tilted up at an angle of 45°, compute the force F which is still horizontal.

CONSERVATION
of ENERGY

33. Introduction

The general principle of conservation of energy is that energy can neither be created nor destroyed in the absence of nuclear reaction. The first law of thermodynamics states that for any mass system the net heat supplied to the system must equal the increase in internal energy of the system plus all energy which leaves the system as work. A mass system is a defined collection of matter. The mathematical statement of the first law of thermodynamics is

$$\Delta Q_1 = \Delta E + \Delta W_1 \tag{5-1}$$

where Q_1 = heat added to the system
W_1 = work done by the system
E = internal energy of the system

This general principle, conservation of energy, is one which cannot be proved but has never been proved wrong and, therefore, is accepted as a fundamental truth. From Equation 5-1 we shall derive a general mathematical statement which is very useful in solving fluid flow problems.

34. Derivation of the General Energy Equation

The internal energy of a system is a physical property of the system and is independent of the process used in arriving at the particular state. The net heat added to or subtracted from the system and the net work done by or on the system are not properties of the system. The heat and the work terms depend upon the process followed as well as the end states of the system.

Equation 5-1 applies to a mass system.   To be of value in solving fluid mechanics problems, this equation should be derived for a control volume.   Figure 44a shows a mass system which occupies a certain volume at time t.   At time $t + \Delta t$ the mass system has moved to a new position as shown in Fig. 44b.   The volume that the mass system occupied at time t remains fixed in space and is called the control

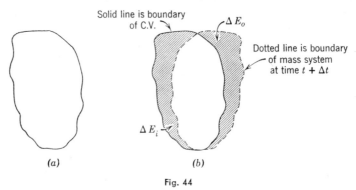

Fig. 44

volume.   We designate this control volume in Fig. 44b by C.V. and the new location of the mass system by dotted lines.

E_1 = internal energy of the mass system at time t
E_2 = internal energy of the mass system at time $t + \Delta t$
E_1' = internal energy of the mass in the control volume at time t
E_2' = internal energy of the mass in the control volume at time $t + \Delta t$

The change ΔE of internal energy of the mass system equals $E_2 - E_1$. Since the mass system completely occupies the control volume at time t, $E_1 = E_1'$.   At time $t + \Delta t$ the internal energy of the mass system will equal the internal energy of the mass in the control volume at time $t + \Delta t$, plus the amount of internal energy that has moved out of the control volume in time Δt, minus the amount of internal energy that has flowed into the control volume in time Δt.   We write this mathematically as

$$E_2 = E_2' + \Delta E_o - \Delta E_i$$

Then, $$E_2 - E_1 = E_2' - E_1' + \Delta E_o - \Delta E_i$$

The change in internal energy ΔE of the mass system equals the change in internal energy in the control volume, plus the internal energy which flowed out of the control volume, minus the internal energy which flowed into the control volume, all in time Δt.   We substitute this

into Equation 5-1 to get

$$\Delta Q_1 = E_2' - E_1' + \Delta E_o - \Delta E_i + \Delta W_1 \qquad (5\text{-}2)$$

The term $\Delta E_o - \Delta E_i$ represents the net ouflow of internal energy through the control surface. We may express this net outflow of internal energy by the product of the flow of mass out of the control surface and the internal energy per unit mass. Figure 45 shows part of the control volume which is the outline of the mass system at time t and the outline of this part of the mass system at time $t + \Delta t$. The area dA is part of the control surface, one dimension appearing in Fig. 45 as a solid line, the other as perpendicular to the figure. We draw the solid line N normal to and outward from the surface dA.

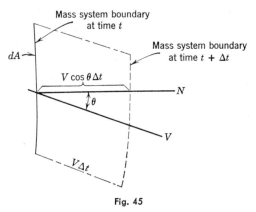

Fig. 45

The angle θ is the angle between the velocity through the area dA and the normal N to this area. We must note that the mass outflow through the surface area dA in time Δt is $\rho V \cos \theta \, dA \, \Delta t$. The product of the mass outflow and the internal energy per unit mass e is the internal energy carried across dA by the mass flow in time Δt. The total internal energy carried across the surface area and out of the control volume is the sum of the internal energy carried out through each area dA. This sum of an infinite number of infinitesimal quantities is an integral.

$$\Delta E_o - \Delta E_i = \Delta t \int_A \rho e V \cos \theta \, dA \qquad (5\text{-}3)$$

In the absence of electricity, magnetism, and capillarity, the internal energy e is the sum of three kinds of energy: potential energy, kinetic energy, and specific internal energy. The specific internal energy denoted by u has the units of energy per unit mass. We sometimes call specific internal energy intrinsic or residual energy. Thus, for the specific energy e we can write

$$e = gz + \frac{V^2}{2} + u$$

When we combine Equations 5-2 and 5-3 with the definition of e, the energy equation becomes

$$\Delta Q_1 = E_2' - E_1' + \Delta t \int_A \rho \left(gz + \frac{V^2}{2} + u \right) V \cos \theta \, dA + \Delta W_1 \quad (5\text{-}4)$$

We can divide the work term, ΔW_1, in the energy equation into two parts. The first part is the work due to the pressure on the control surface acting through a distance in time Δt. The other part of the work term ΔW consists of all other work transferred through the boundary of the control volume.

Figure 46 shows a small segment dA of the control volume surface. The pressure p acts normal to this surface, and the velocity V forms

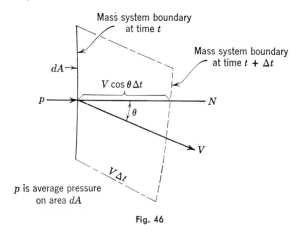

Fig. 46

an angle θ with the outward-drawn normal N. In time Δt the mass system has moved to a new position. The work performed by the pressure forces acting on the area dA in this time Δt will be the product of the pressure, the area, and the distance moved in the direction of the pressure, which we write as $p \, dA \, V \cos \theta \, \Delta t$. The total work done by all pressure forces is the sum of all these terms taken over the complete surface of the control volume.

$$\int_A pV \cos \theta \, dA \, \Delta t = \Delta t \int_A pV \cos \theta \, dA \quad (5\text{-}5)$$

During time Δt the pressure acting on area dA undergoes a change in moving the distance $V \cos \theta \, \Delta t$. In computing the pressure work, we should take into account this small change; but, since it leads to infinitesimals of a higher order, it is not included in this derivation.

The work term ΔW_1 is

$$\Delta W_1 = \Delta W + \Delta t \int_A pV \cos \theta \, dA = \Delta W + \Delta t \int_A \frac{p}{\rho} \rho V \cos \theta \, dA$$

We substitute this value of ΔW_1 into Equation 5-4 to get

$$\Delta Q = E_2' - E_1' + \Delta t \int_A \left(\frac{p}{\rho} + \frac{V^2}{2} + gz + u \right) \rho V \cos \theta \, dA + \Delta W$$

We divide by Δt and take the limit as $\Delta t \to 0$

$$\lim_{\Delta t \to 0} \left(\frac{\Delta Q}{\Delta t} \right) = \lim_{\Delta t \to 0} \left(\frac{E_2' - E_1'}{\Delta t} + \frac{\Delta W}{\Delta t} \right) + \int_A \left(\frac{p}{\rho} + \frac{V^2}{2} \right.$$
$$\left. + gz + u \right) \rho V \cos \theta \, dA$$

$$\frac{dQ}{dt} = \frac{E_2' - E_1'}{dt} + \frac{dW}{dt} + \int_A \left(\frac{p}{\rho} + \frac{V^2}{2} \right.$$
$$\left. + gz + u \right) \rho V \cos \theta \, dA \quad (5\text{-}6)$$

where Q = heat added across the control surface

W = work, except for pressure work transferred out of the control surface

In its most general form this is the energy equation for a control volume. No restrictions are placed upon this equation except those applying to the first law of thermodynamics and restricting the internal energy to potential energy, kinetic energy, and specific internal energy. In the event that electricity, magnetism, or capillarity enters into a specific problem, we must add those energies to the internal energy of a fluid. This equation applies equally well to steady and unsteady flow.

We previously broke down the work term dW_1 into two terms, the pressure work and all remaining work dW. In choosing the boundaries of the control volume, we often find it expedient to select solid boundaries of the fluid and surfaces normal to the fluid flow. The pressure work term applies only at those surfaces through which fluid flows. On the solid boundaries of the control volume through which fluid does not pass there may exist a shear stress. At all solid boundaries in fluid flow the velocity of the fluid relative to the boundary is zero.   Therefore, the shear forces on the solid boundaries do no work.

Problems of unsteady motion are, in general, beyond the scope of this book.   The energy equation is simplified to apply only to problems of steady flow.   The internal energy of the fluid in the control volume is constant in steady flow.   Thus, $E_1' = E_2'$, and the rearranged energy equation becomes

$$\frac{dQ}{dt} - \frac{dW}{dt} = \int_A \left(\frac{p}{\rho} + \frac{V^2}{2} + gz + u \right) \rho V \cos \theta \, dA \qquad (5\text{-}7)$$

This general energy equation for steady flow appears quite formidable; however, Illustrative Problems 1 and 2 demonstrate that it is not as complicated as it might seem.

▶Illustrative Problem 1.   A perfect gas flows steadily in a 1 ft dia. pipe that suddenly enlarges to 2 ft in diameter.   The temperature is constant at 70°F.   The engineering gas constant is 53-lb$_f$-ft/lb$_m$°R.   Compute the rate of heat transfer either to or from the pipe enlargement.

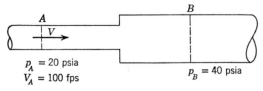

P_A = 20 psia
V_A = 100 fps

P_B = 40 psia

Sketch 33

Solution: The equation of state for a perfect gas may be written as

$$\frac{p}{\rho} = g_c RT$$

where p = pressure, in lb/ft^2
ρ = mass density, in slugs/ft^3
g_c = Newton proportionality constant = 32.2 lb$_m$-ft/lb$_f$ sec^2
T = temperature, in °R
R = engineering gas constant, in lb$_f$-ft/lb$_m$°R

Select the control volume as the walls of the pipe and as two surfaces normal to flow.   The control volume then is

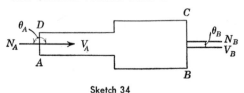

Sketch 34

The angle θ is $\pi/2$ between the outward-drawn normal and the velocity vector at every surface of the control volume except AD and BC. Therefore, evaluate the integral which appears in the energy Equation 5-7, as follows:

$$\int_A \left(\frac{p}{\rho} + \frac{V^2}{2} + gz + u \right) \rho V \cos \theta \, dA = \int_{AD+BC} \left(\frac{p}{\rho} + \frac{V^2}{2} \right.$$
$$\left. + gz + u \right) \rho V \cos \theta \, dA$$

Here $\theta = \pi$ at surface AD, and $\theta = 0$ at surface BC.

$$\left.
\begin{aligned}
\int_A \left(\frac{p}{\rho} + \frac{V^2}{2} + gz + u \right) \rho V \cos \theta \, dA = &- \int_{AD} \left(\frac{p}{\rho} + \frac{V^2}{2} \right. \\
+ gz + u \Big) \rho V \, dA + \int_{BC} \left(\frac{p}{\rho} \right. & \left. + \frac{V^2}{2} + gz + u \right) \rho V \, dA
\end{aligned}
\right\} \quad \text{(P)}$$

Since the properties p, ρ, V, z, and u are considered constant across the surface of integration, you may take them outside the integral sign. The integration over surface AD is

$$(-1) \left(\frac{p_A}{\rho_A} + \frac{V_A^2}{2} + gz_A + u_A \right) \rho_A V_A \int_{AD} dA = - \left(\frac{p_A}{\rho_A} + \frac{V_A^2}{2} \right.$$
$$\left. + gz_A + u_A \right) \rho_A V_A A_A$$

Do the same across the face BC and substitute both into Equation P to get

$$\int_A \left(\frac{p}{\rho} + \frac{V^2}{2} + gz + u \right) \rho V \cos \theta \, dA = -\rho_A A_A V_A \left(\frac{p_A}{\rho_A} + \frac{V_A^2}{2} \right.$$
$$\left. + gz_A + u_A \right) + \rho_B V_B A_B \left(\frac{p_B}{\rho_B} + \frac{V_B^2}{2} + gz_B + u_B \right)$$

With this substitution the energy equation becomes

$$\frac{dQ}{dt} - \frac{dW}{dt} = \rho_B A_B V_B \left(\frac{p_B}{\rho_B} + \frac{V_B^2}{2} + gz_B + u_B \right)$$
$$- \rho_A A_A V_A \left(\frac{p_A}{\rho_A} + \frac{V_A^2}{2} + gz_A + u_A \right)$$

The intrinsic energy u in a perfect gas is a function of only the temperature. Therefore, $u_B = u_A$ since the temperature is constant and the gas may be considered a perfect gas. Measure the elevation z to the center of the pipe. Therefore, $z_B = z_A$.

Next consider the p/ρ terms. For a perfect gas

$$\frac{p}{\rho} = g_c R T$$

Since g_c, R, and T are constant, p/ρ is a constant; therefore,

$$\frac{p_B}{\rho_B} = \frac{p_A}{\rho_A}$$

No work transfers through the control volume and so $dW/dt = 0$.
The energy equation becomes

$$\frac{dQ}{dt} = \rho_B A_B V_B \left(\frac{p_A}{\rho_A} + \frac{V_B{}^2}{2} + gz_A + u_A\right)$$

$$- \rho_A A_A V_A \left(\frac{p_A}{\rho_A} + \frac{V_A{}^2}{2} + gz_A + u_A\right)$$

To simplify, it is necessary to apply the equation of continuity to
the control volume.

$$\int_A \rho V \cos \theta \, dA = 0$$

$$\int_{AD} \rho V \cos \theta \, dA + \int_{BC} \rho V \cos \theta \, dA = 0$$

$$\rho_A V_A(-1) \int_{AD} dA + \rho_B V_B(+1) \int_{BC} dA = 0$$

$$- \rho_A V_A A_A + \rho_B V_B A_B = 0$$

$$\rho_A V_A A_A = \rho_B V_B A_B$$

When you make this substitution, the energy equation becomes

$$\frac{dQ}{dt} = \rho_A A_A V_A \left(\frac{p_A}{\rho_A} + \frac{V_B{}^2}{2} + gz_A + u_A\right)$$

$$- \rho_A A_A V_A \left(\frac{p_A}{\rho_A} + \frac{V_A{}^2}{2} + gz_A + u_A\right)$$

$$\frac{dQ}{dt} = \rho_A A_A V_A \left[\left(\frac{p_A}{\rho_A} \overset{0}{\diagup} \frac{p_A}{\rho_A}\right) + \frac{V_B{}^2 - V_A{}^2}{2} + g(z_A \overset{0}{\diagup} z_A) + (u_A \overset{0}{\diagup} u_A)\right]$$

$$\frac{dQ}{dt} = \rho_A A_A V_A \left(\frac{V_B{}^2 - V_A{}^2}{2}\right)$$

The mass flow rate is

$$\rho_A A_A V_A = \left(\frac{p_A}{g_c R T}\right) A_A V_A = \frac{(20)(144)}{(32.2)(53)(530)} \frac{\pi(1)^2}{4} (100)$$

$$= 0.25 \text{ slug/sec}$$

By continuity $\rho_A A_A V_A = \rho_B A_B V_B$.

Therefore, $(0.25) = \dfrac{(40)(144)}{(32.2)(53)(530)} \dfrac{\pi(4)}{(4)} V_B$

$$V_B = 12.5 \text{ fps}$$

$$\frac{dQ}{dt} = \rho_A A_A V_A \left(\frac{V_B{}^2 - V_A{}^2}{2}\right)$$

$$= (0.25) \left(\frac{156.25}{2} - \frac{10,000}{2}\right) = -1230 \text{ ft-lb/sec}$$

The minus sign signifies that the heat transfers out of the control volume.   ◄

▶Illustrative Problem 2.   An incompressible fluid flows steadily in a 2 in. dia. horizontal pipe at the rate of 0.21812 slug/sec.   The velocity is constant across section 1.   A distance 30 ft down the pipe at section 2, the velocity v_2 varies with the distance R from the centerline of the pipe.   Write the variation as

$$v_2 = 2V_a \left[1 - \left(\frac{R}{R_o}\right)^2\right]$$

where R_o = radius of the pipe, in ft
    V_a = average velocity, in fps

The density of the fluid is 2 slugs/ft^3.   The pressure drop from section 1 to section 2 is 400 lb/ft^2.   Assume zero heat transfer and no work transmittal across the control surface.   Compute the change in intrinsic energy from section 1 to section 2.

Solution: The velocity at section 1 is constant so that $V_1 = V_a = $ average velocity.   Since $dW/dt = dQ/dt = 0$, the energy equation is

$$\int_A \left(\frac{p}{\rho} + \frac{V^2}{2} + gz + u\right) \rho V \cos\theta \, dA = 0$$

Choose the control volume so that the amount of calculations are a minimum and the desired terms appear.   (See Sketch 35.)   The walls of the pipe, a plane at section 1 perpendicular to the flow, and a plane at section 2 perpendicular to the flow are the surfaces of the control volume, as represented by the dotted line in the Sketch 35. Substitute the values of θ_1, θ_2, and θ_3 into the energy equation

$$- \int_{A_1} \left(\frac{p_1}{\rho_1} + \frac{V_1^2}{2} + gz_1 + u_1 \right) \rho_1 V_1 \, dA + \int_{A_2} \left(\frac{p_2}{\rho_2} + \frac{V_2^2}{2} \right.$$
$$\left. + gz_2 + u_2 \right) \rho_2 V_2 \, dA = 0$$

All the quantities are constant across section 1 and so they may be moved outside the integral sign and the remaining integral evaluated.

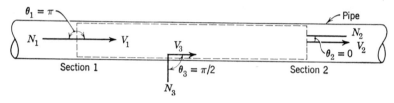

Sketch 35

At section 2 all the quantities except velocity are constant and may be taken outside the integral sign. The energy equation then takes the form

$$-\rho_1 A_1 V_1 \left(\frac{p_1}{\rho_1} + \frac{V_1^2}{2} + gz_1 + u_1 \right) + \left(\frac{p_2}{\rho_2} + gz_2 + u_2 \right) \rho_2 \int_{A_2} v_2 \, dA$$
$$+ \frac{\rho_2}{2} \int_{A_2} v_2^3 \, dA = 0$$

Next evaluate the integrals over A_2. To do so, you must select any area dA over which the velocity v_2 is constant. The velocity varies as the distance from the center of the pipe. Thus, an area (Sketch 36)

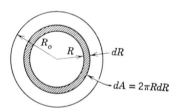

End view of section 2

Sketch 36

that is everywhere the same distance from the center will be an area of constant velocity.

Given $$v_2 = 2V_a \left[1 - \left(\frac{R}{R_o} \right)^2 \right]$$

Thus, $$\int_{A_1} v_2 \, dA = \int_0^{R_o} v_2 2\pi R \, dR = 2\pi \int_0^{R_o} 2V_a \left[1 - \left(\frac{R}{R_o} \right)^2 \right] R \, dR$$

$$= 4\pi V_a \int_0^{R_o} \left[R - \frac{R^3}{R_o^2} \right] dR = V_a \pi R_o^2 = V_a A$$

Evaluate $$\int_{A_2} v_2{}^3 \, dA$$

Now $$v_2{}^3 = 8V_a{}^3 \left[1 - \frac{R^2}{R_o^2} \right]^3$$

and so $$\int_{A_2} v_2{}^3 \, dA = 8V_a{}^3 2\pi \int_0^{R_o} \left[1 - \left(\frac{R}{R_o} \right)^2 \right]^3 R \, dR = 2V_a{}^3 \pi R_o^2$$

$$= 2V_a{}^3 A$$

Substitute the value of the integrals into the energy equation

$$-\rho A V_a \left[\frac{p_1}{\rho} + \frac{V_a{}^2}{2} + gz_1 + u_1 \right] + \left[\frac{p_2}{\rho} + gz_2 + u_2 \right] \rho A V_a$$

$$+ \frac{\rho}{2} 2V_a{}^3 A = 0$$

and divide by $\rho A V_a$

$$- \left[\frac{p_1}{\rho} + \frac{V_a{}^2}{2} + gz_1 + u_1 \right] + \frac{p_2}{\rho} + gz_2 + u_2 + V_a{}^2 = 0$$

Rearrange the energy equation to solve for change of intrinsic energy $u_2 - u_1$.

$$u_2 - u_1 = \frac{p_1 - p_2}{\rho} + \frac{V_a{}^2}{2} - V_a{}^2 + g(z_1 - z_2)$$

0 since $z_2 = z_1$

Given $$p_1 - p_2 = 400 \text{ lb/ft}^2$$

Therefore, $$u_2 - u_1 = \frac{400}{\rho} - \frac{V_a{}^2}{2}$$

Since $\rho A V_a = 0.21812$ slug/sec,

$$V_a = \frac{0.21812}{\rho A} = \frac{0.21812}{(2)\pi(\frac{1}{12})^2} = 5.0 \text{ fps}$$

$$u_2 - u_1 = \frac{400}{\rho} - \frac{V_a^2}{2} = \frac{400}{2} - \frac{(5)^2}{2} = 187.5 \text{ ft-lb/slug}$$

This is an increase in internal energy since $u_2 > u_1$. ◀

35. Comparison of the Energy Equation and the Euler Equation

We derived the Euler equation for flow along a stream tube. When we apply the energy equation to the same stream tube shown in Fig. 47, comparison of the two equations produces some interesting results. When we apply the Euler equation to flow along a stream tube, no work transfers across the boundaries of the stream tube, but heat may

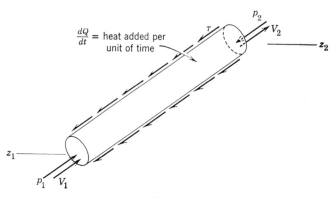

Fig. 47

transfer. The Euler equation for an incompressible fluid applied to this flow between section 1 and section 2 further downstream results in this equation:

$$\frac{V_2^2 - V_1^2}{2} + g(z_2 - z_1) + \frac{(p_2 - p_1)}{\rho} + gh_L = 0 \qquad (5\text{-}8)$$

We substitute the gh_L term for the friction term $\int (\tau/\rho)(dR/dA)\,ds$ which appears in the modified Euler equation, Equation 3-11 in Chapter 3. Head loss h_L appears frequently in pipe flow problems. We write the energy equation for the control volume which is defined by the sides of the stream tube and the two ends 1 and 2. The work term equals 0, and the properties of the fluid are constant across each section so that the following equation emerges:

$$\frac{dQ}{dt} = -\rho_1 A_1 V_1 \left(\frac{p_1}{\rho_1} + \frac{V_1^2}{2} + gz_1 + u_1 \right)$$
$$+ \rho_2 A_2 V_2 \left(\frac{p_2}{\rho_2} + \frac{V_2^2}{2} + gz_2 + u_2 \right) \quad (Q)$$

The application of the equation of continuity to this control volume gives the relation

$$0 = \int_A \rho V \cos \theta \, dA = -\rho_1 A_1 V_1 + \rho_2 A_2 V_2$$

$$\rho_1 A_1 V_1 = \rho_2 A_2 V_2 = \rho A V = \text{mass flow rate}$$

By dividing the energy equation Q by the mass flow rate and rearranging terms, we obtain

$$0 = \frac{p_2 - p_1}{\rho} + \frac{V_2^2 - V_1^2}{2} + g(z_2 - z_1) + u_2 - u_1 - q \quad (5\text{-}9)$$

where $q = \dfrac{dQ}{\rho A V \, dt}$ = heat transferred to the system per mass of fluid flowing

Equations 5-8 and 5-9, written for the same system, are both equal to zero. We equate these results in the following relationship:

$$gh_L = u_2 - u_1 - q \quad (5\text{-}10)$$

which is valid for incompressible flow only.

In this way we demonstrate that the friction term from the Euler equation equals the change in intrinsic energy minus the heat added to the system per mass of fluid flowing. The friction does not cause an energy loss but an increase in intrinsic energy plus heat transferred from the control volume.

▶Illustrative Problem 3. An incompressible, frictionless fluid flows steadily into a machine at section 1 and out at section 2. Heat transfers to the machine at the rate of 300 Btu per minute. The area at section 1 is $\frac{1}{10}$ ft^2 and at section 2 is $\frac{1}{5}$ ft^2. The fluid, water, flows in section 1 at the rate of 2 slugs/sec. The pressure at section 1 is 40 psia and at section 2 is 30 psia. Neglecting the change in elevation, compute the work per slug added to or taken from the machine.

Solution:

The dotted lines in Sketch 37 represent the control surfaces of the control volume. Select this control volume because the cos θ is different from zero only at sections 1 and 2. This selection of the control volume reduces the amount of work.

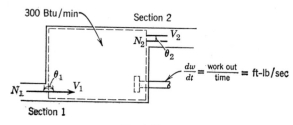

Sketch 37

The general energy equation is

$$\frac{dQ}{dt} - \frac{dW}{dt} = \int_A \left(\frac{p}{\rho} + \frac{V^2}{2} + gz + u \right) \rho V \cos \theta \, dA$$

At section 1, $\theta_1 = \pi$ over the entire section; at section 2, $\theta_2 = 0$ over the entire section. The value of the integral is zero over the remaining surface of the control volume since $\theta = \pi/2$. From this you can get

$$\frac{dQ}{dt} - \frac{dW}{dt} = - \int_{A_1} \left(\frac{p_1}{\rho_1} + \frac{V_1{}^2}{2} + gz_1 + u_1 \right) \rho_1 V_1 \, dA$$

$$+ \int_{A_2} \left(\frac{p_2}{\rho_2} + \frac{V_2{}^2}{2} + gz_2 + u_2 \right) \rho_2 V_2 \, dA$$

All properties of the water at section 1 are constant and can be taken from inside the integral sign. The same is true at section 2.

$$\frac{dQ}{dt} - \frac{dW}{dt} = - \rho_1 V_1 \left(\frac{p_1}{\rho_1} + \frac{V_1{}^2}{2} + gz_1 + u_1 \right) \int_{A_1} dA$$

$$+ \rho_2 V_2 \left(\frac{p_2}{\rho_2} + \frac{V_2{}^2}{2} + gz_2 + u_2 \right) \int_{A_2} dA$$

By definition $\int_{A_1} dA = A_1$ and $\int_{A_2} dA = A_2$

The fluid is water and may be considered incompressible. Therefore, $\rho_1 = \rho_2 = \rho$, and

$$\frac{dQ}{dt} = +300 \text{ Btu/min} = \frac{(300)(778)}{60} = 3890 \text{ ft-lb/sec}$$

Substitute these values in the energy equation.

$$3890 - \frac{dW}{dt} = -\rho A_1 V_1 \left(\frac{p_1}{\rho} + \frac{V_1^2}{2} + gz_1 + u_1 \right)$$
$$+ \rho A_2 V_2 \left(\frac{p_2}{\rho} + \frac{V_2^2}{2} + gz_2 + u_2 \right)$$

From the equation of continuity for steady flow you get

$$\int_A \rho V \cos \theta \, dA = 0$$

and $\quad -\rho A_1 V_1 + \rho A_2 V_2 = 0, \qquad \rho A_1 V_1 = \rho A_2 V_2 = \rho A V$

Divide the energy equation by $\rho A V$ and rearrange.

$$\frac{3890}{\rho A V} - \frac{1}{\rho A V} \frac{dW}{dt}$$
$$= \left(\frac{p_2 - p_1}{\rho} + \frac{V_2^2 - V_1^2}{2} + g(z_2 - z_1) + u_2 - u_1 \right) \text{ ft-lb/slug}$$

For a frictionless incompressible fluid $u_2 - u_1 - q = 0$, and h_L is zero. The q in the above equation is $3890/\rho A V$. Therefore,

$$-\frac{1}{\rho A V} \frac{dW}{dt} = -w_s = \frac{p_2 - p_1}{\rho} + \frac{V_2^2 - V_1^2}{2} + g(z_2 - z_1)$$

Given in the problem that $p_2 = 30$ psia, $\rho = 1.94$ slugs/ft^3, $p_1 = 40$ psia, and $z_1 = z_2$. Therefore,

$$-w_s = \frac{(30 - 40)(144)}{1.94} + \frac{V_2^2 - V_1^2}{2} + g(z_2 - z_1)^0$$

$$-w_s = \frac{-1440}{1.94} + \frac{V_2^2 - V_1^2}{2} \tag{R}$$

From continuity

$$\rho A_1 V_1 = \rho A_2 V_2 = 2 \text{ slugs/sec}$$
$$(1.94)(\tfrac{1}{10}) V_1 = (1.94)(\tfrac{1}{5}) V_2 = 2 \text{ slugs/sec}$$

Therefore, $\qquad V_1 = \dfrac{20}{1.94}, \qquad V_2 = \dfrac{10}{1.94}$

and

$$\frac{V_2^2 - V_1^2}{2} = \frac{1}{2} \left[\left(\frac{10}{1.94} \right)^2 - \left(\frac{20}{1.94} \right)^2 \right] = \frac{1}{2} \left(\frac{1}{1.94} \right)^2 [100 - 400]$$
$$= -39.86 \text{ ft-lb/slug}$$

Substitute this into the energy equation R.

$$-w_s = -\frac{1440}{1.94} - 39.86 = -782.13$$

$$w_s = +782.13 \text{ ft-lb/slug}$$

The plus sign signifies work taken out of the machine.   ◄

36. Compressible Flow in Diverging and Converging Nozzles

The study of steady flow in a nozzle is not fundamental in itself but results in some interesting conclusions. We shall consider flow in a nozzle from a one-dimensional viewpoint, using a short nozzle so that friction and heat transfer will be small enough to neglect. The expansion of the gas, then, is isentropic. Following the usual practice in this book, we consider the gas to be perfect.

The first law of thermodynamics is

$$dQ_1 = dE + dW_1 \tag{5-11}$$

For an isentropic process $dQ_1 = 0$. The work term divides into two parts, the pressure work $d(p/\rho)$ and the remaining work dW. No work transfers from the system and so $dW = 0$. The internal energy E in the absence of other forms of energy is

$$E = \frac{V^2}{2} + gz + u$$

We make these substitutions in the first law with this result

$$d\frac{p}{\rho} + d\left(\frac{V^2}{2} + gz + u\right) = 0$$

or

$$d\left(\frac{p}{\rho}\right) + d\left(\frac{V^2}{2}\right) + g\,dz + du = 0$$

We expand the first term and rearrange to

$$p\,d\left(\frac{1}{\rho}\right) + du + \frac{1}{\rho}\,dp + g\,dz + d\,\frac{V^2}{2} = 0$$

But for an isentropic process, from thermodynamics, we know that

$$p\,d\left(\frac{1}{\rho}\right) + du = T\,ds = 0$$

Therefore, Equation 3-11 becomes

$$\frac{1}{\rho}\,dp + g\,dz + d\,\frac{V^2}{2} = 0$$

For a nozzle the change in z is small and so we can neglect the dz term.

$$\frac{1}{\rho}\,dp + V\,dV = 0 \qquad\qquad (5\text{-}12)$$

We apply the principle of continuity to the flow in the nozzle. Figure 48 shows a closed conduit of varying cross section with section 1 upstream from section 2. We consider the control volume as a plane

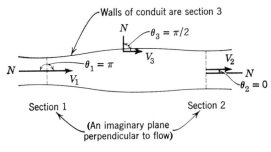

Fig. 48

at section 1 perpendicular to the flow, a plane at section 2 perpendicular to the flow, and the walls of the conduit. The equation of continuity for steady flow is

$$\int_A \rho V \cos \theta \, dA = 0$$

When we apply this to the control volume, there results

$$\int_{A_1} \rho V \cos \theta \, dA + \int_{A_2} \rho V \cos \theta \, dA + \int_{A_3} \rho V \cos \theta \, dA = 0$$

For section 1, $\theta = \pi$; for section 2, $\theta = 0$; and for walls of the conduit, $\theta = \pi/2$. We substitute these values into the above equation to get

$$-\int_{A_1} \rho_1 V_1 \, dA + \int_{A_2} \rho_2 V_2 \, dA = 0$$

Since all the quantities are constant across the section, we may take them outside of the integral sign.

$$-\rho_1 V_1 \int_{A_1} dA + \rho_2 V_2 \int_{A_2} dA = 0$$

or
$$\rho_1 A_1 V_1 = \rho_2 A_2 V_2 = \rho A V$$

This states that the mass flow across any section is constant. Therefore,

$$\rho A V = \text{constant}$$

$$\log_e \rho A V = \log_e (\text{constant})$$

$$\log_e \rho + \log_e A + \log_e V = \log_e (\text{constant})$$

By differentiating this equation, we arrive at

$$\frac{d\rho}{\rho} + \frac{dA}{A} + \frac{dV}{V} = 0 \qquad (5\text{-}13)$$

For an isentropic process

$$\frac{p}{\rho^k} = \text{constant} = K$$

or
$$p = K\rho^k$$

We differentiate this to get $dp = Kk\rho^{k-1} d\rho$, but $K = \dfrac{p}{\rho^k}.$ Therefore,

$$dp = \frac{kp}{\rho^k} \rho^{k-1} d\rho = k \frac{p}{\rho} d\rho$$

or
$$\frac{d\rho}{\rho} = \frac{dp}{kp} \qquad (5\text{-}14)$$

We then substitute Equation 5-14 into Equation 5-13.

$$\frac{dp}{kp} + \frac{dA}{A} + \frac{dV}{V} = 0$$

solve Equation 5-12 for dp, and substitute this into the above equation.

$$\frac{-\rho V \, dV}{kp} + \frac{dA}{A} + \frac{dV}{V} = 0$$

Now we solve for dA/dV.

$$\frac{dA}{dV} = A\left(\frac{\rho V}{kp} - \frac{1}{V}\right) = \frac{A}{V}\left(\frac{\rho V^2}{kp} - 1\right)$$

For an isentropic process $kp/\rho = a^2$, where a is the acoustic velocity, a substitution which leads to

$$\frac{dA}{dV} = \frac{A}{V}\left(\frac{V^2}{a^2} - 1\right)$$

or

$$\frac{dA}{dV} = \frac{A}{V}(M^2 - 1) \qquad (5\text{-}15)$$

where $M = V/a$ and is called the Mach number.

We derived Equation 5-15 for both diverging and converging nozzles. The velocity can be either subsonic, $M < 1$, or supersonic, $M > 1$. The quantities A and V are both positive. From the definition of a differential, dA is positive when the cross-sectional area is increasing and negative when the cross-sectional area is decreasing.

First, we consider subsonic flow, $M < 1$. This means that $M^2 - 1$ is negative. Therefore $A/V(M^2 - 1)$ is negative because both A and V are positive. From Equation 5-15 we see that dA/dV equals this negative quantity. When the area is increasing ($dA > 0$), for dA/dV to be negative dV must be negative. A negative dV indicates decreasing velocity. The velocity must decrease for an area increase. When area is decreasing ($dA < 0$), then dV must be positive for dA/dV to be negative. The velocity is increasing for decreasing area.

Therefore, the subsonic flow is as shown in Sketch 38.

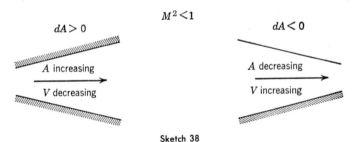

Sketch 38

We consider next the case of supersonic flow $M > 1$. For $M > 1$, $M^2 - 1$ is positive and, from Equation 5-15, dA/dV is also positive. When dA/dV is positive, dA and dV must have the same sign. Therefore, for A increasing, V is increasing; and, for A decreasing, V is decreasing. (See Sketch 39.) This demonstrates that the behavior of a gas is entirely different in the supersonic region from what it is in the subsonic region. From momentum we know that, to increase thrust, we must increase the exit velocity. Because the flow in rocket and jet nozzles is supersonic and because we desire maximum thrust, we design the nozzles to expand in the direction of flow. From previous discussion we know that expansion of a nozzle increases the velocity in supersonic flow.

In supersonic wind tunnel design it is necessary to change the flow from subsonic upstream to supersonic at the test section by converging the nozzle in the subsonic section until the flow becomes sonic. The nozzle then is expanded until the flow reaches the proper velocity.

$$M^2 > 1$$

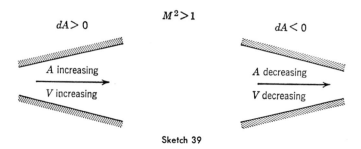

Sketch 39

We can reach the acoustic velocity $M = 1$ only in the throat of a nozzle. Since the fluid passes through the throat, where it reaches acoustic velocity, the question naturally arises as to how it can be made to go either subsonic or supersonic on the downstream section of the nozzle throat. This depends on the pressure downstream from the throat, a subject that is covered completely in more advanced books on compressible flow.

37. Critical Pressure Ratio

A perfect gas fills a large tank (Fig. 49) so that the pressure in the tank is p_1. A converging nozzle is opened in one side of the tank. When the nozzle area is very small compared to the volume of the tank, we may consider the flow steady and isentropic out the nozzle. The walls of the tank, a plane down the inside of the tank, and the walls and throat of the nozzle form the control volume, as shown by the dotted lines in the figure. There is no heat transfer and no work transmittal across the boundaries. The energy equation applied to this control volume is

$$0 = \int_A \left(\frac{V^2}{2} + gz + \frac{p}{\rho} + u \right) \rho V \cos \theta \, dA$$

Here $\cos \theta$ is zero everywhere except at the plane inside the tank and at the throat of the nozzle. We assume that the gas flows into the control volume at the inside plane and out at the throat. Then cos θ at the inside plane equals -1 and at the throat $+1$. The quantities inside the integral sign are constant across secton 1 and may be taken outside

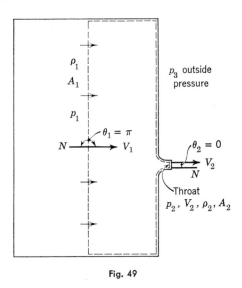

Fig. 49

the integral sign. The same is true at section 2, the throat. The energy equation is

$$-\rho_1 A_1 V_1 \left(\frac{V_1^2}{2} + gz_1 + \frac{p_1}{\rho_1} + u_1 \right)$$
$$+ \rho_2 A_2 V_2 \left(\frac{V_2^2}{2} + gz_2 + \frac{p_2}{\rho_2} + u_2 \right) = 0 \quad (5\text{-}16)$$

We may assume the z term to be small and, therefore, neglect it. For gases

$$\frac{p}{\rho} + u = h$$

where h is called enthalpy. We substitute this equation into Equation, 5-16, obtaining

$$-\rho_1 A_1 V_1 \left(\frac{V_1^2}{2} + h_1 \right) + \rho_2 A_2 V_2 \left(\frac{V_2^2}{2} + h_2 \right) = 0 \quad (5\text{-}17)$$

We apply the equation of continuity for this control volume which results in

$$\rho_1 A_1 V_1 = \rho_2 A_2 V_2 = \rho A V$$

Now A_1 is very large, but V_1 is very small. By substituting them into Equation 17 and dividing by $\rho A V$, we obtain the following results:

$$-\left(\frac{V_1^2}{2} + h_1\right) + \left(\frac{V_2^2}{2} + h_2\right) = 0$$

$$\frac{V_1^2}{2} + h_1 = \frac{V_2^2}{2} + h_2$$

Because the velocity V_1 is small, we can neglect it. Therefore,

$$V_2^2 = 2(h_1 - h_2)$$

From thermodynamics for perfect gases

$$h_1 - h_2 = \frac{k}{k-1}\left(\frac{p_1}{\rho_1} - \frac{p_2}{\rho_2}\right) = \frac{k}{k-1}\frac{p_2}{\rho_2}\left[\frac{p_1}{p_2}\frac{\rho_2}{\rho_1} - 1\right] \quad (5\text{-}18)$$

For an insentropic process $p/\rho^k =$ constant. We rearrange and substitute this into Equation 5-18 to obtain

$$V_2^2 = \frac{2k}{k-1}\frac{p_2}{\rho_2}\left[\left(\frac{p_1}{p_2}\right)^{(k-1)/k} - 1\right] \quad (5\text{-}19)$$

For a converging nozzle the maximum velocity that the gas can attain is sonic velocity. Therefore, $V_2 = a$, for maximum velocity. For an isentropic process, $a^2 = kp/\rho$ which we substitute into Equation 5-19.

$$V_2^2 = a_2^2 = \frac{kp_2}{\rho_2} = \frac{2k}{k-1}\frac{p_2}{\rho_2}\left[\left(\frac{p_1}{p_2}\right)^{(k-1)/k} - 1\right] \quad (5\text{-}20)$$

We obtain the following results by eliminating p_2/ρ_2 in Equation 5-20 and solving for p_2/p_1.

$$\frac{p_2}{p_1} = \left(\frac{2}{k+1}\right)^{k/(k-1)} \quad (5\text{-}21)$$

Thus, we demonstrate that, for a maximum flow through a converging nozzle from a tank, the pressure ratio p_2/p_1 is fixed; we call this fixed pressure ratio the critical pressure ratio. When the pressure outside the tank p_3 is such that p_3/p_1 is greater than the critical pressure ratio, the flow in the nozzle throat is less than sonic. When the pressure p_3 is such that p_3/p_1 equals the critical pressure ratio, the flow in the throat is sonic. For a ratio of p_3/p_1 less than the critical pressure ratio, the velocity in the throat must still be the sonic velocity. This means that the pressure p_2 in the throat is greater than p_3, the pressure outside the nozzle, when p_3/p_1 is less than the critical pressure ratio.

38. Summary

We used the first law of thermodynamics for a mass system to derive the general energy equation (Equation 5-6) for a control volume system.

$$\frac{dQ}{dt} = \frac{dW}{dt} + \int_A \left(\frac{p}{\rho} + \frac{V^2}{2} + gz + u \right) \rho V \cos \theta \, dA \qquad (5\text{-}6)$$

Equation 5-6 is valid for both steady and unsteady flow. Although this equation is a very powerful tool and we used it for many problems, it has some real weaknesses, the greatest of which is determining quantities, such as heat transfer, work done, and change of specific internal energy. Many times we must estimate these quantities or use empirical data to apply the energy equation to the problem. In any work dealing with compressible flow, a complete understanding of thermodynamics is necessary.

PROBLEMS

5-1. Calculate the heat transferred per slug of fluid flowing between sections 1 and 2 in the problem shown in Fig. P.5-1. The fluid may be considered a perfect gas. Neglect height. The following data are given:

$$
\begin{array}{ll}
A_1 = 0.5 \text{ ft}^2 & A_2 = 0.25 \text{ ft}^2 \\
p_1 = 60 \text{ psia} & p_2 = 120 \text{ psia} \\
T_1 = 70°\text{F} & T_2 = 70°\text{F} \\
V_1 = 20 \text{ fps} & \\
\rho_1 = 0.002 \text{ slug/ft}^3 &
\end{array}
$$

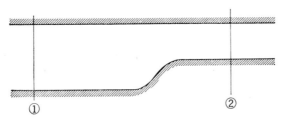

Fig. P.5-1

5-2. A gas that is neither a pure substance nor a perfect gas flows steadily in the heat exchanger (Fig. P.5-2).   No work is done by the gas.   Properties at the three cross sections where fluid flows are:

$\rho_1 = 0.1$ slug/ft^3 $\rho_2 = 0.2$ slug/ft^3 $\rho_3 = 0.15$ slug/ft^3
$A_1 = 0.1$ ft^2 $A_2 = 0.1$ ft^2 $A_3 = 0.2$ ft^2
$V_1 = 70$ fps $V_2 = 40$ fps
$p_1 = 15$ psia $p_2 = 20$ psia

The intrinsic energy is constant.   Compute V_3 and p_3.

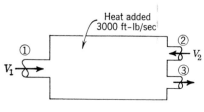

Fig. P.5-2

5-3. The enthalpy h is

$$h = u + \frac{p}{\rho}$$

Consider steady isentropic flow of a perfect gas through a control volume with only one entrance and one exit.   Neglect changes in elevation.   Derive the energy equation for this flow, and put the equation in the form

$$-w = \frac{k}{k-1}\left(\frac{p_2}{\rho_2} - \frac{p_1}{\rho_1}\right) + \frac{v_2{}^2 - v_1{}^2}{2}$$

where w = work done by the system per unit mass.

5-4. A perfect gas flows steadily through the machine shown in Fig. P.5-4. The engineering gas constant for this gas is 40 ft/°R.   One thousand foot-pounds of heat are added per second.   Calculate the shaft work of the machine.

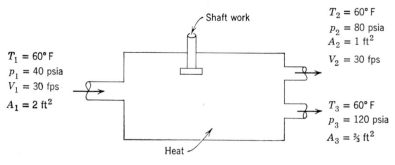

Fig. P.5-4

5-5. As shown in Fig. P.5-5, a real, incompressible fluid enters the machine at areas A_1 and A_2 and leaves at area A_3. The temperature is constant. The mass density of the fluid is 2 slugs/ft³. Consider all openings to be at the same elevation. Calculate the horsepower input or output from the shaft.

$$V_1 = 20 \text{ fps} \qquad V_2 = 40 \text{ fps} \qquad V_3 = 50 \text{ fps}$$
$$p_1 = 100 \text{ psia} \qquad p_2 = 70 \text{ psia} \qquad p_3 = 25 \text{ psia}$$
$$A_1 = 0.1 \text{ ft}^2 \qquad A_2 = 0.2 \text{ ft}^2$$

The flow is steady.

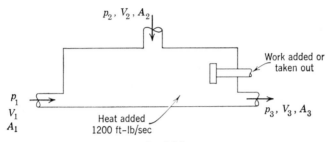

Fig. P.5-5

5-6. Air which may be considered a perfect gas is stored in a large tank at 60 psia. The atmospheric pressure is 15 psia, and the temperature is 70°F. The ratio of the specific heats k is 1.4. The gas flows out a 1 in. dia. hole in the side of the tank. The flow is steady and may be considered isentropic. Calculate the mass flow rate.

5-7. A pure substance which is also a perfect gas is flowing steadily in the horizontal branching pipe (Fig. P.5-7). In a pure substance the residual energy is a function only of the temperature. Consider this a constant temperature flow. When the flow does no work, calculate the heat added or subtracted from the flow per unit mass flowing.

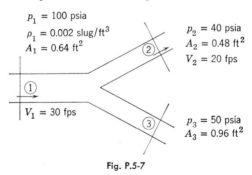

Fig. P.5-7

5-8. You wish to pump a stream of water from a nozzle through the air to a pond 100 ft away. The diameter of the stream at the nozzle is 3 in. The pond is at the same elevation as the nozzle, but the water supply for the stream is 25 ft below the nozzle. Neglecting all friction, determine the minimum horsepower pump required. The pump is 85 per cent efficient.

5-9. In a pump test (Fig. P.5-9) the flow rate is 3 cfs of water. Compute the theoretical pump horsepower. Assume water to be frictionless.

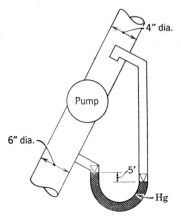

Fig. P.5-9

5-10. Four cubic feet per second of water flows as shown in Fig. P.5-10. Calculate the pump horsepower, neglecting all friction.

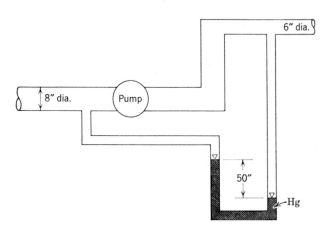

Fig. P.5-10

5-11. A cylinder of infinite length and diameter d is placed in a uniform parallel stream as shown in Fig. P.4-8, p. 162. Assume constant pressure and no heat transfer. Compute the change in intrinsic energy for the flow.

5-12. For the jet engine in Problem 4-12, p. 163, find the heat transfer to the air stream from the burning fuel. The specific internal energy of entering air is 86,000 ft-lb/slug, of leaving gases is 524,000 ft-lb/slug, and of entering fuel is 240,000,000 ft-lb/slug.

5-13. For the nozzle in Fig. P.5-13 find the exit velocity of the air and find the exit area.

Assume isentropic flow.

$p_1 = 20$ psia
$V_1 = 10$ fps
$\rho_1 = 0.002$ slug/ft^3
$A_1 = 1$ ft^2

$p_2 = 15$ psia

Fig. P.5-13

5-14. For the nozzle in Fig. P.5-14 compute the throat velocity and p_t.

Throat

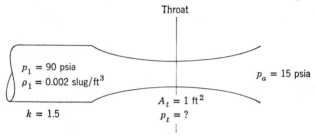

$p_1 = 90$ psia
$\rho_1 = 0.002$ slug/ft^3

$p_a = 15$ psia

$A_t = 1$ ft^2

$k = 1.5$

$p_t = ?$

Fig. P.5-14

5-15. For the flow in Problem 5-13 find the flow rate.

5-16. For the flow in Problem 5-14 find the flow rate.

5-17. For the flow in Problem 5-14 find the throat velocity when $k = 1.8$.

5-18. Determine between sections 1 and 2 the sum of the heat loss plus the increase in the specific internal energy per slug of liquid flowing in the 6 in. dia. pipe (Fig. P.5-18).

$p_1 = 20$ psia $p_2 = 17.92$ psia
$V_1 = 10$ fps $V_2 = 20(1 - 16r^2)$ fps, where r is distance
$\rho = 2$ slugs/ft^3 in feet from center

Section 1   Section 2

Fig. P.5-18

5-19. Determine between sections 1 and 2 the sum of the heat loss and the increase in the residual energy per slug of fluid flowing in the 6 in. dia. pipe (Fig. P.5-18). The conditions at section 1 are the same as in Problem 5-18. At section 2 $p_2 = 19.4$ psia and the velocity profile is

$$v_2 = (12.5)(4y)^{1/7} \text{ fps}$$

where y is measured in feet from the pipe wall.

5-20. In a hydraulic jump which occurs in a channel 10 ft wide, the depth changes from 1 ft to 3.6 ft. The flow rate is 160 cfs. Assuming that the velocity profile at each section is uniform and assuming a hydrostatic pressure distribution across each section, calculate the increase in residual energy when there is no heat transfer.

$$\rho = 1.94 \text{ slugs/ft}^3$$

5-21. In Illustrative Problem 6, Chapter 4 pp. 151–155, compute the work done per second by the water, use an energy analysis. Assume no heat transfer and no change in specific internal energy.

5-22. In Illustrative Problem 7, Chapter 4, p. 155–159, determine the work done per second on the water, use an energy analysis. Assume no heat transfer and no change in specific internal energy.

5-23. The 3 in. dia. circular pipe suddenly enlarges to 9 in. dia. (Fig. P.5-23). The velocity of the water in the 3 in. dia. section is uniform at 27 fps. The pressure in the 3 in. section is 20 psia and in the 9 in. section 21 psia. Assuming no heat transfer, compute the change in intrinsic energy of the water.

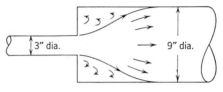

3" dia.   9" dia.

Fig. P.5-23

5-24. A perfect gas flows in a pipe of length L and diameter 1 ft. The pressure at the beginning of the pipe is 50 psia, and the velocity is uniform throughout the pipe at 40 fps. Near the end of the pipe the pressure has dropped to 10 psia. The temperature has been kept constant and so there is no change in residual energy. Compute the heat transfer to or from the pipe. The engineering gas constant is 50 ft/°R, and the temperature is 70°F.

5-25. At the entrance to a natural gas pumping station the velocity of the natural gas is 75 fps, and the pressure is 20 psia. At the exit the pressure is 90 psia. The sum of the change in elevation plus residual energy plus heat transferred, and the change in density can be neglected. The pipe is 3 in. in diameter and the engineering gas constant is 45 ft/°R. Compute the power output of the pump.

5-26. A steady stream of air 1 ft in diameter passes through a normal shock wave. Compute the change in specific internal energy across the shock. Neglect heat transfer, work added, and changes in elevation. Figure P.5-26

M_1		M_2
T_1		T_2
V_1		V_2
ρ_1		ρ_2
p_1		p_2

Shock
wave

Fig. P.5-26

is a sketch of the shock wave showing the properties before and after the shock.

$$M_1 = 2.50 \qquad\qquad M_2 = 0.513$$
$$p_1 = 7.85 \text{ psia} \qquad\qquad p_2 = 42.38 \text{ psia}$$
$$T_1 = 249°\text{R} \qquad\qquad T_2 = 560°\text{R}$$
$$\rho_1 = 0.00249 \text{ slug/ft}^3 \qquad \rho_2 = 0.0083 \text{ slug/ft}^3$$

5-27. A steady stream of air $\frac{1}{2}$ ft in diameter passes through a normal shock wave. Compute the change in specific internal energy across the shock. Neglect heat transfer, work added, and changes in elevation. Figure P.5-26 is a sketch of the shock wave showing the properties before and after the shock

$$M_1 = 1.20 \qquad\qquad M_2 = 0.842$$
$$p_1 = 11.00 \text{ psia} \qquad\qquad p_2 = 16.63 \text{ psia}$$
$$T_1 = 450°\text{R} \qquad\qquad T_2 = 507°\text{R}$$
$$\rho_1 = 0.00205 \text{ slug/ft}^3 \qquad \rho_2 = 0.00274 \text{ slug/ft}^3$$

FRICTION

chapter 6

39. Introduction

Up to this point we have not discussed friction directly. We have taken some of its effects into account without studying what friction really is. This chapter is devoted to a study of friction and how to handle it in different cases.

In fluid flow there are two main types of friction, the first caused by the molecular action of fluid, and the second caused by the agitation of the fluid particles, each of which is made up of billions of molecules. The molecules of a fluid not only have an attraction for each other but also have an attraction for the molecules of any solid with which the fluid comes into contact. This attraction causes the velocity of the fluid immediately adjacent to a solid boundary to approach the velocity of the solid boundary. As the molecules of the fluid come into contact with the molecules of the solid boundary, their collision tends to change the velocity of the fluid molecules to the velocity of the solid molecules. Because the solid molecules are much more rigidly connected to the solid boundary than the fluid molecules are connected to the fluid, the effect is greater on the fluid molecules. The net effect of these two types of molecular action (attraction and collision) on the fluid is to equalize the velocity of the fluid at the solid boundary and the velocity of the solid boundary. The only known exception to this is very high relative velocities between the fluid and the solid boundary in very low density fluids. In all presentations in this book we assume that the velocity of a real fluid at a solid boundary is equal to the velocity of the solid boundary.

40. Definition of Viscosity

We study the friction due to molecular action by examining the problem of two parallel plates separated by a thin film of liquid (Fig.

202

50a). The upper plate is moving with a small velocity V, and the lower plate is stationary. We must apply a force F to the top plate to keep it moving with the constant velocity V. From experimental work we know that this force is proportional to the product of the

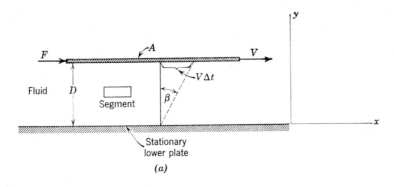

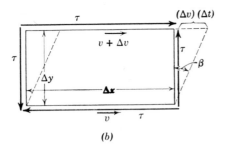

Fig. 50

velocity V and the wetted area A of the underside of the top plate divided by the perpendicular distance between the plates.

$$F \approx \frac{V}{D} A$$

or

$$F = \mu \frac{V}{D} A \qquad (6\text{-}1)$$

The proportionality constant μ is a function of the fluid involved, and we call it the coefficient of viscosity of the fluid. The shear stress τ equals the force F divided by the area A. We divide Equation 6-1 by the area A and substitute τ for F/A to get

$$\tau = \mu \frac{V}{D} \qquad (6\text{-}2)$$

Equation 6-2 is valid when the clearance between the plates is small enough to keep the liquid velocity profile linear, that is, a straight variation in velocity from V at the top plate to zero at the stationary plate, a restriction which makes Equation 6-2 unsatisfactory for general use.   Thus, we are forced to find a more general statement of the relation among these quantities.

We take as the axis system in Fig. 50a the x axis lying on the surface of the stationary plate in the direction of motion of the upper plate and the y axis perpendicular to both plates and positive in the upward direction.   The z axis is perpendicular to both the x and y axes.   We select a small cube of liquid between the plates and put the shear forces on it as in Fig. 50b.   The velocity of the fluid on the bottom of the cube is v and on the top of the cube is $v + \Delta v$.   In time Δt the cube deforms into the shape shown by the dotted lines, a deformation caused entirely by the shear stress τ.   The angle β is a measure of this deformation.   Since the angle is very small, we may consider it as

$$\beta = \frac{\Delta v \, \Delta t}{\Delta y} \qquad \text{or} \qquad \frac{\beta}{\Delta t} = \frac{\Delta v}{\Delta y}$$

The angle β is the same one shown in Fig. 50a because the velocity profile is linear.   From the figure we see that β is also

$$\beta = \frac{V \, \Delta t}{D}$$

or

$$\frac{\beta}{\Delta t} = \frac{V}{D}$$

From above

$$\frac{\beta}{\Delta t} = \frac{\Delta v}{\Delta y}$$

and so

$$\frac{V}{D} = \frac{\Delta v}{\Delta y}$$

We may apply Equation 6-2 to this cube.   The relation among the quantities depends only on the straight line velocity profile.   Thus, we can substitute $V/D = \Delta v/\Delta y$ into Equation 6-2, and the shear stress τ remains the same.   Equation 6-2 becomes

$$\tau = \mu \frac{\Delta v}{\Delta y} \qquad\qquad (6\text{-}3)$$

To determine the shear stress at a point, it is necessary to take Equation 6-3 to the limit as $\Delta y \to 0$

$$\tau = \lim_{\Delta y \to 0} \left(\mu \frac{\Delta v}{\Delta y} \right) = \mu \frac{dv}{dy} \tag{6-4}$$

Equation 6-4 is the general case of friction due to molecular action. It is interesting to note that dv/dy is the rate of deformation of the cube, not the deformation. This indicates that, once a fluid deforms, it does not return to its original shape unless a shear stress is applied. We can treat problems involving shear stress in a manner similar to that used in solid mechanics, but the strain is the rate of deformation rather than the deformation used in solid mechanics.

We can explain the shear stress between two elements of liquid on the basis of the molecular theory. As was pointed out in Chapter 1, molecular attraction holds liquids together. When one liquid element moves relative to another, the attraction between the molecules of the two elements causes a shear force between the elements. This shear force tends to speed up the slower element and slow down the faster element.

A reduction in the temperature of a liquid results in a lower velocity of its molecules. When the velocity of the molecules is slower, the attraction between them is greater. When the attraction between the molecules is increased but nothing else is changed, the shear stress should increase. Thus, a decrease in temperature should cause an increase in shear stress. From Equation 6-4 we see that an increase in shear stress when dv/dy is held constant must mean an increase in the viscosity μ. Therefore, for a liquid the viscosity should increase with a decrease in temperature, and, of course, with an increase in temperature the viscosity should decrease.

Experimental work shows that viscosity in liquids increases with a temperature decrease. Verification does not prove the explanation correct but does give it more credibility.

In gases, the molecules are so far apart that the attraction between them when compared to other forces is small. Figure 51a is a sketch of two adjacent elements of gas. Element 1 travels at a velocity $v + \Delta v$ in the x direction. Element 2 travels at a velocity v in the x direction. Thus, the average velocity of all the molecules in element 1 is $v + \Delta v$. Each molecule has a molecular velocity which transmits some of the molecules in element 1 into element 2. Now the average velocity of the molecules in element 2 is v in the x direction. The molecules from element 1 which have entered element 2 have a greater average velocity in the x direction than molecules in element 2.

When the faster molecules strike the slower ones, they cause the slower molecules to speed up, and at the same time the velocity of the faster molecules is lowered. This increases the average velocity in the x direction of the molecules which are in element 2. The reverse is true when the molecules from element 2 enter element 1. This causes a decrease in the average velocity in the x direction of the molecules in element 1 because the average velocity of the molecules is the velocity of the element. The transfer of molecules tends to speed up the slower

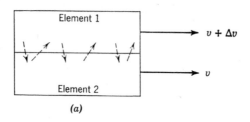

(a)

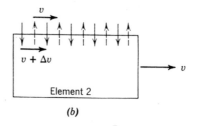

(b)

Fig. 51

elements and slow down the faster elements. Since there is a completely random motion of the molecules between the two elements, there must be the same number of molecules entering and leaving each element.

A more exact way to examine this molecular phenomenon is by momentum transfer. Figure 51b is a sketch of element 2 with a schematic notation for the molecules leaving and entering the element across the top surface. We assume that n number of molecules per unit time, each with a mass m, enter the element across the upper surface. Since the motion of the molecules is random, there must be an equal number of molecules leaving the element through the top surface. The molecules entering the element have an average velocity $v + \Delta v$ and so a momentum per unit time equal to $nm(v + \Delta v)$ transfers across the top surface into element 2. The molecules leaving the element have an average velocity v and so a momentum per unit time equal to *nmv* transfers across the top surface out of element 2. The total momentum per unit time transferring into the element is the difference between that momentum which transfers in and that momentum which transfers out. That is,

$$nm(v + \Delta v) - nmv = nm \, \Delta v \qquad (6\text{-}5)$$

Thus, momentum in the x direction, shown as a shear force on the upper surface, transfers into the lower element. The x momentum that transfers into the lower element transfers out of the upper element. This has the effect of a shear force on the upper element. This shear force is equal and opposite to the one on the lower element.

A temperature increase in a gas causes an increase in the molecular velocity of the molecules which causes more molecules to cross the boundary and, thus, increases n in Equation 6-5. When n increases, more momentum transfers across the boundary, and the shear stress increases.

Therefore, a temperature increase in a gas causes a viscosity increase, and, likewise, a temperature decrease causes a viscosity decrease. Experimental work shows this to be true. The analysis and explanation are justified, at least qualitatively.

The effect of pressure on the viscosity is negligible for both gases and liquids in most cases. Normal pressures compress liquids very slightly and so have very little effect on the attraction between the molecules, an attraction which is the basic cause of viscosity in liquids. Therefore, there is very little change in the viscosity because there is very little change in the molecular attraction.

In gases the pressure has no effect on rate of momentum transfer of the molecules and so the pressure has no effect on the viscosity. From the perfect gas law we know that an increase in pressure usually means an increase in density, which would seem to indicate that more molecules would be involved in the momentum transfer. The increased number of molecules causes more collisions between the molecules, but no more cross the boundary than before. Thus, the viscosity of a gas is independent of the pressure and the density under normal conditions.[1] When the density is reduced to the point where the molecules can travel distances of the order of the size of the container without interference from other molecules, the density has a marked effect on the viscosity.

[1] A complete analysis of the effect of pressure and density on the viscosity of a gas is given in *Theoretical Physics* by Georg Joos, Hafner Publishing Company, New York, 2nd ed., 1950, pp. 560–563.

Figure 52 is a plot of the shear stress τ versus the rate of deformation for some general types of fluids. The slope of the line in each case is the viscosity of the fluid. The fluids in which the viscosity is a constant and for which the curve goes through the origin are called Newtonian fluids. All other fluids are called non-Newtonian fluids. Most fluids in common use today are Newtonian fluids or may be considered Newtonian fluids because the viscosity is close to a constant

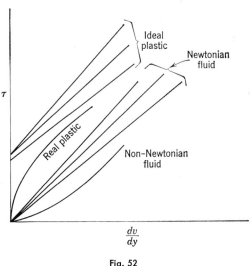

Fig. 52

in the working range. The fluids that we discuss in this book will be Newtonian fluids unless specified otherwise.

The term μ/ρ appears so frequently in fluid mechanics that it has been given a specific name, ν (nu) the kinematic viscosity. It is given the name kinematic viscosity because it has the dimensions of square feet per second. Thus,

$$\nu = \frac{\mu}{\rho}$$ KINEMATIC VISCOSITY

Illustrative Problems 1 and 2 demonstrate the use of viscosity concepts to solve engineering problems.

▶**Illustrative Problem 1.** A plate 4 ft square slides on a thin layer of oil which separates the plate from a horizontal plane. The layer of oil is $\frac{1}{10}$ in. thick, and the plate moves at 40 fps parallel to the plane. Calculate the force necessary to maintain this velocity of the plate when the oil has a viscosity of 0.015 lb sec/ft². (μ)

Solution: The force necessary to maintain this velocity equals the shear stress acting on the bottom of the plate multiplied by the area of the bottom of the plate, the area of which is

$$A = (4)(4) = 16 \text{ ft}^2$$

Compute the shear stress from Equation 6-4.

$$\tau = \mu \frac{dv}{dy}$$

The layer of oil is so thin that you may consider that the velocity of the oil varies linearly from 40 fps at the top plate to 0 at the plane. The velocity of the oil equals the velocity of the surface with which it is in contact.   For the linear velocity profile the term

$$\frac{dv}{dy} = \frac{\Delta v}{\Delta y}$$

The Δv is the change in velocity over the distance Δy, which is the distance between the plates or $(0.1)(\frac{1}{12})$ ft.   Thus, the Δv is the change in velocity between the plates.   Therefore,

$$\frac{\Delta v}{\Delta y} = \frac{40 - 0}{(0.1)(\frac{1}{12})} = 4800 \text{ per sec}$$

Substitute this value into Equation 6-4 along with the viscosity of the oil.

$$\tau = (0.015)(4800) = 72 \text{ lb/ft}^2$$

$$F = \tau A = (72)(16) = 1152 \text{ lb} \qquad \blacktriangleleft$$

▶**Illustrative Problem 2.**   A 2 ft long cylinder with a 6 in. diameter (Fig. 53a) is concentric with and inside of another 2 ft cylinder of 6.12 in. diameter.   The outer cylinder rotates constantly at 400 rpm about the stationary inner cylinder.   Oil with viscosity of 0.012 lb sec/ft^2 fills the space between the cylinders.   Calculate the torque necessary to maintain the 400 rpm velocity and the power input to the outer cylinder.

Solution: Draw a free body diagram of the outer cylinder (Fig. 53b).

$$\Sigma M_c = 0 \quad \overset{\frown}{+}$$

$$-T + \tau(2\pi r)lr = 0$$

$$T = \tau(2\pi r)lr$$

In this problem $r = 3.06/12$ and $l = 2$.   Therefore,

$$T = \tau 2\pi \left(\frac{3.06}{12}\right)^2 2$$

$$T = 0.817\tau$$

The only remaining problem is to compute τ.

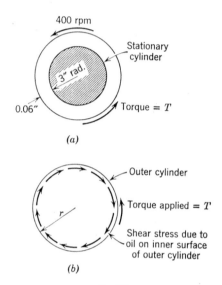

(a)

(b)

Fig. 53

Figure 54 is a greatly enlarged sketch of element $abcd$ of oil a distance r_1 from the center of the cylinders.   In time Δt the element moves to the new position $a'b'c'd'$.   If the element had not deformed in the time Δt, it would have the shape $a'b''c''d'$.   The rate of deformation of the oil is the angle $b'a'b''$ divided by Δt or

$$\text{Rate of deformation} = \frac{\beta}{\Delta t}$$

For small angles

$$\beta = \frac{b'b''}{\Delta r_1}$$

The velocity of the oil at r_1 is v_1, and the velocity of the oil at $r_1 + \Delta r_1$ is $v_1 + \Delta v_1$.   From this you know that

$$\text{arc } aa' = v_1 \,\Delta t, \qquad \text{arc } bb' = (v_1 + \Delta v_1)\,\Delta t$$

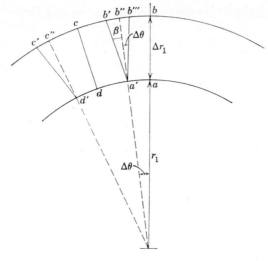

Fig. 54

Draw line $a'b'''$ parallel to ab so that

$$bb''' = aa' = v_1 \, \Delta t$$

and the angle $b''a'b''' = \Delta\theta = \dfrac{v_1 \, \Delta t}{r_1}$

Figure 54 shows that

$$\text{arc } b'b'' = \text{arc } bb' - \text{arc } bb''' - \text{arc } b''b'''$$

$$= (v_1 + \Delta v_1) \, \Delta t - v_1 \, \Delta t - \Delta\theta \, \Delta r_1$$

$$= \Delta v_1 \, \Delta t - \frac{v_1 \, \Delta t}{r_1} \, \Delta r_1$$

$$\beta = \frac{b'b''}{\Delta r_1} = \frac{\Delta v_1 \, \Delta t}{\Delta r_1} - \frac{v_1 \, \Delta t}{r_1}$$

Divide by Δt to get the (average) rate of deformation $\dfrac{\beta}{\Delta t} = \dfrac{\Delta v_1}{\Delta r_1} - \dfrac{v_1}{r_1}$.

Take the limit of the rate of deformation as $\Delta r \to 0$. Thus, the rate of deformation at a point equals $(dv/dr) - (v/r)$. The shear stress is

$$\tau = \mu \left(\frac{dv}{dr} - \frac{v}{r} \right)$$

Assume the velocity profile to be a straight line because the space between the two cylinders is small. From this assumption compute dv/dr as

$$\frac{dv}{dr} = \frac{2\pi r(n-0)}{\text{clearance}} = \frac{2\pi \left(\frac{3.06}{12}\right)\frac{400}{60}}{\frac{0.06}{12}} = 2135 \text{ per sec}$$

To compute the shear stress at the outer cylinder, use the values of v and r at the outer cylinder in the dv/dr term. Thus,

$$\frac{v}{r} = \frac{2\pi r n}{r} = 2\pi n = 2\pi \frac{400}{60} = 41.8 \text{ per sec}$$

The rate of deformation is

$$\frac{dv}{dr} - \frac{v}{r} = (2135 - 41.8) = 2093 \text{ per sec}$$

The shear stress is

$$\tau = \mu \left[\frac{dv}{dr} - \frac{v}{r}\right] = (0.012)(2093) = 25.1 \text{ lb/ft}^2$$

You derived the torque T for this problem as

$$T = (0.817)(\tau) = (0.817)(25.1) = 20.5 \text{ ft-lb}$$

The power input is the product of the torque and the angular velocity. Using this, compute the power as follows:

$$P = \frac{T 2\pi n}{60} = (20.5)(2\pi)\frac{400}{60} = 854 \text{ lb-ft/sec}$$

In most problems of rotating cylinders compute the rate of deformation as dv/dr. Because the v/r is so small compared with dv/dr, you neglect it. To give some idea of the magnitude of this error, consider the value of the shear stress as computed, neglecting the v/r term. Then,

$$\tau = \mu \frac{dv}{dr} = (0.012)(2135) = 25.6 \text{ lb/ft}^2$$

You computed the actual shear stress as

$$\tau = 25.1 \text{ lb/ft}^2$$

The per cent error is

$$\frac{25.6 - 25.1}{25.1} = \frac{0.5}{25.1} = 2 \text{ per cent}$$

In most fluid mechanics work this is a very small error. Continue to calculate the more accurate shear stress so that you do not forget the principle. ◀

41. Reynolds' Experiments

In the late nineteenth century Osborne Reynolds[2] conducted a series of experiments that today we consider classic. Figure 55 is a

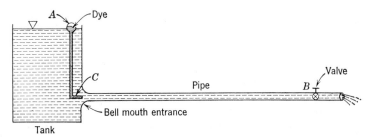

Fig. 55

rough sketch of the equipment that he used. The valve B controlled the outflow of the water filled tank. Dye of the same density as the water filled container A. The dye drained down the tube and into the center of the pipe at C. The dye container was so situated that the dye left the tube at C with the same velocity as the water in the pipe.

Under certain conditions the dye would travel down the center of the pipe in a straight line all the way to the valve. Under other conditions the dye would begin to diffuse through the pipe after traveling only a short distance down the pipe. The first type of flow Reynolds termed "streamline" or "direct" flow. The second type of flow he called "sinuous" flow. For "streamline" or "direct" flow the water traveled down the pipe in a straight line with no velocity component normal to the direction of flow. The water seemed to flow in layers or lamina which would slide one upon another. For this reason

[2] Osborne Reynolds, "An experimental investigation of the circumstances which determine whether the motion of water will be direct or sinuous, and of the law of resistance in parallel channels," *Phil. Trans. Royal Society of London,* **174,** Part III, 935–942 (1883).

we know "direct" flow today as laminar flow. All friction in laminar flow must come from molecular activity. Thus, all the friction discussed in the preceding article applies only to laminar flow.

In sinuous flow the fluid appears to have some motion normal to the centerline of the pipe. This motion causes the dye to diffuse across the entire pipe cross-sectional area. If we choose the x axis as the centerline of the pipe with the y axis vertical and the z axis normal to both, the particles not only have a velocity in the x direction but also at any instant will have small velocities in the y and z directions. We can write the velocity of a particle at any time t as

$$v = \bar{v}_x \dotplus \bar{v}_y \dotplus \bar{v}_z$$

The average velocity of all the particles must be in the x direction because the walls of the pipe constrain the flow in this direction. The components $\bar{v}_y$ and $\bar{v}_z$ of the velocity are thus only fluctuations in velocity which make the liquid always appear disturbed. Thus, we call the flow turbulent. The discussion of friction in the preceding article is not valid for turbulent flow because there is a momentum transfer of particles between elements that causes an additional shear stress. Friction in turbulent flow will be discussed in detail later in this chapter.

The important phase of Reynolds' experiments was not only in recognizing the two distinct types of flow but also in determining the factors that were important. He found out that the density ρ of the liquid, the viscosity μ of the liquid, the diameter d of the pipe, and the velocity v of the liquid were the important quantities. These quantities he arranged in the form: $\rho v d/\mu$ which is called the Reynolds number.

Reynolds discovered that pipe flow is always laminar when the value of the Reynolds number is less than about 2000. For flow with a Reynolds number greater than 2000, the flow can be either laminar or turbulent. If the water in the tank is allowed to become quiet and still before slowly opening the valve, the flow will remain laminar for Reynolds numbers greater than 2000. Once the flow becomes turbulent it is necessary to reduce the velocity until the Reynolds number is below 2000 before the flow will return to laminar. Thus, above a Reynolds number of 2000 the flow is unstable when it is laminar. Experiments since then show that the flow can be laminar for Reynolds numbers in the range of 50,000 to 100,000. We must take extreme care to insure that the water in the tank is completely at rest and that the surfaces of the bell mouth and the pipe are smooth. The number below which the flow is always laminar is called the critical Reynolds number. Later work by Schiller[3] has shown the critical Reynolds number to be 2320.

42. Exchange of Momentum between Layers

In laminar flow, molecular activity causes the friction between adjacent layers of fluid. This molecular activity is a momentum transfer of molecules and an attraction between molecules. In turbulent flow the molecular activity continues as it did in laminar flow, but a momentum transfer on the particle scale contributes even more to the friction. Thus, the definition of shear stress in laminar flow is not valid in turbulent flow.

Before discussing how we can handle the shear stress in turbulent flow, it is necessary to discuss the turbulent flow in some detail.

In turbulent flow there is a high frequency, low magnitude velocity superimposed on the time average velocity at a point. Therefore, in some flow problems where the time average velocity at any point is u, v, and w in the x, y, and z directions, the actual velocity at any instant at any point is

$$u_i = u + u'$$

$$v_i = v + v'$$

$$w_i = w + w'$$

where u', v', and w' are of very low magnitude when compared with u, v, and w and are of very high frequency. When we average the instantaneous velocities u_i, v_i, and w_i over a time interval of the magnitude of $\frac{1}{2}$ sec, they equal u, v, and w.

For simplicity we consider a flow in which v and w are zero and u is some finite value for turbulent flow. The velocity u, in the x direction, can vary in the y direction. Figure 56 is a sketch of two thin control volumes adjacent to each other in this flow. The velocity of the upper control volume is $u + \Delta u$ and the velocity of the lower control volume is u. The particles, each of which contains billions of molecules, in the control volumes move with the average velocity u or $u + \Delta u$ depending upon whether they are in the lower or upper control volume. Superimposed on these average velocities are the high frequency, low magnitude velocities u', v', and w'. The velocity v' causes particles to move continually from one control volume to another. These particles have different average velocities and so transfer different amounts of

[3] L. Schiller, *Forsch. Gebiete Ingenieurw.*, **248**, 16 (1922).

momentum into and out of the control volumes.   The particles that move from the upper control volume into the lower one have a greater amount of momentum in the x direction than the particles that move from the lower control volume into the upper one.   Thus, there is more momentum transferred into the lower control volume than transferred out of it.   This has the effect of a shear force in the positive x direction applied to the top of the lower control volume.   Of course, we must consider an equal and opposite shear force as acting on the

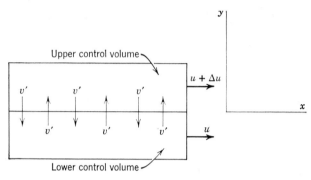

Fig. 56

bottom of the upper control volume.   In addition to these shear forces there are the shear forces due to molecular activity.

Prandtl, in attempting to derive an equation for turbulent shear stress, introduced the concept of the mixing length.   He hypothesized that the particles moved a certain distance and then the molecules in the particles mingled with the molecules in the other particles to form new particles.   The distance that the particles moved before breaking up into new particles Prandtl called the mixing length l.   On this basis he derived the following equation for the turbulent shear stress τ_t:

$$\tau_t = \rho l^2 \left(\frac{du}{dy}\right)^2 \tag{6-6}$$

As stated above, in addition to the turbulent shear stresses τ_t there still is acting the molecular shear stress.   Therefore, the molecular shear stress $\tau_l = \mu(dv/dy)$ must be added to τ_t to get the actual shear stress τ for turbulent flow.

The shear stress in turbulent flow is

$$\tau = \mu \frac{du}{dy} + \rho l^2 \left(\frac{du}{dy}\right)^2 \tag{6-7}$$

Equation 6-7 is the best known and the most widely used equation for shear stress in turbulent flow.

This equation, however, has not been entirely satisfactory.   Work is continuing to obtain a better expression for the turbulent shear stress.

43. Pipe Flow

Figure 57a is a sketch of a liquid flowing from a large reservoir into a circular horizontal pipe of constant diameter through a bell mouth

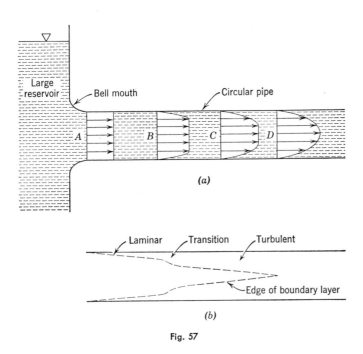

Fig. 57

entrance.   The velocity profile of the fluid in the pipe is shown at sections A, B, C, and D.   When the fluid enters the pipe at A, the velocity is almost constant across the section.   There is only a very small region close to the pipe wall where the fluid is moving with a velocity less than the average velocity V_a.   At section B further down the pipe the effects of wall friction have extended deeper into the fluid. There is still a core in the center of the pipe where the velocity is constant.   This core velocity at B is greater than the average velocity V_a because more fluid near the wall is moving with a velocity less than

V_a. This trend continues at section C where the core diameter of the constant velocity fluid is less than the core diameter at B. At D the core diameter reduces to zero which indicates that the effects of friction extend completely across the pipe diameter. From this point on downstream the velocity profile does not change. When the velocity profile develops and does not change along the pipe, the flow is called fully developed flow.

Figure 57b shows a sketch of the same flow in the same pipe as that in Fig. 57a. The dotted line represents the dividing line between the part of the fluid directly effected by friction and the part of the fluid where the velocity profile is not effected by friction. The layer of fluid adjacent to the wall of the pipe inside the dotted line is called the boundary layer. The dotted line, thus, shows the growth of the boundary layer along the pipe.

When the fully developed flow is laminar, the boundary layer is laminar and grows steadily in size until it fills the pipe. When the fully developed flow is turbulent, the boundary layer is laminar at the beginning of the pipe but increases rapidly in size and becomes turbulent. The turbulent boundary layer continues to grow until it fills the pipe. The zone where the boundary layer changes from laminar to turbulent is called the transition zone, and it is usually three to five diameters long.

In a turbulent boundary layer the fluid adjacent to the pipe wall moves very slowly and cannot have a motion perpendicular to the wall because the fluid would have to penetrate the wall. Thus, it is not possible for the fluid to be turbulent in this layer. The layer of laminar fluid inside a turbulent boundary layer is called the laminar sublayer. The shear stress at the wall depends upon the layer of fluid that touches the wall. Since this layer is the laminar sublayer, we can calculate the shear stress from the equation for laminar flow,

$$\tau = \mu \frac{dv}{dy}$$

In this case τ is the shear stress at the wall, μ is the viscosity of the fluid, and v is the velocity a distance y from the wall. Therefore, dv/dy is the slope of the velocity profile in the laminar sublayer at the wall.

In Chapter 3 we used the Bernoulli equation to solve steady flow pipe problems, neglecting friction and treating the pipe as a stream tube. The velocity used in the $V^2/2$ term was the average velocity of the fluid, and we assumed the pressure to be constant across any

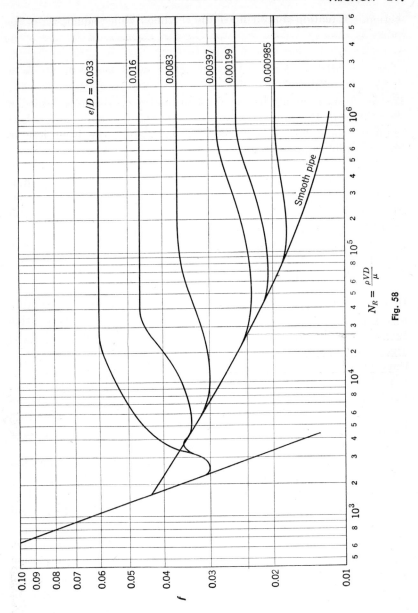

$$N_R = \frac{\rho V D}{\mu}$$

Fig. 58

section. Equation 5-8 changed the modified Euler equation to the form

$$\frac{p_2 - p_1}{\rho} + \frac{V_2{}^2 - V_1{}^2}{2} + g(z_2 - z_1) + gh_L = 0 \qquad (6\text{-}8)$$

The gh_L term accounts for the friction, and h_L is the head loss. In the middle of the nineteenth century Darcy, Weisbach, and others proposed the following equation for calculating the head loss in straight, uniform, long pipes.

$$h_L = f\frac{L}{D}\frac{V^2}{2g} \qquad (6\text{-}9)$$

where f = friction factor
  L = length of pipe between sections 1 and 2
  D = diameter of pipe
  V = average velocity of the fluid
  g = acceleration due to gravity

In this equation, generally called the Darcy equation, the friction factor f is a function of the Reynolds number $\rho V D/\mu$ and the relative roughness of the pipe. The root mean square of the roughness of the pipe divided by the diameter of the pipe is the relative roughness of the pipe. Thus, the relative roughness is e/D.

In 1914, Stanton was the first to make a logarithimic plot of the friction factor f versus the Reynolds number $\rho V D/\mu$. Figure 58 is such a plot of experimental points taken from tests of J. Nikuradse.[4] Even though the curves are from tests by Nikuradse, the diagram is called Stanton's diagram in recognition of his original work.

We use Stanton's diagram in conjunction with the Darcy equation and Equation 6-8 to solve problems of steady flow in long, straight uniform pipes. Before we demonstrate this type of solution, a derivation of the relation between the shear stress at the wall and the head loss h_L would prove helpful.

We consider fully developed flow in a long, straight, uniform pipe. Figure 59a is a sketch of a section of the pipe. We apply Equation 6-8 to the problem to get

$$\frac{p_2 - p_1}{\rho} + \frac{V_2{}^2 - \cancel{V_1{}^2}^{\;0}}{2} + g(\cancel{z_2} - z_1) + gh_L = 0$$

[4] J. Nikuradse, "Strömungsgesetze in rauhen Röhen," *VDI-Forschungsheft* 361, Vol. 4, 1933. Translation in *Nat. Advisory Comm. Aeronaut, Tech. Mem.*, 1292, Nov. 1950.

Velocity V and the elevation z remain unchanged and so the equation becomes

$$\frac{p_2 - p_1}{\rho} = -gh_L \qquad (6\text{-}10)$$

The momentum equation is applied to the control volume in Fig.

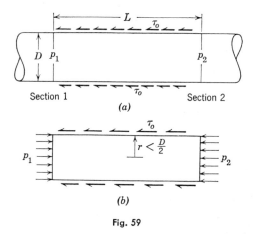

Fig. 59

$59b$. There is no change in momentum so that the following relation results:

$$\tau 2\pi r L - p_1 \pi r^2 + p_2 \pi r^2 = 0$$

$$\tau = \frac{(P_1 - P_2)r}{2L} \qquad (6\text{-}11)$$

We substitute the value of $(p_1 - p_2)$ from Equation 6-10 into Equation 6-11 to get

$$\tau = \left(\frac{\rho g h_L}{2L}\right) r \qquad (6\text{-}12)$$

All the terms in the parentheses are constant across the pipe and so the shear stress varies linearly from zero at the center of the pipe to $(\rho g h_L D)/4L$ at the wall. We obtain the relation between the shear stress at the wall and the head loss h_L from Equation 6-12 by substituting the radius $D/2$ of the pipe for r.

$$\tau_o = \frac{\rho g D}{4L} h_L \qquad (6\text{-}13)$$

By substituting for the h_L term the quantities from the Darcy equation, we obtain the following relation between the friction factor and the shear stress at the wall:

$$\tau_0 = f\frac{\rho V^2}{8} \tag{6-14}$$

The square root of the wall shear stress divided by the density ρ is known as the "friction velocity." From Equation 6-14 the friction velocity v_* is

$$v_* = \sqrt{\tau_0/\rho} = V\sqrt{f/8} \tag{6-15}$$

We do not use the last two equations in this book: we introduce them only because they will be seen frequently in the literature. Illustrative Problems 3 and 4 demonstrate the use of the Darcy equation, Equation 6-8, and the Stanton diagram in solving the steady flow of an incompressible fluid in a long, straight, uniform pipe.

▶**Illustrative Problem 3.**   Water flows steadily at the rate of 3 cfs in a 6 in. dia. straight smooth pipe. The flow is fully developed between section 1 and section 2, 1000 ft down the pipe. Calculate the change in pressure between the two sections when (a) the pipe is horizontal and (b) the elevation of the pipe drops 15 ft.

Solution: Apply the modified Euler Equation 6-8 to the flow between sections 1 and 2 for both parts a and b.

$$\frac{p_2 - p_1}{\rho} + \frac{V_2{}^2 - V_1{}^2}{2} + g(z_2 - z_1) + gh_L = 0 \tag{S}$$

(a) In part a elevation and velocity remain unchanged, and Equation S becomes

$$\frac{p_2 - p_1}{\rho} + gh_L = 0$$

or
$$p_1 - p_2 = \rho g h_L$$

From the Darcy equation evaluate the head loss as follows:

$$h_L = f\frac{L}{D}\frac{V^2}{2g}$$

The length L is 1000 ft, the diameter D is $\frac{1}{2}$ ft, and g is 32.2 ft/sec^2. Determine the value of the velocity V and the friction factor f. The flow rate equals the product of the velocity and the cross-sectional area.

$$Q = VA = \frac{V\pi D^2}{4}$$

$$3 = V\frac{\pi\left(\frac{1}{2}\right)^2}{4} = \frac{V\pi}{16}$$

Therefore,
$$V = \frac{48}{\pi} = 15.2 \text{ fps}$$

Determine the friction factor f from the Stanton diagram in Fig. 58. (You can compute the Reynolds number $\rho VD/\mu$.)

$$\frac{\rho VD}{\mu} = \frac{(1.94)(15.2)\left(\frac{1}{2}\right)}{(2.36)(10)^{-5}} = 625,000$$

From the Stanton diagram (Fig. 58) the value of f for a smooth pipe is

$$f = 0.011$$

Substitute these values in the Darcy equation to compute the head loss.

$$h_L = (0.011)\frac{1000}{\frac{1}{2}}\frac{(15.2)^2}{(2)(32.2)}$$

$$= 79 \text{ ft}$$

Therefore,
$$p_1 - p_2 = \rho g h_L = (1.94)(32.2)(79)$$

$$p_1 - p_2 = 4940 \text{ lb/ft}^2$$

(b) In part b the velocity remains unchanged between sections 1 and 2, but $z_2 - z_1 = -15$ ft. Therefore,

$$\frac{p_2 - p_1}{\rho} + g(-15) + gh_L = 0$$

$$p_1 - p_2 = \rho(gh_L - 15g) \tag{T}$$

There is no difference in the head loss between part a and part b. Therefore, substitute the head loss computed in part a into Equation T.

$$p_1 - p_2 = (1.94)(32.2)(79 - 15) = 1.94(32.2)(64) = 4000 \text{ lb/ft}^2 \quad \blacktriangleleft$$

Head losses caused by other factors in the pipe than wall friction are called minor pipe losses and are computed from an equation of the form

$$h_L = C\frac{V^2}{2g} \tag{6-16}$$

The constant C depends upon the cause of the minor loss. Examples of minor losses and the approximate value of the constant C are listed in the table.

Loss Constant C For Some Minor Losses

Sharp-edged entrance to circular pipe	0.50
Sharp-edged exit from circular pipe	1.00
90° elbow	0.90
45° elbow	0.42
Globe valve (wide open)	10.00
Gate valve (wide open)	0.19
Gate valve (half open)	5.60
Return bend	2.20

These loss coefficients are for only a few of the minor losses that occur in pipe problems. A partial list of the many excellent books which cover in detail the minor losses in pipe flow is included in Appendix E.

The following illustrative problem indicates one type of steady flow pipe problem.

▶**Illustrative Problem 4.** Water flows from a large reservoir into a long pipe system (Fig. 60). Compute the flow rate for a pipe that has a relative roughness of 0.00397.

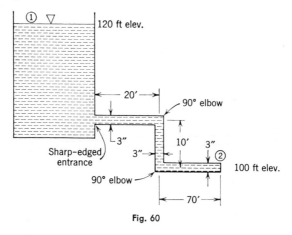

Fig. 60

Solution: Apply the modified Euler equation, Equation 6-8, between the top of the water surface in the reservoir and the end of the pipe, which gives the following equation:

$$\cancel{\frac{p_2 - p_1}{\rho}}^{0} + \frac{V_2{}^2 - V_1{}^2}{2} + g(z_2 - z_1) + gh_L = 0$$

The pressure does not change between sections 1 and 2. Neglect the velocity V_1 at the water surface. Select the elevation 0 as the datum. Substitutions result in

$$\frac{V_2{}^2}{2} + g(100 - 120) + gh_L = 0$$

Solve this equation for V_2.

$$V_2 = (40g - 2gh_L)^{1/2}$$

The head loss term is made up of the wall friction head loss, and the minor losses.

$$h_L = \left(f\frac{L}{D}\frac{V^2}{2g}\right) + (C_1 + C_2 + C_3)\frac{V^2}{2g}$$

where C_1 = loss coefficient due to sharp-edged entrance = 0.50
$C_2 = C_3$ = loss coefficient for 90° elbow = 0.90

Therefore,

$$h_L = f\frac{(20 + 10 + 70)}{\frac{1}{4}}\frac{V^2}{2g} + (0.5 + 0.9 + 0.9)\frac{V^2}{2g}$$

$$h_L = [f(400) + 2.3]\frac{V^2}{2g}$$

The friction factor f is a function of the Reynolds number $\rho V D/\mu$. Until you know the velocity V, you cannot compute the friction factor, but you cannot determine velocity V until you know the friction factor f. Thus, the solution must be a trial and error one. First, assume a value for the friction factor f and then compute V. From V calculate the Reynolds number from which you can determine the value of the friction factor using the Stanton diagram. If it agrees with the assumed f, the solution for V is correct. If it does not agree, pick a new friction factor and repeat the process.

From the Stanton diagram an assumed value of $f = 0.028$ seems reasonable.

Substitute this into the equation for the head loss to get

$$h_L = [(0.028)(400) + 2.3]\frac{V_2{}^2}{2g} = (11.2 + 2.3)\frac{V_2{}^2}{2g}$$

$$= 13.5\frac{V_2{}^2}{2g}$$

Then, substitute this result into the equation for V_2

$$V_2 = \left[40g - 2g(13.5) \frac{V_2{}^2}{2g} \right]^{1/2}$$

or
$$V_2{}^2 = 40g - 13.5V_2{}^2$$

$$14.5V_2{}^2 = 40g$$

$$V_2 = \sqrt{\frac{40g}{14.5}} = \sqrt{88.8}$$

$$V_2 = 9.4 \text{ fps}$$

Reynolds number $= N_R = \dfrac{(1.94)(12.5)(\frac{1}{4})}{(2.36)(10)^{-5}} = 193.000$

From the Stanton diagram the friction factor f from this Reynolds number is

$$f = 0.028$$

You assumed this same value for f before and so the velocity V_2 as computed above is a close approximation. The flow rate is this velocity times the cross-sectional area of the pipe.

$$Q = V_2 A = (9.4) \frac{\pi}{4} (\tfrac{1}{2})^2$$

$$= \frac{(9.4)\pi}{16} = 1.945 \text{ cfs} \qquad \blacktriangleleft$$

44. Friction on Submerged Bodies

In Art. 43 we studied the frictional effects of fluid flowing while surrounded completely by a solid body. In this article we study the problem of a body completely surrounded by a fluid. A solid body moving with respect to a fluid which completely surrounds it must overcome resistance caused by the fluid, resistance in the form of two types of forces, shear stress forces and pressure forces. Figure 61a is a sketch of a thin plate in a fluid flowing with a constant velocity V well upstream of disturbance caused by the plate. The plate is placed in the stream so that its plane is in the direction of the fluid's motion. As fluid flows over the plate's surface, the velocity of the fluid adjacent to the plate changes to the velocity of the plate. Therefore, the fluid

adjacent to the plate is stationary.   The friction between the fluid A
adjacent to the stationary layer and the stationary layer itself B
decelerates the fluid A.   This frictional effect continues until a velocity
profile is established.   It takes time for this friction to move out into
the fluid and change the velocity of the fluid.   As the friction is
affecting the velocity of the fluid further away from the plate, the

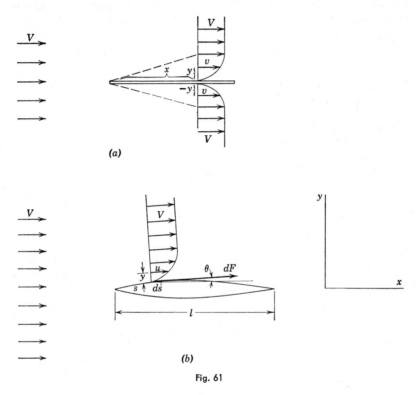

(a)

(b)

Fig. 61

fluid also is moving along the plate.   Thus, a boundary layer forms
along the plate.   As in pipe flow, this boundary layer grows in thickness along the plate in the direction of the flow.   The flow in the
boundary layer may be either turbulent or laminar.   When it is
turbulent, a low magnitude, high frequency velocity is superimposed
on the average velocity.   Even in the turbulent boundary layer a
laminar sublayer exists as in pipe flow.   This sublayer is very thin
when compared to the thickness of the turbulent boundary layer.
Regardless of how thick this sublayer is, when the shear stress at the
surface of the plate is computed, the only friction that we must consider is the friction resulting from molecular action.   Thus, we may

use the equation

$$\tau_o = \mu \left(\frac{du}{dy}\right)_o$$

to compute the shear stress at the surface.

A thin body placed in a stream of fluid that is moving with a uniform velocity V to the left (Fig. 61b) has a length b normal to the sketch. We measure the distance s along the surface of the body in the direction of the flow and show the velocity profile at a point a distance s from the nose.   The velocity u is a function of y, where y is measured normal to the surface.   The force dF of the fluid acting on the area ds by b on the body is

$$dF = \tau_o b \, ds$$

The component in the x direction is

$$dF \cos \theta = \tau_o b \, \frac{ds}{dx} \cos \theta$$

The shear stress at the wall is τ_o which is

$$\tau_o = \mu \left(\frac{du}{dy}\right)_o$$

where $(du/dy)_o$ means du/dy evaluated at $y = o$.

We call the force on a body in the direction of fluid motion the drag force D.   In this case we compute the drag force on the upper surface of the body only and call it D_u.

$$dD_u = dF \cos \theta = \mu \left(\frac{du}{dy}\right)_o b \, ds \cos \theta$$

When we integrate from the front of the body to the rear, we can compute the total drag force D_u.

$$D_u = \int \mu \left(\frac{du}{dy}\right)_o b \, ds \cos \theta$$

From Fig. 61b we see that

$$dx = ds \cos \theta$$

and substitute this in the above to get

$$D_u = \int_o^l \mu \left(\frac{du}{dy}\right)_o b \, dx = \mu b \int_o^l \left(\frac{du}{dy}\right)_o dx$$

From this equation, we learn that we can compute the drag force due to friction when we know the velocity distribution.   The difference in pressure on the front and the back surfaces of the body causes a resultant pressure force in the x direction. We must add this resultant pressure force to the resultant shear forces to obtain the total drag force D. In a thin body similar to the one in Fig. 61b the cross-sectional area of the body is very small as are the pressure differences so that we neglect the resultant pressure force when we compare it with the shear force. The drag force D is twice the drag force D_u computed above when we consider the shear force on both the top and the bottom of the body.

$$D = 2\mu b \int_o^l \left(\frac{du}{dy}\right)_o dx$$

In experimental work we compute the drag force in terms of a drag coefficient C_D and define the drag coefficient by the equation

$$D = C_D \frac{\rho A V^2}{2} \tag{6-17}$$

In Equation 6-17 A is an area of the body. In some cases this area will be the total area in contact with the fluid. In other cases it will be a projection of the body on a plane normal to the undisturbed stream. Thus, the area used in Equation 6-17 must be stated in order to evaluate C_D.

The drag coefficient C_D is a function of the Reynolds number, the Mach number, and the surface roughness. The Reynolds number is $\rho V l/\mu$ where l is some characteristic length. The Mach number is the ratio of the velocity V to the velocity of sound a. If the fluid is an incompressible fluid, the Mach number does not vary, and the drag coefficient is a function of only the Reynolds number and the surface roughness. We use this same drag coefficient for bodies that are floating on the interface of two different fluids; usually, the upper fluid is a gas and the lower fluid a liquid. In this case, the drag coefficient is also a function of the ratio V^2/lg which is called the Froude number.

We should consider the flow of fluid around a flat plate (Fig. 62) that is placed normal to the undisturbed stream. The severe disturbances behind the plate cause a sharp drop in the pressure. The average pressure on the plate's front is p_1 and on its back is p_2. By no means is the pressure constant on either the front or the back of the plate. Rather than chancing the difficulties in determining pressure distribution, we use the average pressures. The only component of the shear stress to act in the x direction must come from the shear stress on the very thin ends. This gives a small force when compared to the force caused by pressure differences. The total drag D is

$$D = 2\tau_o l b + (p_1 - p_2)lb \tag{6-18}$$

The first term $2\tau_o l b$ is so small when compared to $(p_1 - p_2)lb$ that we neglect the first term (which is the shear force) to give

$$D = (p_1 - p_2)lb = C_{D}\rho A V^2$$

We may view most bodies as somewhere between the two extremes of the flat plate parallel to the flow and the flat plate normal to the flow.

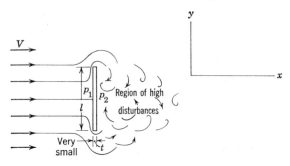

Fig. 62

Thus, in most bodies we must take into account both the pressure forces and shear forces. We here examine three bodies that have a circular cross-sectional area on a plane normal to the flow. These bodies, a disk, a sphere, and a sphere with a streamlined tail added, appear in Fig. 63a, b, and c.

The disk (Fig. 63a) is like the thin plate that we discussed before. There is an appreciable pressure drop from in front of the plate to behind the plate which causes a large pressure force and almost no shear force. Thus,

$$D = (p_1 - p_2)\pi R^2 \tag{6-19}$$

where p_1 and p_2 are average pressures and R is the radius of the disk.

The sphere (Fig. 63b), although it has the same radius R as the disk, does not have as large a region of disturbed or vortex motion as the disk, because the fluid is not required to turn sharp corners on the sphere which it is required to turn on the disk. We can explain this region of vortex motion behind the sphere rather simply on a qualitative basis. Figure 64a is a sketch of the flow around the top half of the sphere. The average velocity of the fluid layer close to the surface of the sphere is very small at A because A is a stagnation point. At B further up the sphere the average velocity is greater and at C on

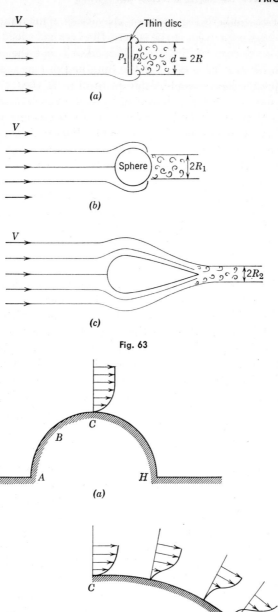

Fig. 63

(a)

(b)

Fig. 64

the top of the sphere the average velocity is a maximum. As the fluid starts down the back of the sphere, the average velocity decreases, causing the pressure to increase. This means that the pressure will slow up the fluid even more. If the fluid had lost no energy to friction, the fluid velocity would decrease until at H the velocity would again be zero. The fluid, however, cannot overcome this pressure increase, and the velocity profile from C to D changes as shown in Fig. 64b. At D we notice that the fluid adjacent to the surface has started to move back up toward C which causes the fluid to have a vortex motion and to separate from the sphere's surface. This separation induces great losses, causing the pressure to drop severely after separation. However, the separation has been delayed in the sphere when compared to the disk. Thus, the area of appreciable pressure difference is reduced. The drag force D on the sphere is

$$D = \text{shear force} + (p_2 - p_1)\pi R^2 \qquad (6\text{-}20)$$

The additional shear force is much less than the reduction in the pressure force so there is a reduction in the drag force D.

We now consider the drag force D on the sphere with the streamlined tail (Fig. 63c). Because the streamlined tail has been added, the pressure drop is not as great on the tail as on the sphere, causing the separation point to appear further back on the tail. This new separation point causes the vortex motion to have a smaller radius R_2 than on the sphere. The drag force on the streamlined sphere is

$$D = \text{additional shear force} + (p_2 - p_1)\pi R_2{}^2 \qquad (6\text{-}21)$$

The greater area over which the fluid flows accounts for the additional shear force. The pressure force lessens because of the reduction of area on which the pressure difference acts. There must be a point where the additional shear force equals the reduction in the pressure force. So up to this point the streamlining will reduce the drag force.

Just as in pipe flow, the boundary layer in flow around submerged bodies will start out as laminar whether the flow outside the boundary layer is laminar or turbulent. After moving along the body as a laminar boundary layer for a certain length, the boundary layer will become turbulent if this is the stable flow for the boundary layer. If the laminar boundary is stable, the boundary layer will remain laminar. Figure 65 is a diagram of the boundary layer growth along a surface, which may be the inside of a pipe or the outside of a submerged body. The characteristics are the same in both cases. The stable flow for this boundary layer is turbulent and so the boundary layer appears first as laminar, then covers a transition zone, and finally is turbulent. Plotted above the surface is the shear stress τ_o at the solid surface.

The shear stress starts very high at the beginning of the laminar zone and decreases in the direction of flow.   In the transition zone the shear stress increases abruptly.   In the turbulent zone the shear stress decreases again but at a slower rate.   From this plot we easily see that two things would reduce the shear stress and, consequently,

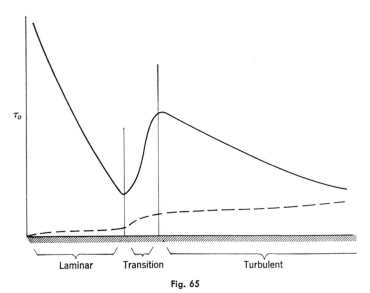

Laminar   Transition   Turbulent

Fig. 65

the drag force.   First, if we could continue the laminar boundary layer, we would decrease the shear stress.   Second, if we could make the boundary layer turbulent from the very beginning, we could eliminate the high shear stress at the start of the laminar boundary layer.

The smaller shear stress causes less loss in the fluid.   This means that the separation point moves further downstream, which means that the pressure forces will decrease.   Thus, a net gain in the reduction of the drag force results.   Research continues into methods to reach one of the two objectives.   Advanced textbooks cover this subject more thoroughly.

45. Secondary Flow

In some types of flow the primary fluid motion sets up forces which in turn start a new flow, which we call a secondary flow.   The secondary flow is superimposed on top of the primary flow. The secondary flow is an entirely different phenomenon than turbulent flow. In turbulent flow a high frequency, low magnitude velocity is superimposed on the average velocity. This low magnitude velocity has a time average velocity of zero. In a secondary flow, however, the time average of the secondary velocity is not zero, and the secondary velocity is not subject to rapid changes.

An excellent example of secondary flow is the flow of fluid in a pipe bend. Figure 66 is a top view of a 90° pipe bend. The dotted lines are the streamlines of the primary flow. The primary flow causes forces which set up a secondary flow as shown in Fig. 67. In Fig. 67a the dotted lines represent an approximate flow pattern of the flow

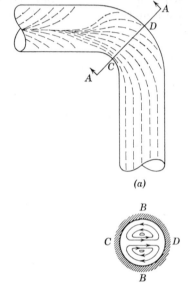

(a)

(b)

Section *AA*

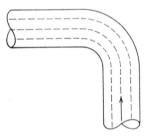

Fig. 66

Fig. 67

adjacent to the wall. This pattern is the result of both the primary and secondary flows. Figure 67b shows a flow pattern of just the secondary flow. We can explain the secondary flow rather easily if we remember to consider the effects of friction. In the center of the pipe the fluid has a high velocity. In the pipe bend, the centrifugal acceleration of the fluid sets up a pressure gradient with a higher pressure p_D at point D on the outer radius and a lower pressure p_C at point C on the inner radius of the bend. The fluid at the pipe walls from D to B to C is almost stationary because of the friction. This low velocity means that a much smaller centrifugal acceleration is set up, and, consequently, there is nothing to prevent the fluid from flowing from D to B to C along the outer edges of the pipe. Thus, the fluid cannot flow from D to C through the center of the pipe because of the fluid's centrifugal acceleration. Along the pipe walls there is no centrifugal acceleration, and the pressure difference from D to B causes the fluid to flow in that direction. The fluid cannot accumulate at point C and so it flows toward D which sets up a pattern as shown in Fig. 67b. We see that the secondary flow is normal to the primary flow. This is a characteristic of secondary flow.

Secondary flows can occur in pipes of any shape, in rotating machinery, in rivers, and channels, and in any other flow which sets up the necessary forces.

PROBLEMS

6-1. Calculate the viscosity of the oil under the plate in Fig. P.6-1.

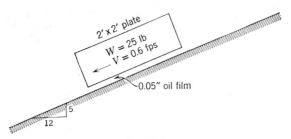

Fig. P.6-1

6-2. If $\mu = 0.015$ lb sec/ft^2, find the angle α (Fig. P.6-2) at which the velocity of blocks A and B will be 1 fps.

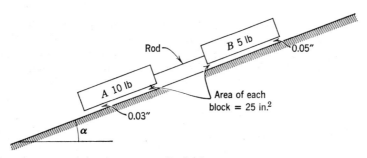

Fig. P.6-2

6-3. In Problem 6-2 compute the force in the bar connecting blocks A and B.

6-4. If the weight shown in Fig. P.6-4 falls at 0.6 fps, what is the viscosity of the oil?   Here $W = 5$ lb.

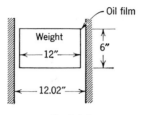

Fig. P.6-4

6-5. If the weight in Fig. P.6-4 with a mass of 1 slug starts from rest and falls in a gravitational field of $g = 10$ ft/sec² and if the oil has a viscosity of $0.2/\pi$ lb sec/ft², derive an expression for the velocity of the weight in terms of the time traveled.

6-6. A device to measure viscosity is made with a rotating shaft A placed inside a drum B (Fig. P.6-6).   While A is rotated at a constant velocity ω, a force P is produced on the drum arm.   Calculate the viscosity in terms of P, ω, and the dimensions shown in the figure.

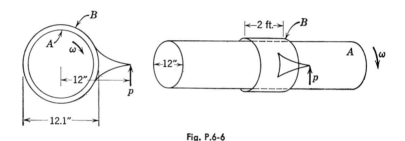

Fig. P.6-6

6-7. What power will be required to produce a 5 lb force when using a fluid of viscosity $\mu = 0.0216$ lb sec/ft² in the setup illustrated in Fig. P.6-6?

6-8. Water flows from a reservoir as shown in Fig. P.6-8.   Consider the only losses to be those in the straight pipe.   Compute the flow rate.

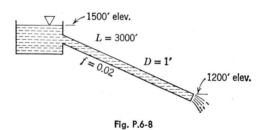

Fig. P.6-8

6-9. Water flows from the reservoir through the horizontal 6 in. pipe for a distance of 500 ft. If the pipe friction factor is 0.02 and the flow velocity is 10 fps, what will be the height x of the water in the open piezometer tube AB? A piezometer tube measures only pressure (Fig. P.6-9).

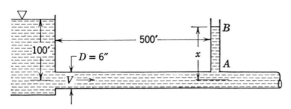

Fig. P.6-9

6-10. Calculate with friction and neglecting friction the maximum flow of water that can occur through this pipe. Barometric pressure is 27.5 in. mercury, vapor pressure of water is 1.50 psia (Fig. P.6-10).

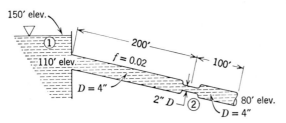

Fig. P.6-10

6-11. Determine the elevation of the water level in reservoir B shown in Fig. P.6-11. No water flows either into or out of the reservoir. Coefficient of pipe friction = 0.02.

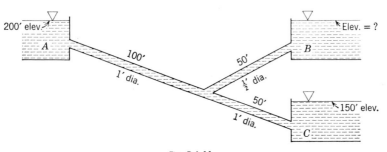

Fig. P.6-11

6-12. In Problem 6-11 the water surface in reservoir B is at 200 ft elevation. Compute the flow rate in each pipe when the coefficient of pipe friction is 0.02 in all pipes.

6-13. Explain a method for computing the flow rate in each pipe in Problem 6-11 when the pipes are smooth and the elevation of reservoir B is 190 ft. The pipe friction coefficient is unknown.

6-14. Water is pumped at the rate of 3 cfs from a large reservoir A to a tank B through the system shown in Fig. P.6-14. Compute the power output of the pump, neglecting friction.

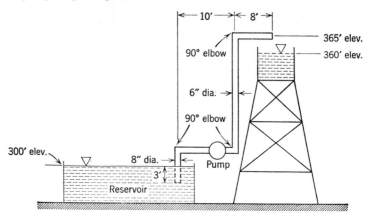

Fig. P.6-14

6-15. Compute the power output of the pump in Problem 6-14 when friction is considered and the pipe is smooth. Do not forget minor losses.

6-16. Compute the ratio of the flow rates in Fig. P.6-16 when (a) friction is neglected and (b) all losses are considered.

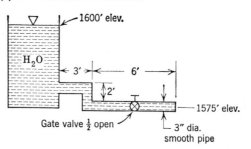

Fig. P.6-16

6-17. A hydraulically smooth pipe (Fig. P.6-17) leads from a reservoir at 500 ft elevation to a 3 in. nozzle at 300 ft elevation. Determine the flow rate within 5 per cent. Neglect minor losses.

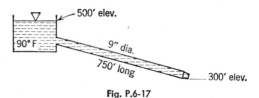

Fig. P.6-17

6-18. A plate 2 ft wide and extending to infinity is placed in a uniform parallel stream of incompressible fluid (Fig. P.6-18). The plate is very thin. Compute the average shear stress on the plate and the drag coefficient C_D.

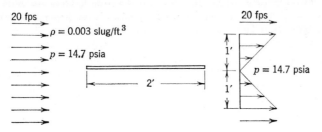

Fig. P.6-18

6-19. The drag coefficient C_D for a flat plate normal to the undisturbed flow is about 1.18 for a plate that has a breadth to length ratio greater than about 0.15. Compute the drag force on a rectangular plate 4 ft by 5 ft by $\frac{1}{2}$ in. when the $\frac{1}{2}$ in. dimension is in the direction of the uniform stream. The velocity of the stream is 70 fps and the fluid has a density of 0.00236 slug/ft³.

6-20. Determine the average shear stress in the Problem 6-19. Explain.

6-21. Table P.6-21 is obtained from actual data for a smooth 4 in. dia. sphere in a uniform air stream. The density of the air is 0.0023 slug/ft³, and the viscosity is $(4)(10)^{-7}$ lb sec/ft². Fill in the values for C_D where they have been omitted. The area A in the formula

$$D = C_D \frac{\rho V^2}{2} A$$

is the projected area normal to the flow.

Table P.6-21

Velocity, fps	Reynolds Number	C_D	Drag, lb
0.001	1.904	15.00	$1.5(10)^{-9}$
0.005	9.52	4.70	$1.2(10)^{-8}$
0.01	19.04		$2.9(10)^{-8}$
0.05	95.20	1.20	$3.0(10)^{-7}$
0.10	190.40	0.85	
1.00	1,904.00	0.40	$4(10)^{-5}$
10.00	19,040.00		$4.3(10)^{-3}$
50.00	95,200.00	0.58	$1.07(10)^{-1}$
100.00	190,400.00	0.43	
150.00	285,600.00	0.18	$4.06(10)^{-1}$
200.00	380,800.00	0.19	$7.2(10)^{-1}$
300.00	571,200.00		1.75

6-22. On log-log paper plot the drag coefficient C_D versus the Reynolds number for the data in Fig. P.6-21. Explain the sharp drop in C_D at a Reynolds number of approximately 225,000.

6-23. Two identical spheres A and B are placed in a stream of uniform flow. Both spheres A and B are smooth, and a patch of sandpaper is placed on the nose of sphere B. The drag coefficient is smaller for sphere B. Explain.

6-24. A sketch of a jet of water leaving a long tube is shown in Fig. P.6-24. The main part of the jet leaves the end of the tube and falls freely under influence of gravity. A very small stream separates from the main jet as shown. An extremely thin sheet of water connects the two jets. Explain this phenomenon.

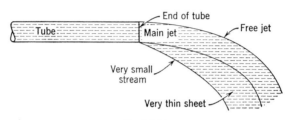

Fig. P.6-24

6-25. A rectangular pipe bends as shown in Fig. P.6-25. Fluid is to flow through the pipe in the indicated direction. Sketch and explain the secondary flow that will occur in cross section A-A.

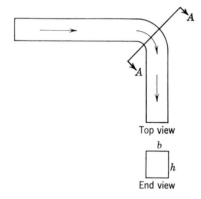

Fig. P.6-25

6-26. A river bed bends through a gentle curve. Will the secondary flow induced cause the bend to become sharper or more gentle? Explain.

DIMENSIONAL ANALYSIS
and MODEL STUDY

chapter **7**

46. Introduction

The use of dimensional analysis did not become general until the beginning of the twentieth century. Since then its importance and use have continued to grow until today it is one of the fundamental tools of fluid mechanics. The science of dimensional analysis is based upon the concept that all quantities to be added must be of the same dimension or combination of dimensions. This makes it possible to use dimensional analysis in a large variety of problems. The general nature of dimensional analysis is at the same time its great strength and its real weakness. We can use it to reduce the amount of work in solving problems, but we cannot use dimensional analysis itself to solve the problems.

The four general applications for which we use dimensional analysis are:

1. To reduce the number of variables in an experimental program.
2. To convert from one set of units to another set.
3. To determine model testing experiments.
4. To check equations.

The term "units" here is used to describe the basic magnitude of each dimension. Therefore, feet and inches are units of length; slugs and kilograms mass are units of mass; pounds and dynes are units of force; hours, seconds, and weeks are units of time. These are only a few of the units in common use.

47. Dimensional Homogeneity

The term "dimension" here means the relation among the dimensional properties by which the quantity is to be measured. This

241

definition differentiates the term from its use in reference to space, such as three-dimensional space, or to dimensions in drawing. The dimension of velocity, therefore, is length divided by time, of area is length squared, of pressure is force divided by length squared, and so forth.

Dimensional analysis demands that equations be dimensionally homogeneous. This merely states that, when two quantities are equated or added, we must measure the quantities in the same dimension. One unit of length plus another unit of length may equal some third unit of length. For example, 1 yard plus 18 inches equals $4\frac{1}{2}$ feet. Although we do not express these three in the same units of length, they are all in the dimension of length. It is impossible, however, to add quantities measured in two different dimensions and arrive at any conclusion. Thus, it is impossible to add 60 miles per hour to 30 pounds and arrive at a logical conclusion.

We notice that all quantities are dimensionally made up of a limited number of fundamental dimensions. It is possible, therefore, to select certain fundamental dimensions and write the dimensions of all quantities in terms of fundamentals. One of the most common sets of fundamental dimensions in fluid mechanics is force, length, time, and temperature, or F, L, T, and Θ. Using this fundamental set, we may write that the dimension of acceleration is length divided by time squared, of energy is force times length, and of power is force times length divided by time. However, when we consider mass, it is difficult to write directly the dimensions of mass in terms of a force, length, time, temperature system. Newton's second law states that force is proportional to mass times acceleration and often is written as force equals mass times acceleration. In this form the law relates the fundamental dimensions of mass and force. Mass, therefore, is force divided by acceleration which dimensionally is force times time squared divided by length or $M = FT^2/L$. By Newton's second law we solve the dilemma of the dimensions of mass.

Another set of fundamental dimensions is the mass, length, time, temperature system, or M, L, T, and Θ. We also solve the dilemma of the dimensions of force in this fundamental dimensional system by Newton's second law. Force equals mass times acceleration and dimensionally equals ML/T^2. Figure 68 lists some of the more familiar quantities and their dimensions in the two sets of fundamental dimensions mentioned above.

The concept of dimensional homogeneity states that in any equation all terms added must have the same dimensions. We consider as a first example the Bernoulli equation.

$$\frac{p}{\rho} + \frac{V^2}{2} + gz = \text{constant}$$

which can be written dimensionally as

$$\frac{F}{L^2}\frac{L}{F}\frac{L^3}{T^2} + \frac{L^2}{T^2} + \frac{L}{T^2}L \overset{d}{=} \frac{L^2}{T^2} + \frac{L^2}{T^2} + \frac{L^2}{T^2}$$

The Bernoulli equation, therefore, is dimensionally homogeneous because each term has the same dimension. We demonstrated it in the F, L, T system, but we could have done it as well in the M, L, T system. We must notice also that the form of the equation does not depend on the units selected, which shows another property of a dimensionally homogeneous equation.

Symbol	Quantity	F–L–T–Θ	M–L–T–Θ
α	acceleration (angular)	T^{-2}	T^{-2}
a,g	acceleration (linear)	LT^{-2}	LT^{-2}
A	area	L^2	L^2
ρ	density	FT^2L^{-4}	ML^{-3}
E	energy	FL	ML^2T^{-2}
F	force	F	MLT^{-2}
R	gas constant (engineering)	$L^2T^{-2}\Theta^{-1}$	$L^2T^{-2}\Theta^{-1}$
M	mass	FT^2L^{-1}	M
β	modulus (bulk)	FL^{-2}	$ML^{-1}T^{-2}$
E	modulus of elasticity	FL^{-2}	$ML^{-1}T^{-2}$
M	momentum	FT	MLT^{-1}
P	power	FLT^{-1}	ML^2T^{-3}
p	pressure	FL^{-2}	$ML^{-1}T^{-2}$
ϕ	radians	$F^0L^0T^0\Theta^0$	$M^0L^0T^0\Theta^0$ (dimensionless)
τ	shearing stress	FL^{-2}	$ML^{-1}T^{-2}$
γ	specific weight	FL^{-3}	$ML^{-2}T^{-2}$
σ	surface tension	FL^{-1}	MT^{-2}
T	temperature	Θ^1	Θ^1
T	torque	FL	ML^2T^{-2}
ω	velocity (angular)	T^{-1}	T^{-1}
V	velocity (linear)	LT^{-1}	LT^{-1}
μ	viscosity (absolute)	FTL^{-2}	$ML^{-1}T^{-1}$
ν	viscosity (kinematic)	L^2T^{-1}	L^2T^{-1}
V	volume	L^3	L^3
Q	volume flow rate	L^3T^{-1}	L^3T^{-1}
W	weight	F	MLT^{-2}
G	weight rate of flow	FT^{-1}	MLT^{-3}

Fig. 68

By the use of Bernoulli's equation we know that we can express the velocity of a free jet of liquid from a hole in the side of a large tank as

$$V = \sqrt{2gh}$$

where V = velocity of jet
  g = gravitational acceleration
  h = vertical distance from hole to liquid surface

This equation is dimensionally homogeneous. The units of V, h, and g must be consistent, but beyond this we can use any set of units. If h is in feet and g is in feet per second squared, the equation is valid, and V will be in feet per second. If h is in meters and g is in meters per hour squared, then V is in meters per hour and the equation is valid. This form, $V = \sqrt{2gh}$ is independent of the units selected. If, however, we substitute $g = 32.2 \text{ ft/sec}^2$ in the equation, it becomes

$$V = 8.08 \sqrt{h}$$

This form of the equation is valid only if the units of h are feet and the units of V are feet per second. We write this equation dimensionally as

$$\frac{\text{L}}{\text{T}} \overset{\text{d}}{=} \text{L}^{\frac{1}{2}}$$

This is not correct, and the equation is not dimensionally homogeneous.

▶**Illustrative Problem 1.**   Calculate the dimension of the constant K in each of the dimensionally homogeneous equations.
  (a) From strength of materials.

$$\frac{M}{EI} = K\frac{d^2y}{dx^2}$$

  (b) From an empirical equation for open channel flow

$$Q = K_1 A R^{\frac{2}{3}} S^{\frac{1}{2}}$$

Solution: (a)

$$\frac{M}{EI} = K\frac{d^2y}{dx^2}$$

where M = bending moment $\overset{\text{d}}{=}$ FL
  E = modulus of elasticity $\overset{\text{d}}{=}$ F/L^2
  I = moment of inertia of area $\overset{\text{d}}{=}$ L^4
  y = deflection of beam $\overset{\text{d}}{=}$ L
  x = distance along beam $\overset{\text{d}}{=}$ L

Substitute the dimensional equivalents into the equation to get

$$\frac{FL}{F/L^2} \frac{1}{L^4} \overset{d}{=} K \frac{L}{L^2}$$

$$K \overset{d}{=} 1$$

Therefore, K is dimensionless.

(b)

$$Q = K_1 A R^{\frac{2}{3}} S^{\frac{1}{2}}$$

where Q = volume flow rate $\overset{d}{=}$ L^3/T
A = area $\overset{d}{=}$ L^2
R = hydraulic radius $\overset{d}{=}$ L
S = slope $\overset{d}{=}$ 1—dimensionless
$Q = K_1 A R^{\frac{2}{3}} S^{\frac{1}{2}} \overset{d}{=} K_1 L^2 L^{\frac{2}{3}} (1)^{\frac{1}{2}}$

Substitute the equivalent dimensions in the above equation to get

$$\frac{L^3}{T} \overset{d}{=} K_1 L^{\frac{8}{3}}$$

Therefore,

$$K_1 \overset{d}{=} \frac{L^{\frac{1}{3}}}{T} \qquad \blacktriangleleft$$

48. Dimensional Analysis

Before attempting to gather experimental evidence on a phenomenon, we can reduce work and cut down the number of independent variables through the use of dimensional analysis. We consider the study of a phenomenon in which the important quantities are q_1, q_2, q_3, $\cdots$, q_n. We may write that some function of all of these quantities equals zero.

$$F(q_1, q_2, \cdots, q_n) = 0 \qquad (7\text{-}1)$$

We further assume possible that we can expand this function in a power series made up of terms similar to

$$\cdots + A_i (q_1^{a_1} q_2^{a_2} \cdots q_n^{a_n})^i$$
$$+ A_{i+1} (q_1^{a_1} q_2^{a_2} \cdots q_n^{a_n})^{i+1} + \cdots \qquad (7\text{-}2)$$

The coefficients A_i, $A_{(i+1)}$, and so on, are pure numbers and, therefore, are dimensionless, which means that in considering dimensional equations we neglect these coefficients. The terms in the power series must all be the same dimension; if they are not, the equation will not be dimensionally homogeneous. This equation is dimensionally homogeneous. Therefore,

$$(q_1{}^{a_1} q_2{}^{a_2} q_3{}^{a_3} \cdots q_n{}^{a_n}) \overset{\mathrm{d}}{=} M^\alpha L^\beta T^\gamma$$

We consider the i term and the $(i + 1)$ term of the power series.

i term $(q_1{}^{a_1} q_2{}^{a_2} q_3{}^{a_3} \cdots q_n{}^{a_n})^i \overset{\mathrm{d}}{=} M^{\alpha i} L^{\beta i} T^{\gamma i}$

$(i + 1)$ term $(q_1{}^{a_1} q_2{}^{a_2} q_3{}^{a_3} \cdots q_n{}^{a_n})^{i+1} \overset{\mathrm{d}}{=} M^{\alpha(i+1)} L^{\beta(i+1)} T^{\gamma(i+1)}$

If these two terms have the same dimension, the exponent of the mass dimension must be the same for both. This is true of the length dimension and the time dimension. Therefore,

$$M^{\alpha i} L^{\beta i} T^{\gamma i} \overset{\mathrm{d}}{=} M^{\alpha(i+1)} L^{\beta(i+1)} T^{\gamma(i+1)}$$

and

$$\alpha i = \alpha(i + 1)$$
$$\beta i = \beta(i + 1)$$
$$\gamma i = \gamma(i + 1)$$

This can only be true when $\alpha = 0$, $\beta = 0$, and $\gamma = 0$. But when $\alpha = 0$, $\beta = 0$, and $\gamma = 0$, the term $(q_1{}^{a_1} q_2{}^{a_2} q_3{}^{a_3} \cdots q_n{}^{a_n})$ must be dimensionless. Therefore,

$$M^0 L^0 T^0 \overset{\mathrm{d}}{=} q_1{}^{a_1} q_2{}^{a_2} \cdots q_n{}^{a_n} \tag{7-3}$$

We assume that we can write all the small q's dimensionally in the form

$$q_n \overset{\mathrm{d}}{=} M^{\alpha_n} L^{\beta_n} T^{\gamma_n}$$

where we know α_n, β_n, and γ_n which limits the problem to one in which the fundamental dimensions are M, L, T. It is no restriction on the method as the procedure could be expanded without change to other systems or to a greater number of fundamental dimensions. When we substitute these in the dimensional equation, Equation 7-3, we obtain the following dimensional equation:

$$M^0 L^0 T^0 \overset{\mathrm{d}}{=} (M^{\alpha_1} L^{\beta_1} T^{\gamma_1})^{a_1} (M^{\alpha_2} L^{\beta_2} T^{\gamma_2})^{a_2} \cdots (M^{\alpha_n} L^{\beta_n} T^{\gamma_n})^{a_n}$$

and we rearrange it to the form

$$M^0 L^0 T^0$$
$$\overset{\mathrm{d}}{=} M^{(\alpha_1 a_1 + \alpha_2 a_2 + \cdots + \alpha_n a_n)} L^{(\beta_1 a_1 + \beta_2 a_2 + \cdots + \beta_n a_n)} T^{(\gamma_1 a_1 + \gamma_2 a_2 + \cdots + \gamma_n a_n)}$$

For this equation to be dimensionally homogeneous, we must raise the dimensions of mass on both sides of the equal sign to the same power, in this case zero, which is true of both length and time. Setting these three sets of exponents equal to zero, we obtain the following three equations:

$$\left. \begin{array}{l} 0 = \alpha_1 a_1 + \alpha_2 a_2 + \cdots + \alpha_n a_n \\ 0 = \beta_1 a_1 + \beta_2 a_2 + \cdots + \beta_n a_n \\ 0 = \gamma_1 a_1 + \gamma_2 a_2 + \cdots + \gamma_n a_n \end{array} \right\} \qquad (7\text{-}4)$$

From the simultaneous solution of these three equations it is possible to solve for three of the unknowns in terms of the other unknowns. We assume a_1, a_2, a_3 as solved in terms of the others, which gives equations of the following form:

$$\left. \begin{array}{l} a_1 = {}_1k_4 a_4 + {}_1k_5 a_5 + \cdots + {}_1k_n a_n \\ a_2 = {}_2k_4 a_4 + {}_2k_5 a_5 + \cdots + {}_2k_n a_n \\ a_3 = {}_3k_4 a_4 + {}_3k_5 a_5 + \cdots + {}_3k_n a_n \end{array} \right\} \qquad (7\text{-}5)$$

We substitute Equations 7-5 into Equation 7-3 to get

$$M^0 L^0 T^0 \overset{\mathrm{d}}{=} q_1{}^{({}_1k_4 a_4 + {}_1k_5 a_5 + \cdots + {}_1k_n a_n)} q_2{}^{({}_2k_4 a_4 + {}_2k_5 a_5 + \cdots + {}_2k_n a_n)}$$
$$q_3{}^{({}_3k_4 a_4 + {}_3k_5 a_5 + \cdots + {}_3k_n a_n)} q_4{}^{a_4} \cdots q_n{}^{a_n}$$

and we collect q's to the same exponent:

$$M^0 L^0 T^0 \overset{\mathrm{d}}{=} (q_1{}^{{}_1k_4} q_2{}^{{}_2k_4} q_3{}^{{}_3k_4} q_4)^{a_4} (q_1{}^{{}_1k_5} q_2{}^{{}_2k_5} q_3{}^{{}_3k_5} q_5)^{a_5} \cdots$$
$$(q_1{}^{{}_1k_n} q_2{}^{{}_2k_n} q_3{}^{{}_3k_n} q_n)^{a_n}$$

Since we solved Equations 7-4 to give a dimensionless answer, each of the above terms is necessarily dimensionless, and each is called a π term.

$$\left. \begin{array}{l} \pi_1 = q_1{}^{{}_1k_4} q_2{}^{{}_2k_4} q_3{}^{{}_3k_4} q_4 \\ \pi_2 = q_1{}^{{}_1k_5} q_2{}^{{}_2k_5} q_3{}^{{}_3k_5} q_5 \\ \pi_3 = q_1{}^{{}_1k_6} q_2{}^{{}_2k_6} q_3{}^{{}_3k_6} q_6 \\ \cdots \cdots \cdots \cdots \cdots \\ \pi_{n-3} = q_1{}^{{}_1k_n} q_2{}^{{}_2k_n} q_3{}^{{}_3k_n} q_n \end{array} \right\} \qquad (7\text{-}6)$$

Therefore, we have reduced the original power series term on Equation 7-2 to the form

$$+ A_i (\pi_1{}^{a_4} \pi_2{}^{a_5} \pi_3{}^{a_6} \cdots \pi_{n-3}{}^{a_n})^i + A_{i+1} (\pi_1{}^{a_4} \pi_2{}^{a_5} \pi_3{}^{a_6} \pi_4{}^{a_7} \cdots \pi_{n-3}{}^{a_n})^{i+1}$$

and

$$F(q_1, q_2, q_3, \cdots, q_n) = f(\pi_1, \pi_2, \cdots, \pi_{n-3}) \qquad (7\text{-}7)$$

The application of dimensional analysis has reduced the number of variables from n to $(n - 3)$. We accomplished this reduction because the solution of the three equations, Equation 7-4, eliminated three of the variables. Had there been j number of independent equations of the type of Equation 7-4 instead of three equations it would have been possible to eliminate j exponents which would have left $(n - j)\pi$ terms.

▶**Illustrative Problem 2.** Fluid flows in a long pipe. Reduce the variables to π terms for experimental work to determine head loss.

Solution: The first step is always to list all quantities that will affect the problem. This list requires a real understanding of the problem. The quantities and the reasoning behind each are listed below.

Quantity	Reasoning
Head loss, h_L	What you are solving for.
Diameter of pipe, D	Certainly a variable and it could affect head loss.
Roughness of pipe, e	Rougher pipes should cause greater losses.
Length of pipe, l	The longer the pipe, the greater the losses.
Velocity of fluid, V	Friction depends on relative velocity.
Viscosity of liquid, μ	This could seem necessary in any problem involving friction.
Gravitational acceleration, g	To take care of elevation changes in the pipe.
Density of fluid, ρ	In problems of motion add the mass for inertia forces.

Therefore,

$$F(h_L, D, e, l, g, V, \mu, \rho) = 0$$

Notice that the reasoning seems vague in some cases, the typically weakest point of the dimensional analysis approach. Selecting the proper quantities is the most difficult part of the problem.

Use the M, L, T system of fundamental dimensions in this problem, although the selection is completely arbitrary because the F, L, T system works as well. List all quantities with their proper dimensions.

$$h_L \overset{\text{d}}{=} L, \quad D \overset{\text{d}}{=} L, \quad e \overset{\text{d}}{=} L, \quad V \overset{\text{d}}{=} L/T, \quad l \overset{\text{d}}{=} L, \quad \mu \overset{\text{d}}{=} \frac{M}{LT},$$

$$\rho \overset{\text{d}}{=} \frac{M}{L^3}, \quad g \overset{\text{d}}{=} \frac{L}{T^2}$$

For this problem write Equation 7-3, which is the mathematical statement of dimensional homogeneity.

$$M^0 L^0 T^0 \overset{d}{=} h_L{}^{a_1} D^{a_2} e^{a_3} l^{a_4} V^{a_5} \mu^{a_6} \rho^{a_7} g^{a_8} \tag{U}$$

Substitute the dimensional equivalent,

$$M^0 L^0 T^0 \overset{d}{=} L^{a_1} L^{a_2} L^{a_3} L^{a_4} \left(\frac{L}{T}\right)^{a_5} \left(\frac{M}{LT}\right)^{a_6} \left(\frac{M}{L^3}\right)^{a_7} \left(\frac{L}{T^2}\right)^{a_8}$$

Rearrange to

$$M^0 L^0 T^0 \overset{d}{=} M^{a_6 + a_7} L^{a_1 + a_2 + a_3 + a_4 + a_5 - a_6 - 3a_7 + a_8} T^{-a_5 - a_6 - 2a_8}$$

Equate the exponents of mass, length, and time to get

M: $0 = a_6 + a_7$

L: $0 = a_1 + a_2 + a_3 + a_4 + a_5 - a_6 - 3a_7 + a_8$

T: $0 = -a_5 - a_6 - 2a_8$

You can solve these equations for any three constants in terms of the others. In this case, solve for constant a_6, a_2, a_8.

$$a_2 = -a_1 - a_3 - a_4 - \tfrac{1}{2}a_5 + \tfrac{3}{2}a_7$$

$$a_6 = -a_7$$

$$a_8 = \tfrac{1}{2}a_7 - \tfrac{1}{2}a_5$$

The following develops by substituting these values into Equation U.

$$M^0 L^0 T^0 \overset{d}{=} h_L{}^{a_1} D^{(-a_1 - a_3 - a_4 - \frac{1}{2}a_5 + \frac{3}{2}a_7)} e^{a_3} l^{a_4} V^{a_5} \mu^{-a_7} \rho^{+a_7} g^{\frac{1}{2}a_7 - \frac{1}{2}a_5}$$

Collecting terms with the same exponent gives

$$M^0 L^0 T^0 \overset{d}{=} \left(\frac{h_L}{D}\right)^{a_1} \left(\frac{e}{D}\right)^{a_3} \left(\frac{l}{D}\right)^{a_4} \left(\frac{V}{\sqrt{gD}}\right)^{a_5} \left(\frac{\rho g^{\frac{1}{2}} D^{\frac{3}{2}}}{\mu}\right)^{a_7}$$

These terms are dimensionless, π terms.

$$\pi_1 = \frac{h_L}{D}, \quad \pi_2 = \frac{e}{D}, \quad \pi_3 = \frac{l}{D}, \quad \pi_4 = \frac{V}{\sqrt{gD}}, \quad \pi_5 = \frac{\rho g^{\frac{1}{2}} D^{\frac{3}{2}}}{\mu}$$

Therefore,

$$F(h_L, D, e, l, V, \mu, \rho, g) = f(\pi_1, \pi_2, \pi_3\, \pi_4, \pi_5) = 0$$

Now, you have reduced the number of unknowns from eight to five, which you could have predicted. ◀

▶**Illustrative Problem 3.** A solid sphere travels under the surface of the ocean. Reduce the number of variables to π terms to be used to experimentally determine the drag force.

Solution: List all the variables that affect the drag force.

Quantity	Reasoning
Drag force, D	This is the quantity of primary interest.
Density of liquid, ρ	As the sphere moves through the water it accelerates fluid particles. Thus, the mass density of these particles contributes to the force.
Size of sphere, l	Size of the sphere certainly affects the drag force.
Viscosity of water, μ	This determines the friction forces.
Velocity of sphere, V	This affects the shear forces on the side of the sphere.

The M, L, T system of fundamental dimensions was used in Illustrative Problem 2, and so here the F, L, T system will be used to demonstrate that the method is the same for both. List quantities with the proper dimensions.

$$D \stackrel{\mathrm{d}}{=} F, \quad \rho \stackrel{\mathrm{d}}{=} \frac{FT^2}{L^4}, \quad \mu \stackrel{\mathrm{d}}{=} \frac{FT}{L^2}, \quad l \stackrel{\mathrm{d}}{=} L, \quad V \stackrel{\mathrm{d}}{=} \frac{L}{T}$$

Write Equation 7-3 for this problem.

$$F^0 L^0 T^0 \stackrel{\mathrm{d}}{=} D^{a_1} \rho^{a_2} \mu^{a_3} l^{a_4} V^{a_5} \tag{V}$$

Substitute the dimensional equivalents into Equation V to get

$$F^0 L^0 T^0 \stackrel{\mathrm{d}}{=} F^{a_1} \left(\frac{FT^2}{L^4}\right)^{a_2} \left(\frac{FT}{L^2}\right)^{a_3} L^{a_4} \left(\frac{L}{T}\right)^{a_5}$$

Rearrange

$$F^0 L^0 T^0 = F^{a_1 + a_2 + a_3} L^{-4a_2 - 2a_3 + a_4 + a_5} T^{2a_2 + a_3 - a_5}$$

Equate the exponents of force, length, and time.

$$F: \quad 0 = a_1 + a_2 + a_3$$

$$L: \quad 0 = -4a_2 - 2a_3 + a_4 + a_5$$

$$T: \quad 0 = 2a_2 + a_3 - a_5$$

Here are three equations and five unknowns of which three can be solved in terms of the other two.

$$a_1 = -a_2 - a_3$$

$$a_4 = 2a_2 + a_3$$

$$a_5 = 2a_2 + a_3$$

Substitute these into Equation V.

$$F^0L^0T^0 \stackrel{d}{=} D^{(-a_2-a_3)}\rho^{a_2}\mu^{a_3}l^{2a_2+a_3}V^{2a_2+a_3}$$

Collect terms with the same exponent.

$$F^0L^0T^0 \stackrel{d}{=} \left(\frac{\rho V^2 l^2}{D}\right)^{a_2}\left(\frac{\mu V l}{D}\right)^{a_3}$$

Terms to the same exponent are dimensionless and are π terms.

$$\pi_1 = \frac{\rho V^2 l^2}{D}, \qquad \pi_2 = \frac{\mu V l}{D}$$

$$F(D, \rho, \mu, l, V) = f(\pi_1, \pi_2) = 0$$

You have reduced the number of unknowns, therefore, from five to two. ◀

49. Dimensionless Ratios or π Terms

In Illustrative Problem 2 we eliminated the exponents a_2, a_6, and a_8 and, on that basis, formed the π terms π_1, π_2, π_3, π_4 and π_5. If we had eliminated exponents other than a_2, a_6, and a_8, we would have formed π terms other than π_1, π_2, π_3, π_4, and π_5. The arbitrary selection of exponents to be eliminated determines the π terms used, but forming these π terms does not complete the work by any means. We must rearrange the π terms and even change them to a form that we can best use. In this article we discuss a method to follow.

We assume that the problem requires a solution in the form

$$q_1 = f(q_2, q_3, q_4, \cdots, q_n)$$

By dimensional analysis we can get a solution in the form

$$F(\pi_1, \pi_2, \pi_3, \cdots, \pi_{n-j}) = 0$$

where π_1, π_2, π_3, $\cdots$, π_{n-j} are combinations of the quantities q_1,

$q_2, q_3, \cdot \cdot \cdot, q_n$. The complete set of π terms for the problem must use every q at least once.

If q_1, the quantity to be solved, appears in only one term π_1, it is easy to solve for q_1. We rewrite the equation in the form

$$\pi_1 = f_1(\pi_2, \pi_3, \cdot \cdot \cdot, \pi_{n-j})$$

Then we solve for q_1

$$q_1 = f_1(\pi_2, \pi_3, \cdot \cdot \cdot, \pi_{n-j})g\left(\frac{q_1}{\pi_1}\right)$$

where $g(q_1/\pi_1)$ is not a function of q_1. This is a simple and straightforward method. In Illustrative Problem 3

$$f(\pi_1, \pi_2) = 0$$

where $\pi_1 = \rho V^2 l^2/D$, $\pi_2 = \mu V l/D$. To solve for ρ in this problem, we rearrange the terms in the order below.

$$\pi_1 = f_1(\pi_2)$$

$$\pi_1 = \frac{\rho V^2 l^2}{D} = f_1(\pi_2)$$

$$\rho = f_1(\pi_2)\frac{D}{V^2 l^2}$$

In this problem,

$$\frac{D}{V^2 l^2} = g\left(\frac{q_1}{\pi_1}\right) = \frac{\rho D}{\rho V^2 l^2}$$

We next consider the case where q_1 appears in more than one π term. We manipulate the π terms to change them so that q_1 appears in only one π term. Here we discuss the rules of such manipulation.

The product of two π terms is a dimensionless term that may be considered a new π term. The quotient of two π terms is a dimensionless term and, therefore, a new π term. Thus, it is possible from a given set of π terms to get an infinite number of π terms. A complete set of π terms for any problem must include every quantity q that appears in the problem. We can determine when a complete set of π terms is formed by checking to see that we have used each q at least once. However, this does not insure the minimum number of π terms needed to make a complete set, a subject which we take up in the next article.

▶Illustrative Problem 4.   Rearrange the π terms in Illustrative Problem 2 to the form of Darcy's equation.

$$h_L = f \frac{l}{D} \frac{V^2}{2g}$$

Solution: Given

$$\pi_1 = \frac{h_L}{D}, \quad \pi_2 = \frac{e}{D}, \quad \pi_3 = \frac{l}{D}, \quad \pi_4 = \frac{V}{\sqrt{gD}}, \quad \pi_5 = \frac{\rho g^{\frac{1}{2}} D^{\frac{3}{2}}}{\mu}$$

Select new π terms.

$$\pi_6 = \frac{\pi_1}{\pi_4{}^2} = \frac{h_L}{D \dfrac{V^2}{gD}} = \frac{h_L}{\dfrac{V^2}{g}}$$

$$\pi_7 = \pi_4 \pi_5 = \frac{\rho g^{\frac{1}{2}} D^{\frac{3}{2}}}{\mu} \frac{V}{g^{\frac{1}{2}} D^{\frac{1}{2}}} = \frac{\rho V D}{\mu}$$

The new π terms are

$$\pi_2 = \frac{e}{D}, \quad \pi_3 = \frac{l}{D}, \quad \pi_4 = \frac{V}{\sqrt{gD}}, \quad \pi_6 = \frac{h_L}{V^2/g}, \quad \pi_7 = \frac{\rho V D}{\mu}$$

$$\pi_6 = f(\pi_2, \pi_3, \pi_4, \pi_7)$$

$$h_L = f_1(\pi_2, \pi_3, \pi_4, \pi_7) \frac{V^2}{2g}$$

Experiments shown that $V/\sqrt{gD}$ is not important and that the head loss varies directly with L/D.   Therefore,

$$h_L = f_2(\pi_2, \pi_7) \frac{l}{D} \frac{V^2}{2g}$$

$$f = f_2(\pi_2, \pi_7) = f_2\left(\frac{e}{D}, \frac{\rho V D}{\mu}\right)$$

Finally,

$$h_L = f \frac{l}{D} \frac{V^2}{2g} \qquad\qquad ◀$$

▶Illustrative Problem 5.   Rearrange the π terms in Illustrative Problem 3 to the form

$$D = C_D \rho V^2 l^2$$

where C_D is independent of D.

Solution: Given

$$\pi_1 = \frac{\rho V^2 l^2}{D}, \quad \pi_2 = \frac{\mu V l}{D}$$

Form a new π term that does not include the drag force D

$$\pi_3 = \frac{\pi_1}{\pi_2} = \frac{\rho V^2 l^2}{D} \frac{D}{\mu V l} = \frac{\rho V l}{\mu}$$

where the last term is the Reynolds number.

$$F(\pi_1, \pi_3) = 0$$

$$\pi_1 = f(\pi_3)$$

In these two π terms you must include all of the quantities in the problem.

$$\frac{\rho V^2 l^2}{D} = f\left(\frac{\rho V l}{\mu}\right)$$

$$D = \frac{1}{f\left(\dfrac{\rho V l}{\mu}\right)} \rho V^2 l^2 = C_D \rho V^2 l^2$$

where
$$C_D = \frac{1}{f\left(\dfrac{\rho V l}{\mu}\right)} = f_1\left(\frac{\rho V l}{\mu}\right) \qquad \blacktriangleleft$$

50. Determination of Minimum Number of π Terms

In this article we explain a much more orderly way to set up the dimensional analysis problem than the method used up to this point.

In Art. 48 we considered a phenomenon which included the variables $q_1, q_2, q_3, \cdots, q_n$. One term of a power series that mathematically defined the phenomenon we wrote in the form

$$q_1{}^{a_1} q_2{}^{a_2} q_3{}^{a_3} \cdots q_n{}^{a_n} \overset{\mathrm{d}}{=} M^0 L^0 T^0 \tag{7-3}$$

where each q was made up of dimensions such that

$$q_n \overset{\mathrm{d}}{=} M^{\alpha_n} L^{\beta_n} T^{\gamma_n}$$

Figure 69a is an orderly array of numbers for this phenomenon. Across the top we write the variables. Down the left side we write the fundamental dimensions, in this case M, L, T.   Here we could include other fundamental dimensions or a completely different set of fundamental dimensions.   Under q_1 we write the numbers that correspond to the dimensions of q_1, such as

$$q_1 \stackrel{\text{d}}{=} M^{\alpha_1}L^{\beta_1}T^{\gamma_1}$$

We place α_1 in the M row under q_1, β_1 in the L row under q_1, and γ_1 in the T row under q_1.   The columns are vertical, and the rows horizontal.   We continue placing all the quantities in this manner until

	q_1	q_2	q_3	q_4	$\cdots$	q_n
M	α_1	α_2	α_3	α_4	$\cdots$	α_n
L	β_1	β_2	β_3	β_4	$\cdots$	β_n
T	γ_1	γ_2	γ_3	γ_4	$\cdots$	γ_n

(a)

	D	ρ	μ	l	V
F	1	1	1	0	0
L	0	-4	-2	1	1
T	0	2	1	0	-1

(b)

Fig. 69

the array is complete.   Using this array, which we call a matrix, we can tell at a glance the fundamental dimensions of any quantity in the matrix.   By looking in the column under the quantity being examined, we find the numbers that give the mass dimension, length dimension, and time dimension for that quantity.   This, of course, will work for any set of fundamental dimensions.

Figure 69b is the matrix for Illustrative Problem 3.   A glance at the density ρ column shows that

$$\rho \stackrel{\text{d}}{=} F^1L^{-4}T^2 = \frac{FT^2}{L^4}$$

This is handy but certainly not sufficient reason for using a matrix. Another interesting property of this matrix allows us to write the independent equation directly.   In the general term of the power series, q_1 is raised to the a_1 power, q_2 to the a_2 power, and so on up to q_n which is raised to the a_n power.   The product $a_1\alpha_1$ is the total mass dimension in the general term due to q_1.   The same is true of $a_2\alpha_2$, $a_3\alpha_3$, $\cdots$,

$a_n \alpha_n$. The sum of all these products must be zero. Considering the M row in Fig. 69a, we multiply the α's by the corresponding a's, add the quantities, and set them equal to zero with this result

$$\alpha_1 a_1 + \alpha_2 a_2 + \alpha_3 a_3 + \cdots + \alpha_n a_n = 0$$

which is one of the Equations 7-4. The α's are the coefficients of the powers a_1, a_2, $\cdots$, a_n. This is true for the second row and the third row. Then we multiply every number in the q column by the exponent to which that q is raised. We add each row and set it equal to zero.

Returning to Illustrative Problem 3 and the matrix (Fig. 69b), we find it possible to write the equation corresponding to Equation 7-4 directly.

$$\left.\begin{array}{llllll}
\text{F:} & (1)a_1 + & (1)a_2 + & (1)a_3 + (0)a_4 + & (0)a_5 = 0 \\
\text{L:} & (0)a_1 + & (-4)a_2 + & (-2)a_3 + (1)a_4 + & (1)a_5 = 0 \\
\text{T:} & (0)a_1 + & (2)a_2 + & (1)a_3 + (0)a_4 + (-1)a_5 = 0
\end{array}\right\} \quad (7\text{-}8)$$

We throw out the terms with zero coefficient to get

$$a_1 + a_2 + a_3 = 0$$

$$-4a_2 - 2a_3 + a_4 + a_5 = 0$$

$$2a_2 + a_3 - a_5 = 0$$

These are the same equations that we arrived at in Illustrative Problem 3.

It begins to look as though the matrix might be quite useful. However, we have saved the most important use of the matrix until last. Matrices have so many different applications that a thorough investigation has been made of them and has led to many important theorems, of which the most important to us is the one which allows us to determine how many of the Equations 7-4 are independent equations. Article 48 stated that with n quantities and j independent equations there would be $(n - j)\,\pi$ terms. Finding the number of quantities is just a matter of counting them. Finding the number of equations is also just a matter of counting them. However, we must determine if these equations are independent. We do this next.

A theorem states that from a matrix there will be a number of independent equations equal to the order of the highest order determinant of the matrix which is different from zero. The determinant may have a positive or negative value just as long as it differs from zero.

This presents several problems at once:

(1) What is a determinant?
(2) How do we evaluate a determinant?
(3) What is a determinant of a matrix?
(4) What is the order of a determinant?

First, a determinant is an orderly array of numbers similar to a matrix except that it must have an equal number of rows and columns and a numerical value.   A matrix has no numerical value.

Second, the evaluation of a determinant is covered in college algebra textbooks.   Any student who was not taught it or has forgotten it

$$\begin{vmatrix} \alpha_1 & \alpha_2 & \alpha_3 \\ \beta_1 & \beta_2 & \beta_3 \\ \gamma_1 & \gamma_2 & \gamma_3 \end{vmatrix} \qquad \begin{vmatrix} \alpha_2 & \alpha_4 & \alpha_1 \\ \beta_2 & \beta_4 & \beta_1 \\ \gamma_2 & \gamma_4 & \gamma_1 \end{vmatrix}$$
$$(a) \qquad\qquad (b)$$

$$\begin{vmatrix} \alpha_n & \alpha_3 & \alpha_5 \\ \beta_n & \beta_3 & \beta_5 \\ \gamma_n & \gamma_3 & \gamma_5 \end{vmatrix} \qquad \begin{vmatrix} \alpha_1 & \alpha_6 \\ \beta_1 & \beta_6 \end{vmatrix}$$
$$(c) \qquad\qquad (d)$$

$$\begin{vmatrix} \alpha_5 & \alpha_2 \\ \gamma_5 & \gamma_2 \end{vmatrix} \qquad \begin{vmatrix} \beta_n & \beta_4 \\ \gamma_n & \gamma_4 \end{vmatrix}$$
$$(e) \qquad\qquad (f)$$

Fig. 70

should look it up in a good college algebra textbook.   To evaluate a determinant is a simple task which we shall not consider further in this book.

Third, rows and columns make up a matrix.   In dimensional analysis there usually are more columns than rows.   Because a determinant is a matrix with an equal number of rows and columns, we can select different columns from the matrix and combine them into the determinant.   A matrix may have many determinants.   Figure 70 shows some of the determinants made from the matrix in Fig. 69a.   Figure 70a is the first three columns.   Figure 70b is the second, fourth, and first columns.   We can arrange these columns in any order, but the column itself must remain unchanged.

Figure 70c is another example of a determinant that is three columns by three rows.   Figure 70d, e, and f are examples of determinants that are two rows by two columns, accomplished by eliminating a row and taking a determinant from one of the remaining rows.   Figure 70d shows the time row eliminated and the determinant chosen from the remaining two rows.   Again we could have chosen a number of determinants from the two rows.   This is only a typical example.   The same is true of Fig. 70e and f except that we eliminated different rows in each case.   Figure 70 demonstrates that a matrix has not one determinant but many determinants.

Fourth, the order of a determinant is the number of columns or rows in the determinant.   In Fig. 70, the first three determinants have three columns and three rows.   These are third-order determinants. The others have only two columns and two rows and are second-order determinants.   We see that the order of a determinant is an easy number to calculate.

We now have defined all the terms in the theorem and should be in a position to use it.   Illustrative Problems 6 and 7 help clear up any difficulties.

▶**Illustrative Problem 6.**   Make a complete set of π terms from the quantities of surface tension σ, length l, density ρ, force F, and acceleration of gravity g.

Solution: First, make the matrix.   Use the F, L, T system although you could use the M, L, T system.

	σ	l	ρ	F	g
F	1	0	1	1	0
L	−1	1	−4	0	1
T	0	0	2	0	−2

Calculate the order of the highest order determinant of this matrix that is different from zero.

Evaluate the first three columns as the determinant.

$$\begin{vmatrix} 1 & 0 & 1 \\ -1 & 1 & -4 \\ 0 & 0 & 2 \end{vmatrix} = 1 \begin{vmatrix} 1 & -4 \\ 0 & 2 \end{vmatrix} - 0 \begin{vmatrix} -1 & -4 \\ 0 & 2 \end{vmatrix} + 1 \begin{vmatrix} -1 & 1 \\ 0 & 0 \end{vmatrix}$$

$$= 1(2 - 0) - 0(-2 - 0) + 1(0 - 0) = 2$$

This determinant is different from zero.   The highest order determinant possible is a third-order determinant since there are only three rows.   Therefore, this third-order determinant is the highest order determinant different from zero.

The number of π terms is the number of quantities n minus the number of independent equations j:

$$n - j = 5 - 3 = 2\pi \text{ terms}$$

$$\sigma^{a_1} l^{a_2} \rho^{a_3} F^{a_4} g^{a_5} \overset{d}{=} F^0 L^0 T^0$$

From the matrix:

$$\text{F:} \quad (1)a_1 + (0)a_2 + \quad (1)a_3 + (1)a_4 + \quad (0)a_5 = 0$$

$$\text{L:} \quad (-1)a_1 + (1)a_2 + (-4)a_3 + (0)a_4 + \quad (1)a_5 = 0$$

$$\text{T:} \quad (0)a_1 + (0)a_2 + \quad (2)a_3 + (0)a_4 + (-2)a_5 = 0$$

$$a_1 + a_3 + a_4 = 0$$

$$-a_1 + a_2 - 4a_3 + a_5 = 0$$

$$2a_3 - 2a_5 = 0$$

Therefore,

$$a_3 = a_5$$

$$a_1 = -a_5 - a_4$$

$$a_2 = 2a_5 - a_4$$

$$\sigma^{-a_5-a_4} l^{2a_5-a_4} \rho^{a_5} F^{a_4} g^{a_5} = \left(\frac{F}{\sigma l}\right)^{a_4} \left(\frac{\rho g l^2}{\sigma}\right)^{a_5}$$

$$\pi_1 = \frac{F}{\sigma l}, \qquad \pi_2 = \frac{\rho g l^2}{\sigma} \qquad \blacktriangleleft$$

▶**Illustrative Problem 7.** Determine the rate of heat flow between two points on a bar.

Solution: Take as fundamental dimensions temperature Θ, length L, time T, and heat or thermal energy H.

$$Q = \text{rate of heat flow} \overset{d}{=} \text{H/T}$$

$$T_1 = \text{temperature at point 1} \overset{d}{=} \Theta$$

$$T_2 = \text{temperature at point 2} \overset{d}{=} \Theta$$

$$l = \text{distance between points} \overset{d}{=} \text{L}$$

$$d = \text{diameter of rod} \overset{d}{=} \text{L}$$

$$h = \text{thermal conductivity} \overset{d}{=} \text{H/LT}\Theta$$

The matrix is

	Q	T_1	T_2	l	d	h
H	1	0	0	0	0	1
T	−1	0	0	0	0	−1
L	0	0	0	1	1	−1
Θ	0	1	1	0	0	−1

The highest possible determinant is fourth order, and so check the fourth-order determinants to see if any are different from 0.

Any determinant that has a row or column made up of all zeros must be zero. The determinant of the middle four columns here is zero. Evaluate the first four columns.

$$
\begin{vmatrix} 1 & 0 & 0 & 0 \\ -1 & 0 & 0 & 0 \\ 0 & 0 & 0 & 1 \\ 0 & 1 & 1 & 0 \end{vmatrix} = 1 \underbrace{\begin{vmatrix} 0 & 0 & 0 \\ 0 & 0 & 1 \\ 1 & 1 & 0 \end{vmatrix}}_{\substack{\| \\ 0}} - 0 \overset{0}{\cancel{\begin{vmatrix} \\ \\ \end{vmatrix}}} + 0 \overset{0}{\cancel{\begin{vmatrix} \\ \\ \end{vmatrix}}} - 0 \overset{0}{\cancel{\begin{vmatrix} \\ \\ \end{vmatrix}}} = 0
$$

the top row is zero

The determinants which are made up of any combination of the first column and any three of the middle four and of the last column and any combination of the middle four are also zero. This leaves only the first and last columns and two of the middle four. Try the first, second, third, and last columns.

$$
\begin{vmatrix} 1 & 0 & 0 & 1 \\ -1 & 0 & 0 & -1 \\ 0 & 0 & 0 & -1 \\ 0 & 1 & 1 & -1 \end{vmatrix}
$$

$$
= 1 \underbrace{\begin{vmatrix} 0 & 0 & -1 \\ 0 & 0 & -1 \\ 1 & 1 & -1 \end{vmatrix}}_{\substack{\| \\ 0}} - 0 + 0 - 1 \underbrace{\begin{vmatrix} -1 & 0 & 0 \\ 0 & 0 & 0 \\ 0 & 1 & 1 \end{vmatrix}}_{\substack{\| \\ 0}}
$$

the middle row is zero

Try first, second, fourth, and last.

$$\begin{vmatrix} 1 & 0 & 0 & 1 \\ -1 & 0 & 0 & -1 \\ 0 & 0 & 1 & -1 \\ 0 & 1 & 0 & -1 \end{vmatrix}$$

$$= 1\begin{vmatrix} 0 & 0 & -1 \\ 0 & 1 & -1 \\ 1 & 0 & -1 \end{vmatrix} - 0 + 0 - 1\begin{vmatrix} -1 & 0 & 0 \\ 0 & 0 & 1 \\ 0 & 1 & 0 \end{vmatrix}$$

$$= 1(-1)(-1) - 1(-1)(-1) = 1 - 1 = 0$$

Try first, fourth, fifth, and last.

$$\begin{vmatrix} 1 & 0 & 0 & 1 \\ -1 & 0 & 0 & -1 \\ 0 & 1 & 1 & -1 \\ 0 & 0 & 0 & -1 \end{vmatrix} = 1\begin{vmatrix} 0 & 0 & -1 \\ 1 & 1 & -1 \\ 0 & 0 & -1 \end{vmatrix} - 1\begin{vmatrix} -1 & 0 & 0 \\ 0 & 1 & 1 \\ 0 & 0 & 0 \end{vmatrix}$$

$$= 0 - 0 = 0$$

Any other combinations possible end up as one of these determinants. Therefore, there is no fourth-order determinant different from zero. Try a third-order determinant. Eliminate the top row and try columns one, two, and four.

$$\begin{vmatrix} -1 & 0 & 0 \\ 0 & 0 & 1 \\ 0 & 1 & 0 \end{vmatrix} = -1\begin{vmatrix} 0 & 1 \\ 1 & 0 \end{vmatrix} = -1(0 - 1) = +1$$

This is different from zero and so there are only three independent equations.

With six quantities and three independent equations there are $6 - 3 = 3\pi$ terms. You see at once that two of these π terms are l/d and T_1/T_2. This leaves the job of finding the third, which must include Q and h because they have not been used.

Try Q/h.

$$Q/h \stackrel{\mathrm{d}}{=} \frac{\mathrm{HTL\Theta}}{\mathrm{TH}} = \mathrm{L\Theta}$$

To be dimensionless, a combination of quantities that have the dimensions of $(L\Theta)^{-1}$ must be determined. The combination could be xT_1. Try it.

$$\frac{Q}{h}\frac{1}{xT_1} = \frac{Q}{hxT_1} \stackrel{d}{=} \frac{HTL\Theta}{THL\Theta} \stackrel{d}{=} 1$$

which checks.

$$\pi_1 = \frac{l}{d}, \qquad \pi_2 = T_1/T_2, \qquad \pi_3 = \frac{Q}{hxT_1}$$

Put in the form

$$f(\pi_1, \pi_2, \pi_3) = 0$$

or

$$\pi_3 = F(\pi_1, \pi_2)$$

$$\frac{Q}{hxT_1} = F(\pi_1, \pi_2) \qquad \text{or} \qquad Q = F(\pi_1, \pi_2)hxT_1 \qquad \blacktriangleleft$$

51. Model Testing

Many engineering problems are too difficult to solve by analytical means. One method of solving such problems is by model studies. Model studies are inexpensive when compared with the money and lives saved by their use: money saved by not redesigning and rebuilding all or part of any expensive structure when flaws become apparent, and lives saved by the assurance that a structure will not collapse before a flaw becomes apparent. However, the cost of model studies is high compared to analytical methods. We should attempt model studies only when analytical methods are unsatisfactory.

A model study creates on a smaller scale a problem to be studied. We examine effects of the variables on this scale; then we can predict effects on the full scale. In studying the problem, we know what quantities $q_1, q_2, \cdots, q_n$ are important and what we must consider. Some relation among them exists such that a test can be run in which known quantities can be set at their numerical values and unknown quantities measured. When we test these quantities at the numerical values that they will reach in the problem, we must make the entire structure of the problem full scale. In other words, we try to solve the problem by building a full-scale (prototype) model and a method of trial and error, a ridiculously expensive procedure and, in the case of some structures, an impossible one to consider.

A dimensional analysis of the problem reduces it to the form

$$\pi_1 = F(\pi_2, \pi_3, \cdots, \pi_n)$$

When the π terms are equal in the small replica (model) and in the prototype, complete similarity exists.

In dimensionally analyzing the problem we should include all the different lengths as quantities, which gives a number of π terms that are ratios of two lengths. When each of these π terms is the same in model and prototype, the ratio of lengths is the same. For example, consider a pipe flow problem. The *length* dimensions to be considered would be the length l, the diameter d, and the roughness e of the pipe. This gives two π terms that are the ratio of lengths.

$$\pi_1 = \frac{l}{d}, \qquad \pi_2 = \frac{e}{d}$$

For dynamic similarity the π terms must be the same in model and prototype.

$$\pi_{1_m} = \pi_{1_p}, \qquad \pi_{2_m} = \pi_{2_p}$$

$$\left(\frac{l}{d}\right)_m = \left(\frac{l}{d}\right)_p, \quad \left(\frac{e}{d}\right)_m = \left(\frac{e}{d}\right)_p$$

$$\frac{l_m}{l_p} = \frac{d_m}{d_p}, \qquad \frac{e_m}{e_p} = \frac{d_m}{d_p}$$

or

$$\frac{l_m}{l_p} = \frac{d_m}{d_p} = \frac{e_m}{e_p}$$

For the π terms that are length ratios to be equal in model and prototype, the ratio of all corresponding lengths must be made equal in model and prototype. This is just a way of saying that the model and prototype must be geometrically similar and proves that, for dynamic similarity to exist, the model and the prototype must be geometrically similar. Because of this geometric similarity, when we make a dimensional analysis to determine the π terms, we include only one length dimension in the quantities. This is called the characteristic length, which is considered any length dimension in the dimensional analysis until the π terms are determined. This length then changes into the particular length that makes the most sense in each π term. The easiest way to understand this is to look at a few examples.

▶Illustrative Problem 8. A 6 in. dia. sphere which is a model of a 2 ft dia. sphere is to be tested in a wind tunnel. The 2 ft prototype travels at a speed of 60 mph through standard air. Compressibility effects are assumed to be negligible.

(a) What should be the speed of the air in the wind tunnel for the model flow to be dynamically similar to the prototype?

(b) The drag force on the model is 7 lb.   Calculate the drag on the prototype.

Solution: (a) Illustrative Problem 5 shows that the π terms are

$$\pi_1 = \frac{\rho V^2 l^2}{D}, \qquad \pi_3 = \frac{\rho V l}{\mu}$$

For the flows to be dynamically similar the π terms must be equal in model and prototype.

$$\pi_{1_m} = \pi_{1_p}, \qquad \pi_{3_m} = \pi_{3_p}$$

The drag force D is known in π_1, and so set $\pi_{3_m} = \pi_{3_p}$.

$$\frac{\rho_m V_m l_m}{\mu_m} = \frac{\rho_p V_p l_p}{\mu_p}$$

$$\rho_m = \rho_p, \qquad \mu_m = \mu_p$$

The same air is used in both cases.

$$V_m = \frac{\rho_p V_p l_p}{\mu_p} \frac{\mu_m}{\rho_m l_m} = \frac{l_p}{l_m} V_p$$

$$V_m = 4 V_p = (4)(60) = 240 \text{ mph}$$

(b) Illustrative Problem 5 shows the equation of the drag force to be

$$D = f\left(\frac{\rho V l}{\mu}\right) \rho V^2 l^2$$

Since $\rho V l / \mu$ is the same in model and prototype, $f(\rho V l / \mu)$ must be the same in both.   Therefore,

$$\left(\frac{D}{\rho V^2 l^2}\right)_m = f\left(\frac{\rho V l}{\mu}\right) = \left(\frac{D}{\rho V^2 l^2}\right)_p$$

$$D_p = \frac{\rho_p}{\rho_m} \frac{V_p^2}{V_m^2} \frac{l_p^2}{l_m^2} D_m$$

$$= \frac{0.00238}{0.00238} \frac{(60)^2}{(240)^2} \frac{(24)^2}{(6)^2} 7$$

$$D_p = 7 \text{ lb} \qquad \blacktriangleleft$$

▶**Illustrative Problem 9.** A centrifugal pump 4 ft in diameter, running at 600 rpm, is to maintain a pressure difference of 30 psi while pumping 2500 gpm of water. A $\frac{1}{4}$ scale model of this pump is built to pump water.

(a) What pressure difference and what revolutions per minute of the model should be maintained for dynamic similitude?

(b) Determine the flow rate of the model.

(c) Calculate the power input to the prototype if the power input to the model is 200 hp.

Solution:

$$l = \text{characteristic length}$$
$$p = \text{pressure difference}$$
$$n = \text{revolutions per minute of pump}$$
$$\mu = \text{viscosity of water}$$
$$\rho = \text{density of water}$$
$$P = \text{power input to pump}$$
$$Q = \text{flow rate}$$

	l	p	n	μ	ρ	P	Q
M	0	1	0	1	1	1	0
L	1	−1	0	−1	−3	2	3
T	0	−2	−1	−1	0	−3	−1

$$M^0 L^0 T^0 \overset{\text{d}}{=} l^{a_1} p^{a_2} n^{a_3} \mu^{a_4} \rho^{a_5} P^{a_6} Q^{a_7}$$

$$\text{M:} \quad 0 = a_2 + a_4 + a_5 + a_6$$

$$\text{L:} \quad 0 = a_1 - a_2 - a_4 - 3a_5 + 2a_6 + 3a_7$$

$$\text{T:} \quad 0 = -2a_1 - a_3 - a_4 - 3a_6 - a_7$$

$$a_2 = -a_4 - a_5 - a_6$$

$$a_1 = 2a_5 - 3a_6 - 3a_7$$

$$a_3 = a_4 + 2a_5 - a_6 - a_7$$

$$1 \overset{\text{d}}{=} l^{(2a_5 - 3a_6 - 3a_7)} p^{(-a_4 - a_5 - a_6)} n^{(a_4 + 2a_5 - a_6 - a_7)} \mu^{a_4} \rho^{a_5} P^{a_6} Q^{a_7}$$

$$1 \overset{\text{d}}{=} \left(\frac{n\mu}{p}\right)^{a_4} \left(\frac{l^2 n^2 \rho}{p}\right)^{a_5} \left(\frac{P}{l^3 pn}\right)^{a_6} \left(\frac{Q}{nl^3}\right)^{a_7}$$

$$\pi_1 = \frac{n\mu}{p}, \qquad \pi_2 = \frac{\rho n^2 l^2}{p}, \qquad \pi_3 = \frac{P}{l^3 pn}, \qquad \pi_4 = \frac{Q}{nl^3}$$

$$\pi_5 = \frac{\pi_2}{\pi_1} = \frac{\rho n^2 l^2}{p \dfrac{n\mu}{p}} = \frac{\rho nl^2}{\mu}$$

$$\pi_3 = f(\pi_2, \pi_4, \pi_5)$$

For dynamic similitude

$$\pi_{2m} = \pi_{2p}, \qquad \pi_{3m} = \pi_{3p}, \qquad \pi_{4m} = \pi_{4p}, \qquad \pi_{5m} = \pi_{5p}$$

Because $\pi_{5m} = \pi_{5p}$

$$\left(\frac{\rho nl^2}{\mu}\right)_m = \left(\frac{\rho nl^2}{\mu}\right)_p$$

$$\frac{(1.94)(n_m)(1)^2}{(2.2)(10)^{-5}} = \frac{(1.94)(200)(4)^2}{(2.2)(10)^{-5}}$$

$$n_m = 600(16) = 9600 \text{ rpm}$$

$$\left(\frac{\rho n^2 l^2}{p}\right)_m = \left(\frac{\rho n^2 l^2}{p}\right)_p$$

$$\frac{(1.94)(9600)^2(1)^2}{p_m} = \frac{(1.94)(600)^2(4)^2}{30}$$

$$p_m = \frac{1.94(9600)^2(1)^2}{1.94(600)^2(4)^2} \, 30 = 480 \text{ psi}$$

Because $\pi_{4m} = \pi_{4p}$

$$\left(\frac{Q}{nl^3}\right)_m = \left(\frac{Q}{nl^3}\right)_p$$

$$\frac{Q_m}{(9600)(1)^3} = \frac{2500}{(600)(4)^3}$$

$$Q_m = \frac{(2500)(9600)}{(600)(4)^3} = 625 \text{ gpm}$$

Because $\pi_{3m} = \pi_{3p}$

$$\left(\frac{P}{l^3 pn}\right)_m = \left(\frac{P}{l^3 pn}\right)_p$$

$$P_p = \left(\frac{l_p}{l_m}\right)^3 \left(\frac{p_p}{p_m}\right) \left(\frac{n_p}{n_m}\right) P_m$$

$$= (4)^3 \, \frac{30}{480} \, \frac{600}{9600} \, 200 = 50 \text{ hp} \quad \blacktriangleleft$$

52. Incomplete Dynamic Similarity

Two or more designs of a racing sailboat model will be tested to determine which hull has the least resistance. The quantities are velocity of the boat V, density of the water ρ, viscosity of the water μ, a characteristic length of the boat l, drag force on the boat D, and gravitational acceleration g. We need the latter to account for losses due to wave formation.

The matrix is

	V	ρ	μ	l	D	g
M	0	1	1	0	1	0
L	1	-3	-1	1	1	1
T	-1	0	-1	0	-2	-2

The last three columns form the determinant.

$$\begin{vmatrix} 0 & 1 & 0 \\ 1 & 1 & 1 \\ 0 & -2 & -2 \end{vmatrix} = -1 \begin{vmatrix} 1 & 1 \\ 0 & -2 \end{vmatrix} = +2$$

This is different from zero and so the highest order determinant that is different from zero is of the third order. The number of π terms is

$$n - j = 6 - 3 = 3$$

By inspection, three π terms that will include all the quantities are

$$\pi_1 = \frac{\rho V l}{\mu}, \qquad \pi_2 = \frac{V^2}{lg}, \qquad \pi_3 = \frac{D}{\rho V^2 l^2}$$

The π terms must be equal in model and prototype. We use the first two π terms.

$$\left(\frac{\rho V l}{\mu}\right)_m = \left(\frac{\rho V l}{\mu}\right)_p; \qquad \left(\frac{V^2}{lg}\right)_m = \left(\frac{V^2}{lg}\right)_p$$

Since g is the same in both model and prototype,

$$\frac{V_m^2}{l_m} = \frac{V_p^2}{l_p}; \qquad V_m = \left(\frac{l_m}{l_p}\right)^{1/2} V_p$$

We substitute this value of V_m in π_1.

$$\frac{\rho_m \left(\dfrac{l_m}{l_p}\right)^{1/2} V_p l_m}{\mu_m} = \frac{\rho_p V_p l_p}{\mu_p}$$

$$\frac{\rho_m}{\mu_m} = \left(\frac{l_p}{l_m}\right)^{3/2} \frac{\rho_p}{\mu_p} \qquad (7\text{-}9)$$

If the liquid used in testing the model is the same water as that in which the prototype sails, then

$$\frac{\rho_m}{\mu_m} = \frac{\rho_p}{\mu_p}$$

We substitute this into Equation 7-9.

$$\frac{\rho_m}{\mu_m} = \left(\frac{l_p}{l_m}\right)^{3/2} \frac{\rho_m}{\mu_m} \qquad \text{or} \qquad l_p = l_m$$

This is a full-scale model and is really no model at all. The only liquids that are feasible from the standpoint of expense and safety would give l_m/l_p of greater than one-half, which is not enough saving in cost to make model testing worthwhile.

Obviously, if we use water for both model and prototype we cannot satisfy both π_1 and π_2, which brings us to incomplete dynamic similarity. Incomplete dynamic similarity exists when some π terms are not equal in model and prototype. In this case the π_2 term, known as the Froude number, is the same in model and prototype, whereas π_1, known as the Reynolds number, is not the same. We handle this difference of Reynolds number in model and prototype by the skin friction theory.

From dimensional analysis, we may derive the following equation.

$$\left. \begin{array}{l} \pi_3 = f(\pi_1, \pi_2) \\ D = C_D \rho V^2 l^2 \end{array} \right\} \qquad (7\text{-}10)$$

where $C_D = f(\pi_1, \pi_2)$

With complete dynamic similarity C_D is the same in model and prototype. As this is not the case, we divide the coefficient C_D into two coefficients, C_{D_1} and C_{D_2}, where C_{D_1} is a function of the Froude number and C_{D_2} is a function of the Reynolds number. Equation 7-10 changes to

$$D = (C_{D_1} + C_{D_2})\rho V^2 l^2 \qquad (7-11)$$

Since the Froude number is the same in model and prototype, C_{D_1} is the same in both. This leaves the problem of computing C_{D_2} in the model and in the prototype. Here C_{D_1} is a measure of resistance due to surface waves and C_{D_2} is resistance due to friction.

Referring to previous experimental work done on frictional resistance alone, we can find empirical equations for determining C_{D_2}. We should not be surprised to find that these empirical equations for C_{D_2} are in terms of a Reynolds number.

We tow the model through the tank at a velocity that will make the Froude number equal in model and prototype and measure the drag force. We compute the Reynolds number and C_{D_2}, from an empirical equation, for the model. In Equation 7-11 we substitute the values of the drag force and C_{D_2} for the model, and we compute the C_{D_1} for the model. For the prototype we compute the Reynolds number and from this and the empirical equation we figure the value of C_{D_2}. Then we know both C_{D_1} and C_{D_2} for the prototype because C_{D_1} is the same as in the model. These we substitute in Equation 7-11 for the prototype. Then we compute the drag force for the prototype.

This is only one problem of one type of incomplete similarity. In this type all π terms could not be made equal in model and prototype.

Another type of incomplete similarity introduces a different force in the model and the prototype. One helpful use of models is to study rivers, harbors, and dams. To make a river model feasible we must use a scale of the order of 1000 ft of prototype to 1 ft of model which changes the depth of the model river to a fraction of an inch. With this shallow stream in the model, surface tension begins to have noticeable effect, whereas in the prototype it is negligible. The model, therefore, is not dynamically similar to the prototype. To solve problems of this nature, we find it necessary to use different scales for the horizontal and the vertical lengths. This is called a distorted model and is beyond the scope of this book.

We have by no means thoroughly covered dimensional analysis and model studies here. We direct the student to the references at the end of the book for more complete coverage.

At this point we should reiterate that dimensional analysis and model studies are effective methods which depend upon the engineer's knowledge of the phenomenon. If he should include too few quantities in his dimensional analysis of the problem, the answer will be incomplete and almost useless. If he includes too many quantities in his analysis, there will be no saving in time or money and it will be impossible to have complete similarity.

In most model studies' problems, complete dynamic similarity is impossible. This calls for a complete understanding of the phenomenon plus some ingenuity. It makes dimensional analysis and model studies powerful tools, but dangerous when used incorrectly.

PROBLEMS

7-1. Determine the dimensions of velocity V, density ρ, viscosity μ, and surface tension in an M, F, L system.

7-2. Determine the dimensions of torque, pressure, velocity, and acceleration in an F, V, L system.

7-3. Compute the dimensions of volume flow rate, temperature, horsepower, and length in an M, V, T, Θ system.

7-4. Calculate the dimensions of angular acceleration, velocity, engineering gas constant, and specific weight in a heat, force, time system. Heat is dimensionally equal to force times length.

7-5. Determine the dimensions of horsepower, velocity, acceleration, and shearing stress in terms of M, F, L.

7-6. Derive a set of independent dimensionless numbers made up of velocity, length, acceleration due to gravity, and mass density.

7-7. Derive a set of independent dimensionless numbers made up of surface tension, length, force, and velocity.

7-8. Derive a set of independent dimensionless numbers made up of velocity, sonic velocity, and mass density.

7-9. Derive a set of independent dimensionless numbers made up of the bulk modulus, mass density, velocity, and acceleration due to gravity.

7-10. Derive a set of independent dimensionless numbers made up of velocity, pressure, mass density, surface tension, and length.

7-11. The Prandtl number is a dimensionless combination of the specific heat c, the viscosity μ, and the thermal conductivity k. The dimensions of c are $FL/M\Theta$, the dimensions of μ are FT/L^2, and the dimensions of k are $H/TL\Theta$ where H is heat or thermal energy, T is time, and Θ is temperature. The relation between thermal energy and work is $H \stackrel{d}{=} FL$. Derive the Prandtl number.

7-12. The Weber number is a dimensionless combination of density ρ, velocity V, length l, and surface tension σ. Derive the Weber number.

7-13. The Peclet number is a dimensionless combination of velocity V, length l, density ρ, thermal conductivity k ($k \stackrel{d}{=} H/TL\Theta$), and specific heat at constant pressure c ($c \stackrel{d}{=} FL/M\Theta$). Derive the Peclet number.

7-14. The Nusselt number is a dimensionless combination of coefficient h, or heat transfer ($h \stackrel{\mathrm{d}}{=} H/TL^2\Theta$), length L, and thermal conductivity k ($k \stackrel{\mathrm{d}}{=} H/TL\Theta$). Derive the Nusselt number.

7-15. The Knudsen number is a dimensionless combination of the mean free path of molecules and a characteristic length. Derive the Knudsen number.

7-16. A dimensionless number seen frequently in gas dynamics and boundary layer theory is made up of kinematic viscosity ν, velocity V, distance y normal to surface, and distance x along the surface. Calculate the number.

7-17. Evaluate the determinant below.

$$\begin{vmatrix} 3 & 5 \\ 2 & 1 \end{vmatrix}$$

7-18. Evaluate the determinant below.

$$\begin{vmatrix} 1 & 0 \\ 5 & 0 \end{vmatrix}$$

7-19. Evaluate the determinant below.

$$\begin{vmatrix} 3 & 1 & 0 \\ 0 & 1 & -1 \\ 2 & 1 & 2 \end{vmatrix}$$

7-20. Evaluate the determinant below.

$$\begin{vmatrix} 2 & 2 & -2 \\ 0 & 1 & 0 \\ 3 & 5 & -18 \end{vmatrix}$$

7-21. Evaluate the determinant below.

$$\begin{vmatrix} 1 & 1 & 1 \\ 2 & -2 & 2 \\ 3 & 3 & 3 \end{vmatrix}$$

7-22. Evaluate the determinant below.

$$\begin{vmatrix} 2 & 1 & 0 & 0 \\ 1 & 0 & 0 & 0 \\ 3 & 5 & 2 & 1 \\ 0 & -3 & -1 & 0 \end{vmatrix}$$

7-23. Determine the rank of the matrix below.

$$\begin{vmatrix} 1 & 3 & 2 & 5 \\ 1 & -1 & 0 & 1 \\ 1 & 0 & 1 & 1 \end{vmatrix}$$

7-24. Determine the rank of the matrix below.

$$
\begin{vmatrix}
2 & -1 & 2 & 0 & 3 \\
4 & -2 & 4 & 0 & 6 \\
1 & 1 & -2 & 1 & 0
\end{vmatrix}
$$

7-25. Determine the rank of the matrix below.

$$
\begin{vmatrix}
1 & 1 & 1 & 1 & 1 & 1 \\
2 & 1 & 0 & 0 & 0 & 0 \\
0 & 1 & 0 & 0 & 0 & 0 \\
3 & 1 & 0 & 2 & 1 & 0
\end{vmatrix}
$$

7-26. Determine the rank of the matrix below

$$
\begin{vmatrix}
5 & 2 & 1 & 0 \\
3 & 0 & 0 & 1
\end{vmatrix}
$$

7-27. Determine the rank of the matrix below.

$$
\begin{vmatrix}
1 & 2 & -3 & 0 & 5 & 7 \\
-4 & 5 & 3 & 0 & 0 & 0 \\
2 & 4 & -6 & 0 & 10 & 14 \\
1 & 0 & 1 & 0 & 1 & 0
\end{vmatrix}
$$

7-28. Determine the rank of the matrix below.

$$
\begin{vmatrix}
3 & 3 & 3 \\
-1 & -1 & -1 \\
0 & 1 & 0
\end{vmatrix}
$$

7-29. Determine an expression for the velocity V of a bubble in a stationary liquid. The following variables are involved: density ρ, a length l, dynamic viscosity μ, and surface tension, σ. Surface tension σ has the dimensions of mass divided by time to the second power.

7-30. If the force necessary to propel a ship through water depends upon the size of the ship l, the viscosity μ, the density of the water ρ, the velocity of the ship V, and the acceleration due to gravity g, derive an expression for the drag force as a function of the other variables.

7-31. A pump of diameter d, rotating at an angular velocity ω, delivers a rate of flow Q of a fluid of density ρ. Derive by dimensional analysis an expression for power required in terms of the above variables.

7-32. The power output of a certain turbine is a function of the diameter of the turbine, the mass density of the liquid, the height of water above the turbine, the acceleration due to gravity, the revolutions per minute of the turbine, and the flow rate.   Derive an expression for the power output of the turbine.

7-33. Consider a rotating shaft in a well-lubricated bearing.   You judge that the tangential friction force R depends upon the normal force P on the shaft, the number of revolutions per unit time N, the viscosity of the lubricant, and the shaft diameter d.   Find a convenient set of variables, and write a formal expression for the relation among them.

7-34. Assume that the drag force on a submerged object in a viscous compressible fluid depends upon the velocity, viscosity, density, length, and sound velocity in the fluid.   Simplify the assumed dependence relation.

7-35. Derive an expression for the period T of vibration of a weight W on a spring that has a spring constant k.   The original displacement from equilibrium is x_o.

7-36. Derive an expression for the period T of vibration of the spring mass system in Problem 7-35 when there is a damping constant $c \overset{\mathrm{d}}{=} \mathrm{FT/L}$ to consider.

7-37. In the study of the transportation of discrete matter in a fluid the following variables are important: velocity V of the fluid, density ρ of the fluid, some length l of the boundaries of the fluid, viscosity μ of the fluid, some size d of the matter, the specific weight γ_m of the matter, standard deviation σ_d from the size of the matter, and concentration of the matter.   Derive a set of independent, dimensionless numbers for this phenomenon.

7-38. A star is assumed to be a liquid mass which is held together by its own gravity.   The star is free to vibrate in many ways, the most important of which is the vibration in which the surface of the star alternately assumes oblate and prolate forms which are symmetrical about a fixed axis.   This is assumed to be a frictionless vibration in which each particle performs simple harmonic motion.   Any such vibration has a natural frequency n which is constant and a function of the mass density ρ of the star, the diameter D of the star, and the gravitational constant k.   The dimensions of k are $\mathrm{M^{-1}L^3T^{-2}}$. Derive an expression for the natural frequency of the star.

7-39. Determine a formula for the velocity of raindrops which fall in still air.   The velocity v is a function of density ρ_w of water, density ρ_a of air, viscosity μ_a of air, diameter d of a drop, and the gravitational acceleration g.

7-40. The slipper bearing shown in Fig. 7-40 will support a certain load F. Derive an equation for F in terms of h, α, viscosity μ, velocity V, and length l.

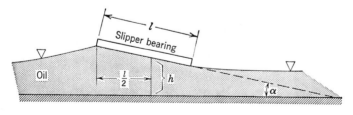

Fig. P.7-40

7-41. Derive an equation for the volume flow rate Q of a fluid through a rectangular channel of width w, depth d, average roughness e, and slope α.

7-42. A submarine 300 ft long travels at 20 mph while submerged in salt water. At what velocity must a 10 ft model be towed for dynamic similitude?

7-43. The dirigible "Hindenburg" was 600 ft long. A $\frac{1}{10}$ scale model is tested in a wind tunnel. The "Hindenburg" traveled 30 mph. At what velocity must the model operate in air for dynamic similitude?

7-44. An airplane wing of a chord length 10 ft moves 200 mph through still air at 60°F and 14.7 psia. Determine the velocity in a variable density wind tunnel when the pressure is 185 psi and the temperature is 60°F. Consider the viscosity as a function of only temperature. The model wing is 1 ft chord length. The drag force on the model is 100 lb. What is the drag force on the prototype?

7-45. To determine the wind forces on a sign 30 ft by 40 ft when the wind velocity is 20 mph, a model is tested in a wind tunnel. The length dimensions of the model are one-tenth that of the prototype. (*a*) Calculate the wind tunnel velocity to assure dynamic similarity between the model and prototype. (*b*) Determine the ratio of the wind forces on the model to the wind forces on the prototype.

7-46. It is necessary to make a model of a 100 ft high chimney to determine a relation between the angle through which the chimney will sway and the wind velocity. (*a*) Calculate the dimensionless ratios that should be taken into account and put them in the form of an equation for the angle of sway. (*b*) The sway of a model 4 ft high is $\frac{1}{4}$ ft. What is the sway of the prototype when dynamic similitude is maintained between model and prototype?

7-47. Spheres of different diameters and different specific weights are dropped in liquids of different properties. What dimensionless number must be the same in model and prototype for the flow around the spheres to be similar? The spheres fall freely under the attraction due to gravity.

7-48. Water is to be siphoned from a lake into a river. The pipe is to be 300 ft long, and the change in elevation between the lake surface and the river bed is 50 ft. A $\frac{1}{20}$ scale model is to be made of this siphon. The model pipe has a diameter of $1\frac{1}{2}$ in. The flow rate in the model is 0.13 cfs. What is the diameter of the prototype? Calculate the approximate flow rate.

7-49. A steel beam 50 ft long has a moment of inertia about the neutral axis of 560 in.[4] A load of 6 tons is to be placed on the beam. A $\frac{1}{10}$ scale model of the beam is made. Compute the magnitude of the load in the scale model for similar bending. The model deflects 0.0001 in. at the center. Compute the prototype deflection.

7-50. A $\frac{1}{10}$ scale model of a large valve is built to test the pressure drop across the valve when it is partially closed. If the velocity of the water in the prototype immediately in front of and immediately behind the valve is 10 fps, what is the velocity of the water for dynamic similitude in the model. Compute the pressure drop in the prototype when a pressure drop of 10 psi occurs in the model.

7-51. An airplane model built to one-sixteenth of the linear size of the prototype is to be tested in a wind tunnel at an air speed equal to the flying speed of the prototype. Calculate the pressure in the tunnel. The temperature is the same in model and prototype.

7-52. An ocean vessel 600 ft long is to travel at 12 knots. Calculate the speed of a model 15 ft long towed in water for studies of surface wave resistance.

7-53. Air at a specified temperature and pressure flows through a 3 in. dia. pipe at an average velocity of 100 fps. For dynamically similar flow, compute the average velocity for air at the same pressure and temperature when it flows in an 8 in. dia. pipe.

7-54. A gangster has bought an automobile with $\frac{3}{4}$ in. thick bulletproof glass in all windows. He does not know if the glass is bulletproof for all types of pistols. He cannot obtain anymore of the same glass. However, he does own a pane of the same type glass $\frac{1}{2}$ in. thick. A .32 automatic bullet barely breaks this glass. The bullet weighs 88 grains and travels 700 fps. Will a .38 automatic bullet weighing 158 grains and traveling 850 fps break the $\frac{3}{4}$ in. glass in his car?

7-55. In Problem 7-54 will a .45 automatic bullet break the automobile glass? The .45 slug weighs 230 grains and travels 850 fps.

7-56. In Problem 7-54 will a .357 magnum slug weighing 158 grains and traveling 1430 fps break the glass?

POTENTIAL FLOW

53. Introduction

The introduction to Chapter 1 mentions the work of the mathematicians and other theoretical men. This chapter considers some of the results of their work which had to be done with a nonexistent, incompressible, frictionless fluid called an ideal fluid.

In many flow problems, the changes in fluid density are small enough to be neglected. All problems of liquid flow under normal pressures in conduits, liquid flow around bodies such as ships and abutments, and gas flow where pressure changes are slight and the velocity is less than about 300 mph are considered problems of incompressible flow. Equation 3-18 shows the correction for compressibility effects on a streamline. Therefore, the limitation of constant density, which is incompressible flow, still leaves many problems in which potential flow analysis is valid. The limitation of a frictionless fluid was a much more severe restriction until Ludwig Prandtl postulated the boundary layer theory. Simply stated, he showed that all flow outside a very thin layer adjacent to solid boundaries may be considered frictionless and that all friction occurs inside the thin layer called the boundary layer.

All the fluid outside the boundary layer, therefore, may be considered ideal fluid if it does not undergo high pressure changes or move at velocities exceeding 300 mph. We should always keep in mind that this use of an ideal fluid is a reasonably correct approximation under the stated conditions. These conditions leave many problems of flow around objects or inside objects which we can solve approximately by the method of potential flow. We correct the analysis when the pressure changes or when the velocities become too great for the fluid to be considered an ideal fluid. We do not discuss such corrections in this book, but the student must know that the general approach applies to supersonic as well as subsonic flow.

To make the work less complicated, we deal primarily with two-dimensional flow in this book. Furthermore, we restrict the analysis to a cartesian coordinate axis system. We could use spherical or cylindrical axis systems, but they entail difficulties in which we do not become involved.

54. Continuity

We select a cube Δx by Δy by Δz (Fig. 71) which is a control volume with its center at point x, y, z in an orthogonal x, y, z axis system. The

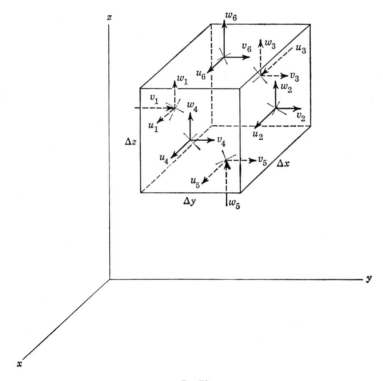

Fig. 71

fluid flowing through the cube has a velocity q at the center of the cube at time t. The velocity q is a vector with three components u, v, and w in the x, y, and z directions respectively. The velocity components of q appear on each face of the control volume.   We apply the general continuity equation to this control volume.

$$0 = \frac{M_2' - M_1'}{dt} + \int_A \rho V \cos \theta \, dA \tag{8-1}$$

This equation is the same as Equation 3-5.

The velocity q at each surface of the control volume breaks down into three x, y, z components at that surface.   At time t the density of the fluid at the center of the cube is ρ_1' and at time $t + \Delta t$ the density at the center of the cube has changed to ρ_2'.   In Equation 8-1 now

$$M_1' = \rho_1' \, \Delta x \, \Delta y \, \Delta z$$

$$M_2' = \rho_2' \, \Delta x \, \Delta y \, \Delta z$$

and

$$\frac{M_2' - M_1'}{\Delta t} = \frac{\rho_2' - \rho_1'}{\Delta t} \Delta x \, \Delta y \, \Delta z \tag{8-2}$$

To evaluate $\int_A \rho V \cos \theta \, dA$ in Equation 8-1, we first apply it to surface 1 on which we number the subscripts 1.

$$\int_{A_1} \rho V \cos \theta \, dA = \left[u_1 \cos \frac{\pi}{2} \rho_1 + \rho_1 v_1 \cos \pi + \rho_1 w_1 \cos \frac{\pi}{2} \right] \Delta x \, \Delta z$$

$$= - \rho_1 v_1 \, \Delta x \, \Delta z$$

We do the same to surface number 2 to get

$$\int_{A_2} \rho V \cos \theta \, dA = \left[\rho_2 u_2 \cos \frac{\pi}{2} + \rho_2 v_2 (\cos 0) + \rho_2 w_2 \left(\cos \frac{\pi}{2} \right) \right] \Delta x \, \Delta z$$

$$= \rho_2 v_2 \, \Delta x \, \Delta z$$

We continue in this manner until we account for all six surfaces of the cube and arrive at

$$\int_A \rho V \cos \theta \, dA = \int_{A_1} \rho V \cos \theta \, dA + \int_{A_2} \rho V \cos \theta \, dA$$

$$+ \int_{A_3} \rho V \cos \theta \, dA + \int_{A_4} \rho V \cos \theta \, dA + \int_{A_5} \rho V \cos \theta \, dA$$

$$+ \int_{A_6} \rho V \cos \theta \, dA$$

$$\int_A \rho V \cos \theta \, dA = (\rho_2 v_2 - \rho_1 v_1) \, \Delta x \, \Delta z + (\rho_4 u_4 - \rho_3 u_3) \, \Delta y \, \Delta z$$

$$+ (\rho_6 w_6 - \rho_5 w_5) \, \Delta x \, \Delta y \tag{8-3}$$

We obtain Equation 8-4 by substituting Equations 8-2 and 8-3 into Equation 8-1.

$$0 = \frac{\rho_2' - \rho_1'}{\Delta t} \Delta x \, \Delta y \, \Delta z + (\rho_2 v_2 - \rho_1 v_1) \, \Delta x \, \Delta z + (\rho_4 u_4 - \rho_3 u_3) \, \Delta y \, \Delta z$$
$$+ (\rho_6 w_6 - \rho_5 w_5) \, \Delta x \, \Delta y = 0 \quad (8\text{-}4)$$

We divide Equation 8-4 by the volume $\Delta x \, \Delta y \, \Delta z$.

$$0 = \frac{\rho_2' - \rho_1'}{\Delta t} + \frac{(\rho_2 v_2 - \rho_1 v_1)}{\Delta y} + \frac{(\rho_4 u_4 - \rho_3 u_3)}{\Delta x} + \frac{(\rho_6 w_6 - \rho_5 w_5)}{\Delta z}$$

and take the limit of this as $\Delta x \to 0$, $\Delta y \to 0$, $\Delta z \to 0$, and $\Delta t \to 0$.

$$0 = \lim_{\Delta t \to 0} \frac{\rho_2' - \rho_1'}{\Delta t} + \lim_{\Delta y \to 0} \frac{\rho_2 v_2 - \rho_1 v_1}{\Delta y} + \lim_{\Delta x \to 0} \frac{\rho_4 u_4 - \rho_3 u_3}{\Delta x}$$
$$+ \lim_{\Delta z \to 0} \frac{\rho_6 w_6 - \rho_5 w_5}{\Delta z}$$

By definition of a partial derivative

$$0 = \frac{\partial \rho}{\partial t} + \frac{\partial (\rho v)}{\partial y} + \frac{\partial (\rho u)}{\partial x} + \frac{\partial (\rho w)}{\partial z} \quad (8\text{-}5)$$

For an ideal fluid ρ is a constant, and we may take it outside of the partial derivative sign and divide by ρ to get the differential equation of continuity for an incompressible fluid in three dimensions.

$$0 = \frac{\partial u}{\partial x} + \frac{\partial v}{\partial y} + \frac{\partial w}{\partial z} \quad (8\text{-}6)$$

Since we use only the two dimensions x and y, Equation 8-6 in these two dimensions is

$$0 = \frac{\partial u}{\partial x} + \frac{\partial v}{\partial y} \quad (8\text{-}7)$$

For unsteady flow, u and v are functions of x, y, and t. For steady flow in two dimensions

$$u = u(x, y)$$
$$v = v(x, y)$$

Illustrative Problems 1 and 2, to a limited extent, demonstrate the uses of Equation 8-7.

▶**Illustrative Problem 1.**   The velocity components of a steady two-dimensional, incompressible flow may be represented by

$$u = ky + 1$$
$$v = kx + 4$$

Determine if this is a possible flow.

Solution: You must satisfy the equation of continuity for a steady incompressible flow for the flow to be possible.   Because this is two-dimensional flow, use Equation 8-7.

$$\frac{\partial u}{\partial x} + \frac{\partial v}{\partial y} = 0$$

$$\frac{\partial u}{\partial x} = \frac{\partial(ky + 1)}{\partial x} = 0, \qquad \frac{\partial v}{\partial y} = \frac{\partial(kx + 4)}{\partial y} = 0$$

Substituting these values into Equation 8-7 gives

$$\frac{\partial u}{\partial x} + \frac{\partial v}{\partial y} = 0 + 0 = 0$$

which satisfies continuity.   ◀

▶**Illustrative Problem 2.**   Determine which of the following functions of u and v are possible steady incompressible flow.

(a) $$u = kxy + y$$
$$v = kxy + x$$

(b) $$u = x^2 + y^2$$
$$v = -2xy$$

(c) $$u = xy^2 + x + y^2$$
$$v = x(x - y) + 3y^3$$

Solution: You must satisfy Equation 8-7 to enable the foregoing to be possible steady flows of an incompressible fluid.

(a) $$\frac{\partial u}{\partial x} = \frac{\partial(kxy + y)}{\partial x} = ky$$

$$\frac{\partial v}{\partial y} = \frac{\partial(kxy + x)}{\partial y} = kx$$

$$\frac{\partial u}{\partial x} + \frac{\partial v}{\partial y} = ky + kx \neq 0$$

Therefore, this is not a possible flow.

(b)
$$\frac{\partial u}{\partial x} = \frac{\partial(x^2 + y^2)}{\partial x} = 2x$$

$$\frac{\partial v}{\partial y} = \frac{\partial(-2xy)}{\partial y} = -2x$$

$$\frac{\partial u}{\partial x} = \frac{\partial v}{\partial y} = 2x - 2x = 0$$

which satisfies Equation 8-7.   Therefore, this is a possible flow.

(c)
$$\frac{\partial u}{\partial x} = \frac{\partial(xy^2 + x + y^2)}{\partial x} = y^2 + 1$$

$$\frac{\partial v}{\partial y} = \frac{\partial[x(x - y) + 3y^3]}{\partial y} = -x + 9y^2$$

$$\frac{\partial u}{\partial x} + \frac{\partial v}{\partial y} = y^2 + 1 - x + 9y^2 = 10y^2 - x + 1 \rightarrow \text{Not zero}$$

Therefore, this is not a possible flow.   ◀

55. Irrotational Flow

In the flow of a two-dimensional fluid, we select point P and draw two perpendicular lines PB and PA which are fixed to the fluid to move with it.   After time Δt the lines are in the new position $A_1P_1B_1$ (Fig. 72).   We select an axis system such that the axes are parallel to the original position of the perpendicular lines and the angular rotation of the fluid immediately adjacent to point P is $\frac{1}{2}(\beta_1 + \beta_2)$. We define the rate of rotation of the fluid, therefore, as

$$\omega = \frac{1}{2}\left(\frac{\beta_1 + \beta_2}{\Delta t}\right) \qquad (8\text{-}8)$$

It is called simply "rotation" and is about an axis normal to the xy plane.

When the two lines AP and BP are part of a solid that is rotating, they must move through the same angle $\omega_1 \Delta t$ where ω_1 is the angular rotation of the body.   The angles β_1 and β_2 of rotation both equal $\omega_1 \Delta t$.   We substitute these in Equation 8-8 to get

$$\omega = \frac{1}{2}\left(\frac{\beta_1 + \beta_2}{\Delta t}\right) = \frac{1}{2}\left(\frac{\omega_1 \Delta t + \omega_1 \Delta t}{\Delta t}\right) = \omega_1$$

Therefore, we see that ω is the angular rotation of a solid.

The velocity of the fluid at point P is u in the x direction and v in the y direction, and we choose the length of the normal lines as Δx

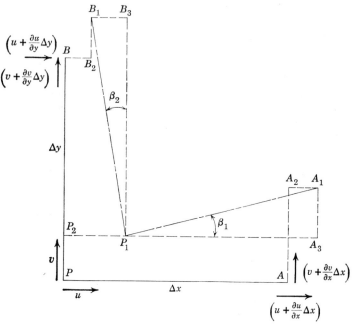

Fig. 72

and Δy. Thus, the velocity components of point B are

$$u + \frac{\partial u}{\partial y} \Delta y \quad \text{in the } x \text{ direction}$$

and

$$v + \frac{\partial v}{\partial y} \Delta y \quad \text{in the } y \text{ direction.}$$

Because the angle β_2 is small, it equals the tangent of the angle.

$$\tan \beta_2 = \frac{\overline{B_1 B_3}}{\overline{P_1 B_3}}$$

$$\tan \beta_2 = \beta_2 = \frac{\overline{B_1 B_3}}{\overline{P_1 B_3}}$$

The distance from B_1 to B_3 must equal $\overline{P_1P_2} - \overline{BB_2}$. In time Δt, point P moves in the x direction a distance equal to the velocity u in the x direction times the time Δt, equal to $\overline{P_1P_2}$. Therefore,

$$\overline{P_1P_2} = u\,\Delta t$$

In the same time, point B moves a distance $\overline{BB_2}$ in the x direction equal to the product of the velocity $u + (\partial u/\partial y)\,\Delta y$ of B in the x direction and the time Δt. Therefore,

$$\overline{BB_2} = \left(u + \frac{\partial u}{\partial y}\,\Delta y\right)\Delta t$$

From the preceding,

$$\overline{B_1B_3} = \overline{P_1P_2} - \overline{BB_2}$$

$$= u\,\Delta t - \left(u + \frac{\partial u}{\partial y}\,\Delta y\right)\Delta t$$

$$= -\frac{\partial u}{\partial y}\,\Delta y\,\Delta t$$

The new length $\overline{P_1B_3}$ of the line PB is Δy plus some small increment which can be neglected. We substitute this into the equation for β_2 to obtain

$$\beta_2 = \frac{\overline{B_1B_3}}{\overline{P_1B_3}} = \frac{-\dfrac{\partial u}{\partial y}\,\Delta y\,\Delta t}{\Delta y} = -\frac{\partial u}{\partial y}\,\Delta t \tag{8-9}$$

By similar reasoning

$$\beta_1 = \frac{\overline{A_1A_3}}{\overline{P_1A_3}}$$

where $$\overline{A_1A_3} = \left(v + \frac{\partial v}{\partial x}\,\Delta x\right)\Delta t - v\,\Delta t = \frac{\partial v}{\partial x}\,\Delta x\,\Delta t$$

$$\overline{P_1A_3} = \Delta x$$

Thus,

$$\beta_1 = \frac{\dfrac{\partial v}{\partial x}\,\Delta x\,\Delta t}{\Delta x} = \frac{\partial v}{\partial x}\,\Delta t \tag{8-10}$$

The following expression for rotation results when we substitute Equations 8-9 and 8-10 into Equation 8-8.

$$\omega_z = \frac{1}{2} \frac{\left(\dfrac{\partial v}{\partial x} \Delta t - \dfrac{\partial u}{\partial y} \Delta t \right)}{\Delta t} \tag{8-11}$$

$$\omega_z = \frac{1}{2} \left(\frac{\partial v}{\partial x} - \frac{\partial u}{\partial y} \right) \tag{8-12}$$

When the particles of the fluid are not rotating, the rotation is zero and the fluid is called irrotational. We can best illustrate the physical

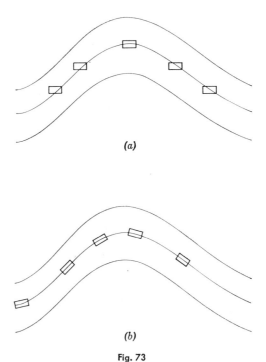

(a)

(b)

Fig. 73

meaning of irrotational flow by sketching two flows, one irrotational (Fig. 73a) and one not (Fig. 73b). On the middle streamline in both figures we see the orientation of a particle as it moves along the streamline. In Fig. 73a the particle does not rotate (irrotational flow) but maintains the same orientation everywhere along the streamline. In Fig. 73b the particle rotates with respect to a fixed axis but maintains the same orientation with respect to the streamline. Thus, the flow is not irrotational. In both figures the particles can undergo deformation without affecting the analysis.

We assume that some function ϕ of x and y exists such that, when we differentiate it in any direction, the result at any point is the negative velocity in the direction at that point.

$$u = -\frac{\partial \phi}{\partial x} \qquad (8\text{-}13a)$$

$$v = -\frac{\partial \phi}{\partial y} \qquad (8\text{-}13b)$$

The function ϕ is called the velocity potential.

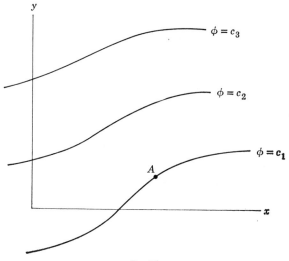

Fig. 74

Figure 74 is a sketch of a family of curves in which ϕ is set equal to various constants and A is a point on the curve $\phi = c_1$. When we differentiate ϕ in the s direction along the curve, the derivative equals zero because ϕ is constant along this curve. Consequently, the velocity at A must be normal to the curve $\phi = c_1$. The same reasoning applies to all points on all curves of ϕ equal to a constant. Therefore, the flow is always normal to the curves $\phi = $ a constant. We can draw a family of curves ϕ set equal to different constants for any function ϕ. Since the velocity is everywhere normal to this family of curves, we can draw a second family of curves everywhere normal to the first family, and, thus, the velocities are everywhere tangent to the second family of curves. This is the definition of a streamline.

Accordingly, we can draw streamlines for the flow represented by each function ϕ. These two families of curves, one family in the velocity direction and the other normal to it, are called a flow net. From each function ϕ it is possible to draw the flow net and to compute the velocity at any point in the flow.

We substitute the velocity components u and v in terms of the velocity potential ϕ into Equation 8-12 for irrotational flow.

$$u = -\frac{\partial \phi}{\partial x}, \qquad v = -\frac{\partial \phi}{\partial y}$$

$$\frac{\partial v}{\partial x} - \frac{\partial u}{\partial y} = \frac{\partial\left(-\dfrac{\partial \phi}{\partial y}\right)}{\partial x} - \frac{\partial\left(-\dfrac{\partial \phi}{\partial x}\right)}{\partial y} = -\frac{\partial^2 \phi}{\partial x\, \partial y} + \frac{\partial^2 \phi}{\partial x\, \partial y}$$

$$= 0$$

Hence, the velocity potential satisfies irrotational flow, and the existence of a velocity potential assures us that the flow is irrotational.

Equation 8-7 is the equation of continuity because the flow is two dimensional. We substitute Equations 8-13a and 8-13b into it to get

$$\frac{\partial u}{\partial x} + \frac{\partial v}{\partial y} = 0$$

$$\frac{\partial\left(-\dfrac{\partial \phi}{\partial x}\right)}{\partial x} + \frac{\partial\left(-\dfrac{\partial \phi}{\partial y}\right)}{\partial y} = -\frac{\partial^2 \phi}{\partial x^2} - \frac{\partial^2 \phi}{\partial y^2} = 0$$

$$\frac{\partial^2 \phi}{\partial x^2} + \frac{\partial^2 \phi}{\partial y^2} = 0 \tag{8-14}$$

All velocity potentials must satisfy Equation 8-14, the Laplace equation, in order to satisfy the principle of conservation of mass. All functions that satisfy the Laplace equation may be considered velocity potentials. Because in fluid mechanics we can use only functions that satisfy the Laplace equation, hereafter a function to be a velocity potential must satisfy it.

We used Equation 8-7 for incompressible fluids, and all velocity potentials automatically presuppose irrotational flow. Therefore, the existence of a velocity potential that satisfies the Laplace equation may be considered the velocity potential for the flow of an incompressible, irrotational fluid. Illustrative Problem 3 gives an indication of the use of the velocity potential.

▶**Illustrative Problem 3.** Determine which of the following functions represent a possible velocity potential, and sketch the flow pattern for these possible cases.

(a) $\qquad\qquad\qquad f = Ux$

(b) $\qquad\qquad\qquad f = Vy$

(c) $\qquad\qquad\qquad f = Kx^3$

(d) $\qquad\qquad\qquad f = \sin(x + y)$

Solution: (a)

$$f = Ux$$

This function must represent a flow field that satisfies the equation of continuity in order to be a possible velocity potential, which means it must satisfy Laplace's equation.

$$\frac{\partial^2 f}{\partial x^2} + \frac{\partial^2 f}{\partial y^2} = 0$$

$$\frac{\partial^2 f}{\partial x^2} = \frac{\partial^2(Ux)}{\partial x^2} = 0$$

$$\frac{\partial^2 f}{\partial y^2} = \frac{\partial^2(Ux)}{\partial y^2} = 0$$

or

$$0 + 0 = 0$$

This function is a velocity potential.

(b) $\qquad\qquad\qquad f = Vy$

This function also must satisfy the Laplace equation.

$$\frac{\partial^2 f}{\partial x^2} = \frac{\partial^2(Vy)}{\partial x^2} = 0; \qquad \frac{\partial^2 f}{\partial y^2} = \frac{\partial^2(Vy)}{\partial y^2} = 0$$

The Laplace equation is

$$\frac{\partial^2 f}{\partial x^2} + \frac{\partial^2 f}{\partial y^2} = 0$$

Substitute for f to get

$$\frac{\partial^2(Vy)}{\partial x^2} + \frac{\partial^2(Vy)}{\partial y^2} = 0 + 0 = 0$$

This function is a velocity potential.

(c)
$$f = Kx^3$$

$$\frac{\partial^2 f}{\partial x^2} + \frac{\partial^2 f}{\partial y^2} = \frac{\partial^2 (Kx^3)}{\partial x^2} + \frac{\partial^2 (Kx^3)}{\partial y^2} = 6Kx$$

This does not satisfy the Laplace equation for it does not equal zero, and, accordingly, it is not a possible velocity potential.

(d)
$$f = \sin (x + y)$$

$$\sin (x + y) = \sin x \cos y + \cos x \sin y$$

$$\frac{\partial^2 f}{\partial x^2} = \frac{\partial^2 (\sin x \cos y + \cos x \sin y)}{\partial x^2} = - \sin x \cos y - \cos x \sin y$$

$$\frac{\partial^2 f}{\partial y^2} = \frac{\partial^2 (\sin x \cos y + \cos x \sin y)}{\partial y^2} = - \sin x \cos y - \cos x \sin y$$

By substituting these values of $\partial^2 f/\partial x^2$ and $\partial^2 f/\partial y^2$ into the Laplace equation, you get

$$(- \sin x \cos y - \cos x \sin y) + (- \sin x \cos y - \cos x \sin y) = 0$$

$$-2 \sin x \cos y - 2 \cos x \sin y = 0$$

$$2 \sin(x + y) = 0$$

which is not necessarily true, and so $f = \sin (x + y)$ is not a velocity potential.

The functions

$$f = Ux$$

$$f = Vy$$

are velocity potentials. Figure 75a is a sketch of the flow pattern represented by $\phi = Ux$. The vertical dotted lines are lines of constant ϕ called equipotential lines. The horizontal lines are everywhere normal to the equipotential lines and, hence, are streamlines. You compute the velocity at any point from the definition of the velocity potential.

$$u = -\frac{\partial \phi}{\partial x}, \qquad v = -\frac{\partial \phi}{\partial y}$$

Consequently,

$$u = -\frac{\partial (Ux)}{\partial x} = -U$$

$$v = -\frac{\partial (Ux)}{\partial y} = 0$$

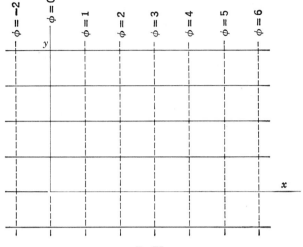

Fig. 75a

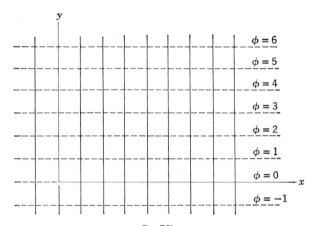

Fig. 75b

The velocity potential $\phi = Ux$ represents horizontal flow of an ideal fluid from higher to lower values of x at a constant velocity U.

Figure 75b is a sketch of the flow pattern represented by $\phi = Vy$. In this case, the horizontal lines are equipotential lines and the vertical lines are streamlines.   Compute velocity as before.

$$u = -\frac{\partial \phi}{\partial x} = -\frac{\partial (Vy)}{\partial x} = 0$$

$$v = -\frac{\partial \phi}{\partial y} = -\frac{\partial (Vy)}{\partial y} = -V$$

Therefore, the flow, with a constant velocity V, is in the negative y direction. ◀

56. Solution to the Laplace Equation

We shall find it beneficial to examine properties of the various solutions before we continue with more difficult solutions of the Laplace equation. We shall assume that ϕ_1 and ϕ_2 are both solutions to the Laplace equation which means

$$\frac{\partial^2 \phi_1}{\partial x^2} + \frac{\partial^2 \phi_1}{\partial y^2} = 0$$

and

$$\frac{\partial^2 \phi_2}{\partial x^2} + \frac{\partial^2 \phi_2}{\partial y^2} = 0$$

We multiply ϕ_1 by a constant c which gives a new function $c\phi_1$ that we substitute into the Laplace equation to find out if the new function is a solution.

$$\frac{\partial^2 (c\phi_1)}{\partial x^2} + \frac{\partial^2 (c\phi_1)}{\partial y^2} = 0$$

Because it is a constant, we take c outside of the derivative which gives

$$c\,\frac{\partial^2 \phi_1}{\partial x^2} + c\,\frac{\partial^2 \phi_1}{\partial y^2} = c\left\{\frac{\partial^2 \phi_1}{\partial x^2} + \frac{\partial^2 \phi_1}{\partial y^2}\right\}$$

The $(\partial^2 \phi_1 / \partial x^2) + (\partial^2 \phi_1 / \partial y^2)$ is zero by definition and, consequently,

$$\frac{\partial^2 (c\phi_1)}{\partial x^2} + \frac{\partial^2 (c\phi_1)}{\partial y^2} = 0$$

Therefore, the product of a constant and a solution to the Laplace equation is also a solution to the Laplace equation.

Next, we try adding a constant to a solution of the Laplace equation which gives $\phi = \phi_1 + c$.

$$\frac{\partial^2 \phi}{\partial x^2} + \frac{\partial^2 \phi}{\partial y^2} = \frac{\partial^2 (\phi_1 + c)}{\partial x^2} + \frac{\partial^2 (\phi_1 + c)}{\partial y^2}$$

$$= \frac{\partial^2 \phi_1}{\partial x^2} + \frac{\partial^2 \phi_1}{\partial y^2} + \frac{\partial^2 c}{\partial x^2} + \frac{\partial^2 c}{\partial y^2}$$

The terms $\partial^2 c/\partial x^2$ and $\partial^2 c/\partial y^2$ are both zero because c is a constant, leaving

$$\frac{\partial^2(\phi_1 + c)}{\partial x^2} + \frac{\partial^2(\phi_1 + c)}{\partial y^2} = \frac{\partial^2 \phi_1}{\partial x^2} + \frac{\partial^2 \phi_1}{\partial y^2} = 0$$

This equals zero because ϕ_1 is by definition a solution to the Laplace equation. We see, therefore, that a constant plus a solution to the Laplace equation gives a new solution to the Laplace equation.

Next we consider a function ϕ which is the sum of two different solutions to the Laplace equation, $\phi = \phi_1 + \phi_2$. We substitute ϕ in the Laplace equation to obtain

$$\frac{\partial^2 \phi}{\partial x^2} + \frac{\partial^2 \phi}{\partial y^2} = \frac{\partial^2(\phi_1 + \phi_2)}{\partial x^2} + \frac{\partial^2(\phi_1 + \phi_2)}{\partial y^2}$$

$$= \underbrace{\frac{\partial^2 \phi_1}{\partial x^2} + \frac{\partial^2 \phi_1}{\partial y^2}}_{0} + \underbrace{\frac{\partial^2 \phi_2}{\partial x^2} + \frac{\partial^2 \phi_2}{\partial y^2}}_{0}$$

$$= 0$$

which equals zero because ϕ_1 and ϕ_2 are solutions to the Laplace equation.

We see, furthermore, that the sum of two solutions to the Laplace equation, that the sum of a solution and a constant, and that the product of a solution and a constant are solutions to the Laplace equation.

Illustrative Problem 4 exemplifies the sum of two velocity potentials.

▶**Illustrative Problem 4.** In Illustrative Problem 3, parts a and b were solutions to the Laplace equation and, hence, were velocity potentials. Prove that the sum of these two velocity potentials is a third velocity potential and explain the flow pattern that this new velocity potential represents.

Solution: From Illustrative Problem 3a

$$\phi_1 = Ux$$

and from Illustrative Problem 3b

$$\phi_2 = Vy$$

New velocity potential ϕ is

$$\phi = Ux + Vy$$

You know that the sum of two velocity potentials is a third one, and, therefore, ϕ is a solution to the Laplace equation. Check this statement once to demonstrate that it is correct.

$$\frac{\partial^2(Ux + Vy)}{\partial x^2} + \frac{\partial^2(Ux + Vy)}{\partial y^2} = 0$$

$$\frac{\partial U}{\partial x} + \frac{\partial V}{\partial y} = 0 + 0 = 0$$

It checks as you know it must.

To explain the flow pattern corresponding to $\phi = Ux + Vy$, first sketch the equipotential lines.

$$\phi = Ux + Vy = c_1$$

$$y = -\frac{U}{V}x + \frac{c_1}{V}$$

This is the equation of a family of straight lines with a slope $-U/V$. The streamlines are normal to the equipotential lines and must have a slope equal to the negative reciprocal of the slope of the equipotential lines. The streamlines also are a family of straight lines.

$$y = \frac{V}{U}x + c_2$$

where c_2 is a different constant for each straight line. Figure 76 is a sketch of the streamlines and equipotential lines.

From the velocity potential definition

$$u = -\frac{\partial \phi}{\partial x}$$

$$v = -\frac{\partial \phi}{\partial y}$$

Thus,

$$u = -\frac{\partial(Ux + Vy)}{\partial x} = -U$$

$$v = -\frac{\partial(Ux + Vy)}{\partial y} = -V$$

Point 1 (Fig. 76) is arbitrary and shows the components of the velocity which are constant throughout the field. The velocity is the

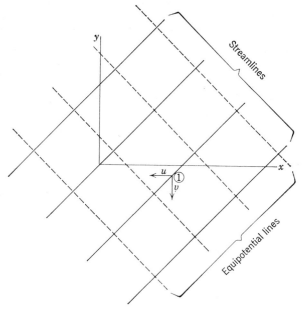

Fig. 76

vector sum of the components which means that the magnitude $|q|$ is

$$|q| = \sqrt{U^2 + V^2}$$

Figure 76 also shows that the flow is downward to the left at a slope V/U. ◀

57. Application to Flow of Fluid in a Corner

This article investigates the velocity potential

$$\phi = A(x^2 - y^2)$$

where A is a real constant. We check to see if it satisfies the Laplace equation to be certain that it is a velocity potential.

$$\frac{\partial^2\phi}{\partial x^2} + \frac{\partial^2\phi}{\partial y^2} = 2A - 2A = 0$$

It checks and so we know $\phi = A(x^2 - y^2)$ is a velocity potential. Figure 77 is a sketch of the equipotential lines

$$A(x^2 - y^2) = \text{constant}$$

and streamlines in the first quadrant which are obtained by drawing curves everywhere normal to the equipotential lines. Both the x and y axes are streamlines.

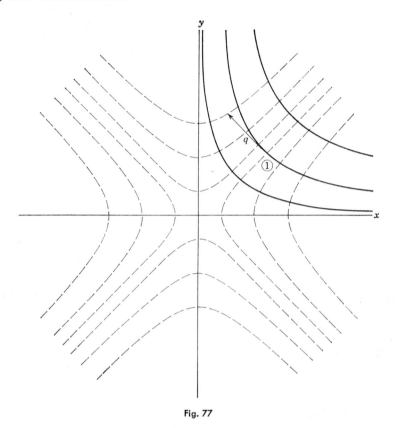

Fig. 77

We compute the velocities from the velocity potential to determine the direction and velocity of flow.

$$u = -\frac{\partial \phi}{\partial x} = -\frac{\partial A (x^2 - y^2)}{\partial x} = -2Ax \qquad (8\text{-}15a)$$

$$v = -\frac{\partial \phi}{\partial y} = -\frac{\partial A (x^2 - y^2)}{\partial y} = 2Ay \qquad (8\text{-}15b)$$

The magnitude of the velocity is

$$|q| = \sqrt{u^2 + v^2} = 2A \sqrt{x^2 + y^2} \qquad (8\text{-}16)$$

We select point 1 (Fig. 77) at $x = 1$ and $y = 1$. From Equations 8-15a, 8-15b, and 8-16 we compute

$$u_1 = -2A, \qquad v_1 = 2A$$

$$q_1 = 2\sqrt{2}\,A$$

The vector q_1 (Fig. 77, point 1) is the only possible vector that will satisfy $u_1 = -2A$, $v_1 = 2A$, which indicates that the fluid flows from the positive x direction in toward the origin and then out the positive y axis. Since both axes are streamlines, no fluid crosses them; the x and y axes may be considered solid boundaries because no fluid can cross a solid boundary. Figure 78 is a sketch of Fig. 77 with the positive x and y axes shown as solid boundaries and the streamlines sketched in to show how the fluid would flow into a 90° corner if the fluid at infinity were flowing parallel to one of the walls.

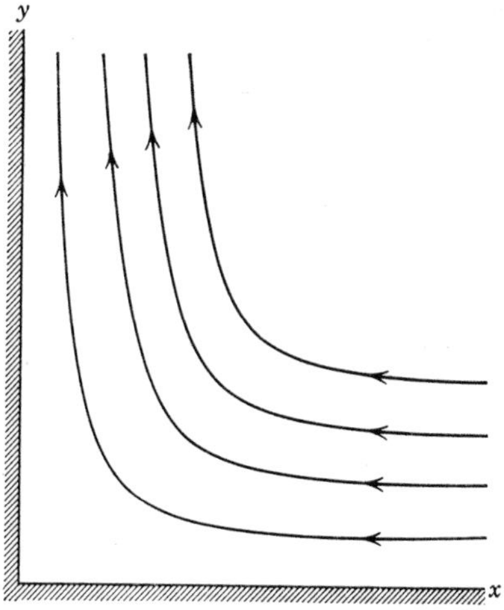

Thus, the velocity potential

$$\phi = A\,(x^2 - y^2)$$

represents the flow we have just described, and we may compute the velocity at any point by Equations 8-15a, 8-15b, and 8-16.

Fig. 78

In this article we introduced the concept that a streamline can be considered a solid boundary. In the foregoing example we took the x and y axes as the boundary, but we could just as well have selected any other streamline to represent a real boundary in a problem. The solid boundary must be a streamline, however.

58. Application of Bernoulli Equation

Figure 79 shows forces in the x direction which may act on an elemental cube Δx, Δy, Δz of an ideal fluid. Surface forces and body forces are the two types of forces which act on the element. For an ideal fluid the shear forces are zero so that the only surface forces are pressure forces. The body forces are forces which depend upon the mass of the body, such as weight and electromagnetic forces. We shall assume that the body force F_{B_x}, F_{B_y}, and F_{B_z} may be written as

$$F_{B_x} = -\frac{\partial \Omega}{\partial x}\, \rho\, \Delta x\, \Delta y\, \Delta z$$

$$F_{B_y} = -\frac{\partial \Omega}{\partial y}\, \rho\, \Delta x\, \Delta y\, \Delta z$$

$$F_{B_z} = -\frac{\partial \Omega}{\partial z}\, \rho\, \Delta x\, \Delta y\, \Delta z$$

where Ω is called the body force potential.

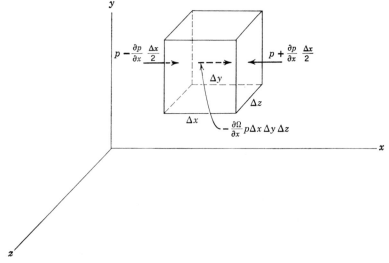

Fig. 79

We know from Newton's second law that the sum of the forces on a body in any direction equals the product of the mass of the body and its acceleration.

$$\Sigma F_x = m a_x$$

We sum the forces on the cube in the x direction and obtain

$$\sum F_x = \left(p - \frac{\partial p}{\partial x}\frac{\Delta x}{2}\right)\Delta y\, \Delta z - \frac{\partial \Omega}{\partial x}\,\rho\,\Delta x\,\Delta y\,\Delta z - \left(p + \frac{\partial p}{\partial x}\frac{\Delta x}{2}\right)\Delta y\, \Delta z$$

$$= -\frac{\partial p}{\partial x}\,\Delta x\,\Delta y\,\Delta z - \frac{\partial \Omega}{\partial x}\,\rho\,\Delta x\,\Delta y\,\Delta z$$

The mass of the cube is $m = \rho \, \Delta x \, \Delta y \, \Delta z$. We substitute these into Newton's second law to get

$$- \frac{\partial p}{\partial x} \Delta x \, \Delta y \, \Delta z - \frac{\partial \Omega}{\partial x} \rho \, \Delta x \, \Delta y \, \Delta z = (\rho \, \Delta x \, \Delta y \, \Delta z) a_x \qquad (8\text{-}17)$$

The acceleration a in the x direction is the rate of change of velocity u. We know from calculus that the change of velocity du is

$$du = \frac{\partial u}{\partial x} dx + \frac{\partial u}{\partial y} dy + \frac{\partial u}{\partial z} dz + \frac{\partial u}{\partial t} dt$$

The rate of change is du divided by the time dt. Therefore,

$$a_x = \frac{du}{dt} = \frac{\partial u}{\partial x} \frac{dx}{dt} + \frac{\partial u}{\partial y} \frac{dy}{dt} + \frac{\partial u}{\partial z} \frac{dz}{dt} + \frac{\partial u}{\partial t} \frac{dt}{dt} \qquad (W)$$

We also know that

$$u = \frac{dx}{dt}, \qquad v = \frac{dy}{dt}, \qquad w = \frac{dz}{dt}$$

and, when we substitute these into Equation W, the acceleration a_x becomes

$$a_x = u \frac{\partial u}{\partial x} + v \frac{\partial u}{\partial y} + w \frac{\partial u}{\partial z} + \frac{\partial u}{\partial t}$$

This expression we substitute for a_x in Equation 8-17 to get

$$- \frac{\partial p}{\partial x} \Delta x \, \Delta y \, \Delta z - \frac{\partial \Omega}{\partial x} \rho \, \Delta x \, \Delta y \, \Delta z$$

$$= \rho (\Delta x \, \Delta y \, \Delta z) \left(u \frac{\partial u}{\partial x} + v \frac{\partial u}{\partial y} + w \frac{\partial u}{\partial z} + \frac{\partial u}{\partial t} \right)$$

We divide by the mass of the element of $\rho \, \Delta x \, \Delta y \, \Delta z$ and obtain the following result:

$$- \frac{1}{\rho} \frac{\partial p}{\partial x} - \frac{\partial \Omega}{\partial x} = u \frac{\partial u}{\partial x} + v \frac{\partial u}{\partial y} + w \frac{\partial u}{\partial z} + \frac{\partial u}{\partial t} \qquad (8\text{-}18)$$

For steady flow the velocity u is not a function of time so that $\partial u / \partial t = 0$. Thus, for steady flow Equation 8-18 is

$$- \frac{1}{\rho} \frac{\partial p}{\partial x} - \frac{\partial \Omega}{\partial x} = u \frac{\partial u}{\partial x} + v \frac{\partial u}{\partial y} + w \frac{\partial u}{\partial z} \qquad (X)$$

For three-dimensional, irrotational flow the following are the criteria:

$$\frac{\partial u}{\partial y} - \frac{\partial v}{\partial x} = 0, \qquad \frac{\partial w}{\partial x} - \frac{\partial u}{\partial z} = 0, \qquad \frac{\partial v}{\partial z} - \frac{\partial w}{\partial y} = 0$$

We have derived the first of the three, and we determine the other two in the same way. From these three equations for irrotational flow we see that

$$\frac{\partial u}{\partial y} = \frac{\partial v}{\partial x}, \qquad \frac{\partial u}{\partial z} = \frac{\partial w}{\partial x}$$

When we substitute into Equation X it becomes

$$-\frac{1}{\rho}\frac{\partial p}{\partial x} - \frac{\partial \Omega}{\partial x} = u\frac{\partial u}{\partial x} + v\frac{\partial v}{\partial x} + w\frac{\partial w}{\partial x} = \frac{1}{2}\frac{\partial u^2}{\partial x} + \frac{1}{2}\frac{\partial v^2}{\partial x} + \frac{1}{2}\frac{\partial w^2}{\partial x}$$

$$-\frac{1}{\rho}\frac{\partial p}{\partial x} - \frac{\partial \Omega}{\partial x} = \frac{1}{2}\frac{\partial}{\partial x}(u^2 + v^2 + w^2) = \frac{1}{2}\frac{\partial}{\partial x}(q^2)$$

since $\qquad q^2 = u^2 + v^2 + w^2$

We rearrange this equation to the form.

$$\frac{\partial}{\partial x}\left(\frac{q^2}{2} + \frac{p}{\rho} + \Omega\right) = 0$$

where ρ = constant because this is an ideal fluid. We integrate the equation and obtain

$$\frac{q^2}{2} + \frac{p}{\rho} + \Omega = f_1(y, z, t) \tag{8-19a}$$

We repeat this entire process for the y and z directions and arrive at

$$\frac{q^2}{2} + \frac{p}{\rho} + \Omega = f_2(x, z, t) \tag{8-19b}$$

$$\frac{q^2}{2} + \frac{p}{\rho} + \Omega = f(x, y, t) \tag{8-19c}$$

From Equations 8-19a, 8-19b, and 8-19c, we see that

$$f_1(y, z, t) = f_2(x, z, t) = f_3(x, y, t)$$

since they all are equal to the same equation. The only possible conditions under which the functions can be equal are when they are independent of x, y, z. Therefore,

$$f_1(y, z, t) = f_2(x, z, t) = f_3(x, y, t) = f(t)$$

For steady flow time is not a variable so that $f(t)$ equals a constant. Then Equations 8-19a, 8-19b, and 8-19c become

$$\frac{q^2}{2} + \frac{p}{\rho} + \Omega = \text{constant} = C \qquad (8\text{-}20)$$

We assume that the only body forces acting on the cube are the ones

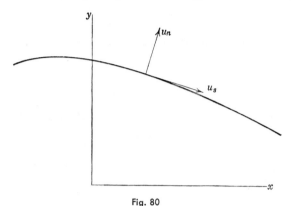

Fig. 80

caused by gravity. We choose the axis system with the positive z axis in the upward direction. Then

$$\Omega = gz$$

We substitute this into Equation 8-20 to get the Bernoulli equation.

$$\frac{q^2}{2} + \frac{p}{\rho} + gz = C \qquad (8\text{-}21)$$

The restrictions on this equation are: (1) the flow is irrotational, and (2) the fluid is an ideal fluid. The advantage is an equation valid throughout the field of flow.

We define the stream function ψ in two dimensions as

$$u = -\frac{\partial \psi}{\partial y}, \qquad v = \frac{\partial \psi}{\partial x} \qquad (8\text{-}22)$$

where x and y are arbitrary orthogonal axes. The stream function cannot be extended directly to three-dimensional flow as the velocity potential can be. It is important that we keep in mind that the stream function can be used in three-dimensional flow only in very special cases.

To examine the stream function further, we look at a sketch of the curve $\psi = \text{constant}$ (Fig. 80). At some arbitrary point P on the curve we consider the velocity and select two directions s and n such that the s direction is tangent to the curve and the n direction is normal to it. Thus, s and n are arbitrary orthogonal axes. The velocity in the s direction is u_s and in the n direction is u_n. The s direction corresponds to x and the n direction to y, and so we write the velocities as

$$u_s = -\frac{\partial \psi}{\partial n}, \qquad u_n = +\frac{\partial \psi}{\partial s} \qquad (8\text{-}23)$$

Because we measure along the curve and the curve is $\psi = $ constant, then

$$u_n = \frac{\partial \psi}{\partial s} = 0$$

which means that no normal component to the curve $\psi = $ constant exists. Therefore, the velocities at all points on the curve $\psi = $ constant are tangential velocities, and the curve is a streamline.

We check to see under what conditions the stream function satisfies continuity and irrotational flow. The equation of continuity is

$$\frac{\partial u}{\partial x} + \frac{\partial v}{\partial y} = 0$$

and we substitute Equation 8-22 into it to get

$$\frac{\partial \left(-\dfrac{\partial \psi}{\partial y}\right)}{\partial x} + \frac{\partial \left(\dfrac{\partial \psi}{\partial x}\right)}{\partial y} = -\frac{\partial^2 \psi}{\partial x\,\partial y} + \frac{\partial^2 \psi}{\partial x\,\partial y} = 0$$

The stream function, therefore, automatically satisfies the equation of continuity.

For irrotational flow

$$\frac{\partial u}{\partial y} - \frac{\partial v}{\partial x} = 0$$

We substitute this into Equation 8-22 and obtain

$$\frac{\partial \left(-\dfrac{\partial \psi}{\partial y}\right)}{\partial y} - \frac{\partial \left(\dfrac{\partial \psi}{\partial x}\right)}{\partial x} = 0$$

$$-\frac{\partial^2 \psi}{\partial y^2} - \frac{\partial^2 \psi}{\partial x^2} = 0$$

$$\frac{\partial^2 \psi}{\partial x^2} + \frac{\partial^2 \psi}{\partial y^2} = 0 \qquad (8\text{-}24)$$

This is the Laplace equation with ψ as the function instead of ϕ. When the stream function satisfies the Laplace equation, the corresponding flow is irrotational and fulfills the requirement of continuity.

All solutions of the Laplace equation are either stream functions or velocity potentials depending upon choice. Illustrative Problem 5 is an example of the stream function and use of the Bernoulli equation.

▶Illustrative Problem 5. Sketch the flow pattern represented by the stream function

$$\psi = Uy\left(1 - \frac{a^2}{x^2 + y^2}\right)$$

The pressure at $x = \pm \infty$ is $p = p_\infty$. Compute the pressure along the line $y = 0$. What is the maximum pressure and where does it occur?

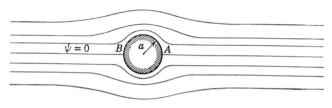

Fig. 81

Solution: Figure 81 is a sketch of the family of curves

$$\psi = \text{constant}$$

or

$$Uy\left(1 - \frac{a^2}{x^2 + y^2}\right) = C$$

The curve $\psi = 0$ is $y = 0$ and $x^2 + y^2 = a^2$.

Take the streamline $\psi = 0$ as a solid boundary and choose the inside of the streamline $\psi = 0$ as solid rather than above or below the streamline $\psi = 0$. A line has zero thickness, and so the only inside section of the streamline that can be considered solid is the inside of the circle $x^2 + y^2 = a^2$. The streamlines outside the circle represent the flow around the cylinder. Do not sketch any streamlines within the circle because this region is considered a solid cylinder.

From the work so far, you do not know what the flow was before the cylinder was placed in its position. The streamlines may have been parallel or in some other pattern. The velocity profile may have been uniform or some function of x and y.

To determine the type of flow into which the cylinder has been placed, examine the flow well upstream of the cylinder, where it has not been disturbed, by examining the stream function ψ for large values of x where the $a^2/(x^2 + y^2)$ term becomes very small compared to one. As an approximation for large values of x, write the stream function as

$$\psi = Uy$$

which is a straight line parallel to the x axis. Consequently, in the limit as x approaches ∞, the streamlines become parallel to the x axis.

Make use of the definition of the stream function to determine the velocity profile.

$$u = -\frac{\partial \psi}{\partial y}, \qquad v = \frac{\partial \psi}{\partial x} \tag{8-22}$$

In this case,

$$u = -\frac{\partial Uy\left(1 - \dfrac{a^2}{x^2 + y^2}\right)}{\partial y} = -U\left(1 - \frac{a^2}{x^2 + y^2}\right) - \frac{2Uy^2 a^2}{(x^2 + y^2)^2}$$

$$= -U\left[1 - \frac{a^2}{x^2 + y^2} + \frac{2a^2 y^2}{(x^2 + y^2)^2}\right]$$

$$v = \frac{\partial Uy\left(1 - \dfrac{a^2}{x^2 + y^2}\right)}{\partial x} = (-1)\frac{[-Uya^2(2x)]}{(x^2 + y^2)^2}$$

$$= \frac{2Ua^2 xy}{(x^2 + y^2)^2}$$

In the limit as $x \to \pm \infty$,

$$\lim_{x \to \pm \infty} u = -U$$

$$\lim_{x \to \pm \infty} v = 0$$

At plus infinity, therefore, the flow is parallel at uniform velocity in the negative direction.

The stream function $\psi = Uy[1 - (a^2/x^2 + y^2)]$ represents the flow around a circular cylinder placed in a stream of uniform parallel flow of an ideal fluid.

For irrotational flow the stream function ψ must satisfy the Laplace equation. Therefore, differentiate ψ twice with respect to each variable.

$$\frac{\partial \psi}{\partial x} = \frac{2Ua^2xy}{(x^2 + y^2)^2}$$

$$\frac{\partial^2 \psi}{\partial x^2} = \frac{2Ua^2y}{(x^2 + y^2)^2} - \frac{8Ua^2x^2y}{(x^2 + y^2)^3}$$

$$\frac{\partial \psi}{\partial y} = +U\left(1 - \frac{a^2}{x^2 + y^2} + \frac{2a^2y^2}{(x^2 + y^2)^2}\right)$$

$$\frac{\partial^2 \psi}{\partial y^2} = +\left(\frac{6ya^2U}{(x^2 + y^2)^2} - \frac{8a^2Uy^3}{(x^2 + y^2)^3}\right)$$

Substitute these into the Laplace equation.

$$\frac{\partial^2 \psi}{\partial x^2} + \frac{\partial^2 \psi}{\partial y^2} = 0$$

$$\frac{2Ua^2y}{(x^2 + y^2)^2} - \frac{8Ua^2x^2y}{(x^2 + y^2)^3} + \frac{6Ua^2y}{(x^2 + y^2)^2} - \frac{8Ua^2y^3}{(x^2 + y^2)^3} = 0$$

$$\frac{8Ua^2y}{(x^2 + y^2)^2}\left[1 - \frac{x^2 + y^2}{x^2 + y^2}\right] = \frac{8Ua^2y}{(x^2 + y^2)^2}[1 - 1] = 0$$

Thus, the flow is irrotational.

The Bernoulli equation is valid for irrotational flow, and you can use it, therefore, to compute the pressure along $\psi = 0$, which is $y = 0$.

$$\frac{p}{\rho} + \frac{q^2}{2} + gz = \text{constant}$$

Assume that the xy plane is horizontal with no change in z throughout. At $x = +\infty$ the velocity is $q = U$, the pressure $p = p_\infty$, and the elevation $z = z_c$. Substitute these values into the Bernoulli equation and calculate the value of the constant.

$$\frac{p_\infty}{\rho} + \frac{U^2}{2} + gz_c = \text{constant}$$

You can write the Bernoulli equation, then, for any point in the flow as

$$\frac{p}{\rho} + \frac{q^2}{2} + gz_c = \frac{p_\infty}{\rho} + \frac{U^2}{2} + gz_c$$

Solve for p to get

$$p = \rho \left\{ \frac{U^2 - q^2}{2} \right\} + p_\infty \tag{8-25}$$

You previously computed the equations for u and v

$$u = -U \left(1 - \frac{a^2}{x^2 + y^2} + \frac{2a^2 y^2}{(x^2 + y^2)^2} \right)$$

$$v = + \frac{2Ua^2 xy}{(x^2 + y^2)^2}$$

Substitute $y = 0$ into these equations to get the values of u and v on the x axis.

$$u = -U \left[1 - \frac{a^2}{x^2} \right]$$

$$v = 0$$

Therefore,

$$q = \sqrt{u^2 + v^2} = -U \left[1 - \frac{a^2}{x^2} \right] \quad \text{on the } x \text{ axis}$$

Substitute this value of q into Equation 8-25 for p to get the equation for p on the x axis.

$$p = \rho \left\{ \frac{U^2 - U^2 \left[1 - \frac{a^2}{x^2} \right]^2}{2} \right\} + p_\infty$$

$$= p_\infty + \frac{\rho U^2}{2} \left\{ 1 - 1 + \frac{2a^2}{x^2} - \frac{a^4}{x^4} \right\}$$

$$p = p_\infty + \frac{\rho U^2}{2} \left\{ \frac{a^2}{x^2} \left(2 - \frac{a^2}{x^2} \right) \right\} \tag{8-26}$$

From Equation 8-25 you can see that the pressure p will be a maximum when the velocity q is zero. The equation for the velocity on the x axis is

$$q = -U \left(1 - \frac{a^2}{x^2} \right)$$

Set q equal to zero and solve for x.

$$0 = U \left(1 - \frac{a^2}{x^2} \right)$$

$$x = \pm a$$

From this, note that the velocity is zero at $x = \pm a$, the two points A and B (Fig. 81) are stagnation points, and the pressure at these points can be computed by substituting $q = 0$ into Equation 8-25.

$$p = p_\infty + \frac{\rho U^2}{2}$$

In this illustrative problem you computed the pressure variation along the streamline $\psi = 0$. It can be computed along any streamline in a similar manner. Therefore, you can compute the pressure at any point in the fluid. ◀

59. Comparison of Theoretical and Actual Pressure Distribution on Cylinders

In Illustrative Problem 5 we derived Equation 8-25 for the pressure distribution anywhere in the fluid when the flow at infinity is uniform with a velocity U and a pressure p_∞.

$$p = \rho \left(\frac{U^2 - q^2}{2} \right) + p_\infty \qquad (8\text{-}25)$$

In the case of uniform flow around a cylinder of infinite length the velocity q is

$$q = (u^2 + v^2)^{\frac{1}{2}}$$

where $$u = -U \left[1 - \frac{a^2}{x^2 + y^2} + \frac{2a^2 y^2}{(x^2 + y^2)^2} \right]$$

$$v = \frac{2Ua^2 xy}{(x^2 + y^2)^2}$$

For simplicity we change to polar coordinates r and θ where

$$r = (x^2 + y^2)^{\frac{1}{2}}$$

$$\theta = \arctan \frac{y}{x}$$

or $x = r \cos \theta,$ $\quad y = r \sin \theta$

We substitute these for x and y and get the following equations for u and v.

$$u = -U \left[1 - \frac{a^2}{2} + \frac{2a^2 \sin \theta}{r^2} \right]$$

$$v = \frac{2Ua^2 \sin \theta \cos \theta}{r^2}$$

We solve for q^2.

$$q^2 = u^2 + v^2$$

$$q^2 = U\left(1 - \frac{2a^2}{r^2}(1 - 2\sin^2\theta) + \frac{a^2}{r^2}\right)$$

and substitute this into Equation 8-25 to get the pressure p at any point in the flow.

$$p = \frac{\rho}{2}\left[U^2 - U^2\left(1 - \frac{2a^2}{r^2}(1 - 2\sin^2\theta) + \frac{a^2}{r^2}\right)\right] + p_\infty$$

To evaluate the force caused by the pressure on the cylinder, we must calculate the pressure on the surface of the cylinder. We substitute $r = a$ and get

$$p = \frac{\rho U^2}{2}[1 - 1 + 2(1 - 2\sin^2\theta) - 1] + p_\infty$$

$$= p_\infty + \frac{\rho U^2}{2}(1 - 4\sin^2\theta) \tag{8-27}$$

To compute the drag force per unit width on the cylinder we must sum the pressure forces on it. We sketch the cylinder (Fig. 82) and compute the drag force for an elemental area (1) ds. The arc length ds equals $a\,d\theta$, and, therefore, the force dF due to pressure is

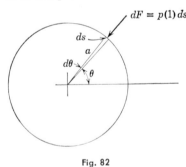

Fig. 82

$$dF = p\,ds = pa\,d\theta$$

We substitute Equation 8-27 for p to get

$$dF = \left(p_\infty + \frac{\rho U^2}{2}[1 - 4\sin^2\theta]\right)a\,d\theta$$

The drag force dF_D is the horizontal component of dF.

$$dF_D = dF\cos\theta$$

Therefore,

$$dF_D = \left(p_\infty + \frac{\rho U^2}{2}[1 - 4\sin^2\theta]\right)a\cos\theta\,d\theta$$

The total drag force is the integral of dF_D taken completely around the cylinder from $\theta = 0$ to $\theta = 2\pi$.

$$\int dF_D = \int_0^{2\pi} \left(p_\infty + \frac{\rho U^2}{2} [1 - 4 \sin^2 \theta] \right) a \cos \theta \, d\theta$$

$$= + \left(p_\infty + \frac{\rho U^2}{2} \right) a \sin \theta \Big|_0^{2\pi} - 4 \frac{\rho U^2}{2} a \frac{\sin^3 \theta}{3} \Big|_0^{2\pi}$$

$$= 0 + 0 = 0$$

Thus, the drag force on the cylinder is zero. We know from experience, however, that the drag force is not zero. This discrepancy

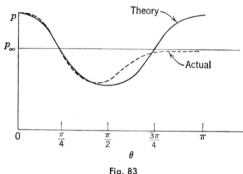

Fig. 83

is called d'Alembert's paradox. We can best explain it if first we look at a plot (Fig. 83) of p versus θ for the actual pressure and for the pressure that we get from the theory. The plot shows only the upper half of the cylinder because the cylinder is symmetrical about the horizontal axis.

We see that the two curves are almost identical until they reach a point just beyond $\theta = \pi/3$. Here the actual pressure starts to increase and continues greater than the theoretical pressure until it reaches the back of the cylinder. Thus, there is a pressure difference between the fronts and back of the cylinder which causes a drag force.

In the actual flow, friction slows up the velocity of the fluid in the boundary layer and causes the flow to separate from the back of the cylinder. This accounts for the pressure increase near the top of the cylinder and the pressure drop at the back. We know from Chapter 6 that the exact shape of the pressure curve in Fig. 83 is a function of the Reynolds number.

From this comparison of theory and practice we can draw some very important conclusions. The pressure as predicted by the theory is very accurate on the front of the cylinder where the boundary layer is very thin.   This leads to the conclusion that, as long as the boundary layer is thin, the potential theory will give good results.   Experience with other problems bears out this conclusion.

Even where the boundary layer is larger, the theory gives results which are usable but not as accurate.   When the boundary layer breaks down completely and a large wake forms, the theory breaks down completely.   Thus, we conclude that we can use the theory when wake effects do not predominate.   Experience with other problems also bears out this conclusion.

60. Source and Vortex

Two notable types of potential flow are the source and the vortex. These two can be combined with each other and with other types to give flows that are of great practical importance.   The flow around a cylinder, discussed in Illustrative Problem 5, is just one example of a combination flow including sources or vortices.   It is much easier to use polar coordinates to discuss these two types of flow, and so we examine them first.

When we use the polar coordinates r and θ, the following relations must hold:

$$x = r \cos \theta, \qquad y = r \sin \theta$$

$$r = \sqrt{x^2 + y^2}, \qquad \theta = \text{arc tan}\, \frac{y}{x}$$

Now $u_r = $ velocity component in r direction

$\qquad\qquad u_\theta = $ velocity component in θ direction

$$u_r = -\frac{1}{r}\frac{\partial \psi}{\partial \theta} = -\frac{\partial \phi}{\partial r}$$

$$u_\theta = +\frac{\partial \psi}{\partial r} = -\frac{1}{r}\frac{\partial \phi}{\partial \theta} \tag{8-28}$$

The Laplace equation in polar coordinates is

$$\nabla^2 \psi = \frac{\partial^2 \psi}{\partial r^2} + \frac{1}{r^2}\frac{\partial^2 \psi}{\partial \theta^2} + \frac{1}{r}\frac{\partial \psi}{\partial r} = 0 \tag{8-29}$$

For a source located at the origin, the stream function ψ and the velocity potential ϕ are

$$\phi = -K \ln r, \qquad \psi = -K\theta \tag{8-30}$$

A plot (Fig. 84) of lines of constant ϕ, equipotential lines, and of lines of constant ψ, streamlines, shows that the streamlines are radial lines and the equipotential lines are concentric circles. The velocity must be in the radial direction and is, thus, u_r.

$$u_r = -\frac{\partial \phi}{\partial r} = -\left(-\frac{K}{r}\right) = \frac{K}{r}$$

From this equation, we see that the velocity u_r is positive and, therefore, in the direction of increasing r. Thus, the flow is always

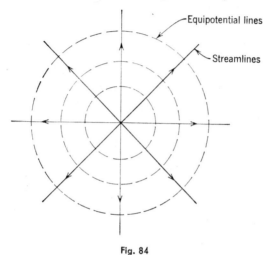

Fig. 84

away from the origin, which means that we can look upon the origin as a line out of which fluid is flowing. This line normal to both the x and y axes appears as a source of fluid, hence, the name source. We can determine the rate at which fluid is flowing out of the line source by computing the flow through a cylinder of radius r_1. This cylinder is considered to have a thickness l normal to the xy plane. The velocity normal to the cylinder's surface is $u_r = K/r_1$ and is constant. Thus, the outflow Ql is $u_r 2\pi r_1 l$

$$Ql = u_r 2\pi r_1 l = \frac{K}{r_1} 2\pi r_1 l = 2\pi l K$$

The outflow Q per unit length of source is

$$Q = 2\pi K$$

We see that Q is not a function of r_1 so that Q must be constant regardless of where we measure it. The strength of the source is K.

If we had chosen ϕ and ψ as positive instead of negative, the flow would have been into the origin instead of out from it. A negative source such as this one is called a sink.

A special combination of a source and a sink is called a doublet. The doublet is a source and a sink of equal strength brought together

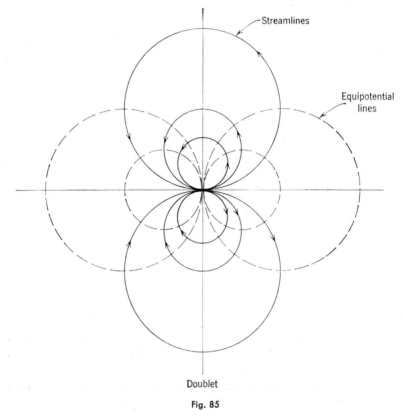

Doublet

Fig. 85

in such a way that the product of the strength K of the source and sink, and the distance between them is a constant. The stream function and the velocity potential for a doublet in both cartesian and polar coordinates are

$$\psi = -\frac{Ay}{x^2 + y^2} = -\frac{A \sin \theta}{r}$$

$$\phi = \frac{Ax}{x^2 + y^2} = \frac{A \cos \theta}{r}$$

(8-31)

Figure 85 shows the flow net for a doublet.

When we add the stream function ψ_1 for a doublet to the stream function ψ_2 for uniform flow parallel to the x axis, we get the same

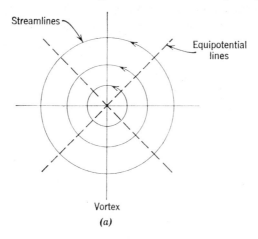

Fig. 86

stream function ψ as used in Illustrative Problem 5 for flow around a cylinder; that is,

$$\psi = \psi_2 + \psi_1 = Uy - \frac{Ay}{x^2 + y^2} = Uy\left(1 - \frac{a^2}{x^2 + y^2}\right)$$

A very important flow net results when the stream function and the velocity potential in Equation 8-30 are reversed. When the symbol for the constant is changed to μ, we get

$$\psi = +\mu \ln r$$

$$\phi = -\mu\theta$$

(8-32)

This flow net called a vortex (Fig. 86a) looks the same as the one for a source (Fig. 84); however, for a vortex the streamlines are concentric circles and the equipotential lines are the radial lines. We determine the direction of the velocity by computing tangential velocity u_θ because the radial velocity is zero.

$$u_\theta = \frac{\partial \psi}{\partial r} = \frac{\mu}{r}$$

Thus, the velocity is independent of θ which means that the velocity is constant for each circle but varies from circle to circle. Figure 86b is a plot of the velocity u_θ versus r.

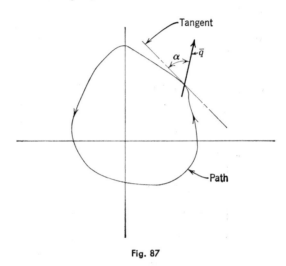

Fig. 87

Just as we measure the strength of a source by the rate at which fluid flows from the source, we measure the strength of a vortex by the circulation. The equation for the circulation is

$$\mathbf{\Gamma} = \oint \bar{q} \cdot ds = \oint q \cos \alpha \, ds \qquad (8\text{-}33)$$

The symbol $\oint$ denotes the line integral taken around any closed path, and α is the angle between the velocity vector $\bar{q}$ and the tangent to the path (Fig. 87). The positive direction of integration around the path is the direction which we would move if we walked around the path with the region enclosed by the path always to our left.

We shall calculate the circulation for the vortex

$$\psi = -\mu \ln r$$

$$q = u_\theta = \frac{\mu}{r}$$

The path of integration will be a circle of radius r_1 with its center at the origin.

$$\Gamma = \oint q \cos \alpha \, ds \qquad (8\text{-}33)$$

The elemental length ds of the path is $r_1 \, d\theta$, the velocity $q = \mu/r_1$, and the angle α between the tangent and the velocity vector $\bar{q}$ is 0. Thus,

$$\Gamma = \oint q \cos \alpha \, ds = \frac{\mu}{r_1}(\cos 0) \int_0^{2\pi} r_1 \, d\theta = 2\pi\mu$$

Therefore, the circulation is $2\pi\mu$ and μ is called the strength of the vortex.

61. Flow Around a Cylinder with Circulation

As discussed in Illustrative Problem 5, we add circulation to the stream function for flow around a cylinder. We do this by adding to the stream function

$$\psi_3 = Uy\left(1 - \frac{a^2}{x^2 + y^2}\right)$$

the stream function for a vortex $\psi_4 = +\mu \ln r$. The resulting stream function is

$$\psi = Uy\left(1 - \frac{a^2}{x^2 + y^2}\right) + \mu \ln r$$

We change to polar coordinates and get

$$\psi = Ur \sin \theta \left(1 - \frac{a^2}{r^2}\right) + \mu \ln r$$

$$= U\left(r - \frac{a^2}{r}\right) \sin \theta + \mu \ln r$$

We set the stream function equal to $\mu \ln a$ and get a streamline which is a circle of radius a. Thus, the flow is still around a cylinder. Next we must examine the flow at great distances from the origin to see if it is uniform flow. First we calculate the velocity from Equation 8-28

$$u_r = -\frac{1}{r}\frac{\partial \psi}{\partial \theta}$$

$$\qquad\qquad\qquad (8\text{-}28)$$

$$u_\theta = +\frac{\partial \psi}{\partial r}$$

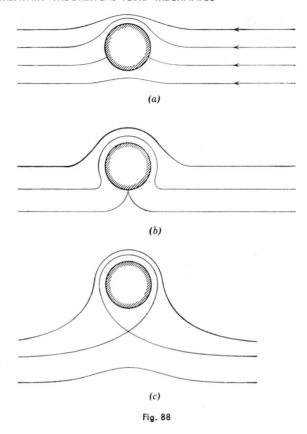

(a)

(b)

(c)

Fig. 88

We carry out the differentiation to get

$$u_r = -U\left(1 - \frac{a^2}{r^2}\right)\cos\theta$$

$$u_\theta = U\sin\theta\left(1 + \frac{a^2}{r^2}\right) + \frac{\mu}{r}$$

and convert this to the components u_x in the x direction and u_y in the y direction by equations

$$u_x = -u_\theta\sin\theta + u_r\cos\theta$$

$$u_y = u_\theta\cos\theta + u_r\sin\theta$$

(8-34)

Thus, in this problem

$$u_x = -U\left(1 + \frac{a^2}{r^2}\right)\sin^2\theta + \frac{\mu}{r}\sin\theta - U\left(1 - \frac{a^2}{r^2}\right)\cos^2\theta$$

$$u_y = U\left(1 + \frac{a^2}{r^2}\right)\sin\theta\cos\theta + \frac{\mu}{r}\cos\theta - U\left(1 - \frac{a^2}{r^2}\right)\cos\theta\sin\theta$$

At great distances from the origin, r is large and we can neglect all terms with r in the denominator.

When we complete this, we find u_x and u_y at great distances from the origin to be

$$u_x = -U\sin^2\theta + 0 - U\cos^2\theta = -U(\sin^2\theta + \cos^2\theta) = -U$$

$$u_y = U\sin\theta\cos\theta + 0 - U\sin\theta\cos\theta = 0$$

We see, then, that at distances great enough for the flow to be considered undisturbed by the cylinder, the velocity is parallel and uniform. Thus, this stream function represents a rotating cylinder placed in a uniform stream. The possible flow patterns are shown in Fig. 88a, b, c. In Fig. 88a the strength of the vortex is small compared with the uniform stream velocity U and the strength of the doublet; in Fig. 88b the relation between the variables is such that there is only one stagnation point; and in Fig. 88c the stagnation point has moved off the cylinder.

Because the flow is symmetrical about the y axis, we can see that drag force on the cylinder is impossible. It is not obvious what the force, called the lift force, in the

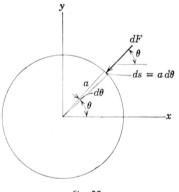

Fig. 89

y direction will be. We compute the lift force L per unit length by integrating the y component of the pressure forces acting all around the cylinder. Thus, from Fig. 89 we see that the y component of the infinitesimal force dF is $-dL$. The minus sign appears because the component is in the negative y direction

$$dL = -dF\sin\theta = -p_1 a\, d\theta \sin\theta$$

$$L = -a\int_0^{2\pi} p\sin\theta\, d\theta \tag{8-35}$$

We compute the pressure from Bernoulli's equation and assume that the pressure at infinity is p_∞. We neglect changes in elevation as small.

$$\frac{p_1}{\rho} + \frac{q^2}{2} = \frac{p_\infty}{\rho} + \frac{U^2}{2}$$

$$p = p_\infty + \frac{\rho}{2}(U^2 - q^2)$$

On the surface of the cylinder the radial velocity u_r is zero and $q = u_\theta$. Also $r = a$ on the surface of the cylinder. So, from the foregoing

$$q = u_\theta = U \sin\theta \left(1 + \frac{a^2}{r^2}\right) + \frac{\mu}{r} = 2U \sin\theta + \frac{\mu}{a}$$

We substitute this into the equation of the pressure p to get

$$p = p_\infty + \frac{\rho}{2}\left[U^2 - \left(2U \sin\theta + \frac{\mu}{a}\right)^2\right]$$

and simplify it

$$p = p_\infty + \frac{\rho}{2}\left(U^2(1 - 4\sin^2\theta) - 4\frac{U\mu}{a}\sin\theta - \frac{\mu^2}{a^2}\right)$$

We substitute this value of p into Equation 8-35 and solve for the lift L.

$$L = -a \int_0^{2\pi}\left[p_\infty + \frac{\rho}{2}\left(U^2(1 - 4\sin^2\theta) - 4\frac{U\mu}{a}\sin\theta - \frac{\mu^2}{a^2}\right)\right]\sin\theta\, d\theta$$

$$= -a\left[\left(p_\infty + \frac{\rho}{2}U^2 - \frac{\rho\mu^2}{2a^2}\right)\int_0^{2\pi}\sin\theta\, d\theta - 2\rho U^2 \int_0^{2\pi}\sin^3\theta\, d\theta\right.$$

$$\left. - \frac{2\rho U\mu}{a}\int_0^{2\pi}\sin^2\theta\, d\theta\right]$$

The first two integrals are zero but

$$\int_0^{2\pi}\sin^2\theta\, d\theta = \pi$$

Therefore, the lift is

$$L = a\frac{2\rho U\mu}{a}\pi = \rho U 2\pi\mu$$

but the circulation $\Gamma = 2\pi\mu$ so that

$$L = \rho U\Gamma \qquad (8\text{-}36)$$

We see from Equation 8-36 that a cylinder with circulation in a uniform stream experiences a thrust normal to the direction of the stream. Thrust on a cylinder can be extended to spheres in three-dimensional work. This explains how a baseball can curve and why tennis balls and golf balls slice and hook when they are hit into a spin.

62. Airfoil Theory

Kutta and Joukowski derived an equation identical to Equation 8-36 for the lift in two dimensions on a right cylinder of any cross section. Joukowski also was able to transform the right circular cylinder into a two-dimensional airfoil. This is known as the Joukowski transformation. We can develop an airfoil with lift using the right circular cylinder with circulation.

Munk, Glauert, and Birnbaum made the main contributions to airfoil theory, generally known as the thin airfoil theory. However, we still calculate the lift in the thin airfoil by a refined use of the Kutta and Joukowski theorem of airfoil lift.

63. Summary

The most important idea in Chapter 8 states that potential flow is a completely theoretical method of computing forces and drawing flow nets. The major limitation of this method demands that the wake effects be very small. Potential flow is the flow of an incompressible, nonviscous fluid.

The existence of a velocity potential ϕ means that a possible flow must be irrotational. For the velocity potential ϕ to represent a possible flow, it must satisfy the Laplace equation. The existence of a stream function ψ signifies that the equation of continuity is satisfied. When the stream function is a solution of the Laplace equation, the flow is also irrotational.

The following equations for two-dimensional flow are important and definitely should be remembered:

$$\text{Equation of continuity (incompressible fluid) } \frac{\partial u}{\partial x} + \frac{\partial v}{\partial y} = 0$$

$$\text{Laplace equation} \begin{cases} \text{cartesian coordinates } \dfrac{\partial^2 \phi}{\partial x^2} + \dfrac{\partial^2 \phi}{\partial y^2} = 0 \\[2em] \text{polar coordinates } \dfrac{\partial^2 \phi}{\partial r^2} + \dfrac{1}{r^2}\dfrac{\partial^2 \phi}{\partial \theta^2} + \dfrac{1}{r}\dfrac{\partial \phi}{\partial r} = 0 \end{cases}$$

Cartesian coordinates

$$u_x = -\frac{\partial \phi}{\partial x} = -\frac{\partial \psi}{\partial y}, \qquad u_y = -\frac{\partial \phi}{\partial y} = \frac{\partial \psi}{\partial x} \qquad (Y)$$

Polar coordinates

$$u_r = -\frac{1}{r}\frac{\partial \psi}{\partial \theta} = -\frac{\partial \phi}{\partial r}, \qquad u_\theta = +\frac{\partial \psi}{\partial r} = -\frac{1}{r}\frac{\partial \phi}{\partial \theta} \qquad (Y)$$

We note that for a certain flow the stream function ψ and the velocity potential ϕ are related by Equation Y, which suggests a method for calculating one when we know the other.

For a right cylinder of any cross section with circulation Γ the lift L in a uniform stream is

$$L = \rho V \Gamma$$

PROBLEMS

8-1. Determine which of the velocities below, composed of velocity components u_x and u_y, satisfy the equation of continuity.

(a) $u_x = Vx$
  $u_y = -Vy$
(b) $u_x = Vx$
  $u_y = Vx$
(c) $u_x = V(x + y)$
  $u_y = -V(x + y)$
(d) $u_x = V(x + y)$
  $u_y = V(x - y)$

(e) $u_x = V(x^2 + xy - y^2)$

  $u_y = V(y^2 + x^2)$

(f) $u_x = A \sin\left(\dfrac{\pi x y}{l^2}\right)$

  $u_y = A \sin\left(\dfrac{\pi x y}{l^2}\right)$

(g) $u_x = A \ln (xy)$

  $u_y = -\dfrac{Ay}{x}$

(h) $u_x = A \sin\left(\dfrac{\pi x}{l}\right)$

  $u_y = \dfrac{-\pi A y}{l} \sin\left(\dfrac{\pi x}{l}\right)$

8-2. Calculate the unknown velocity component so that the two satisfy the equation of continuity.

(a) $u_x = A(x^2 + y^2)$

  $u_y =$
(b) $u_x =$

  $u_y = A \cos\left(\dfrac{\pi y}{l}\right)$

(c) $u_x = -A \ln\left(\dfrac{x}{l}\right)$

  $u_y =$
(d) $u_x =$

  $u_y = xy + Ay^2 + x^4$

(e) $u_x = Ae^x$
  $u_y =$
(f) $u_x =$
  $u_y = Ax + By^2 + Cx^2y^3$

8-3. Derive the equation of continuity in polar coordinates r and θ.

8-4. Determine which of the following velocity fields could represent irrotational flow.

(a) $u_x = A$
$u_y = B$

(b) $u_x = Vx$
$u_y = Vy$

(c) $u_x = Ax^2 + Bx^3$

(d) $u_x = A \sin\left(\dfrac{\pi x}{l}\right)$

$u_y = Ay + B \sin y$

$u_y = -\dfrac{\pi Ay}{l} \sin\left(\dfrac{\pi x}{l}\right)$

(e) $u_x = A \ln xy$

(f) $u_x = Ax^2y + By^2$

$u_y = -\dfrac{Ay}{x}$

$u_y = \dfrac{Ax^3}{3} + 2Byx$

8-5. Calculate the unknown velocity component so that the two velocity components satisfy the conditions of irrotational flow.

(a) $u_x = A \sin\left(\dfrac{\pi y}{l}\right)$

(b) $u_x = Ax^2 + Bxy + C$

$u_y =$

$u_y =$

(c) $u_x =$

(d) $u_x =$

$u_y = A \ln\left(\dfrac{x}{l}\right)$

$u_y = Aye^x + x$

8-6. Calculate the velocity components of q for the velocity potential ϕ given below.

(a) $\phi = Axy$

(b) $\phi = A \sin\left(\dfrac{\pi x}{l}\right) + B \sin\left(\dfrac{\pi y}{l}\right)$

(c) $\phi = Ax^2 + By^2$

(d) $\phi = \dfrac{x^2 + y^2}{x - y}$

8-7. Compute the velocity q at points $(3, 2)$, $(1, -2)$ and $(0, 4)$ for the following velocity potentials:

(a) $\phi = x^2 - y^2$

(b) $\phi = A \arcsin\left(\dfrac{y}{x}\right)$

8-8. Which of the velocity potentials in Problem 8-6 satisfy the law of conservation of matter?

8-9. Determine which of the following functions f is a possible velocity potential for ideal fluid flow:

(a) $f = x^2 - y^2$

(b) $f = A \arcsin\left(\dfrac{y}{x}\right)$

(c) $f = K \arctan \dfrac{2yB}{x^2 + y^2 - B^2}$

(d) $f = -Ay + K \dfrac{y}{x^2 + y^2}$

(e) $f = A \sin\left(\dfrac{\pi xy}{l^2}\right)$

(f) $f = -\dfrac{\Gamma}{2\pi} \ln \sqrt{x^2 + y^2}$

8-10. Sketch the flow net for the velocity potential

$$\phi = \frac{Ax}{x^2 + y^2}$$

8-11. In Problem 8-10 compute the velocity q at $(x = 1, y = 1)$, $(x = -2, y = 0)$ and $(x = 4, y = 5)$.

8-12. Sketch the flow net for the velocity potential

$$\phi = -Ay + \frac{Ky}{x^2 + y^2}$$

8-13. In Problem 8-12 compute the velocity q at $(x = 0, y = 0)$ and $(x = 3, y = -3)$.

8-14. In Problem 8-10 the pressure at $x = \infty$, $y = 0$ is p_∞. Derive an equation for the pressure p anywhere in the fluid.

8-15. In Problem 8-12, the pressure at $(x = \infty, y = 0)$ is p_∞. Derive an expression for the pressure p anywhere in the fluid.

8-16. The velocity potential $\phi = V_o(x^2 - y^2)$ represents potential flow in a corner. The pressure at $(x = \infty, y = 0)$ is p_∞. Compute the pressure at $(x = 0, y = 0)$ and $(x = 1, y = 1)$.

8-17. The velocity potential

$$\phi = V_o\left(r + \frac{a^2}{r}\right) \cos \theta - \frac{k}{2\pi} \theta$$

represents flow around a cylinder without circulation. At $r = \infty$ the pressure is p_∞. Compute the pressure at the nose of the cylinder and at the top of the cylinder.

8-18. Which of the following stream functions ψ are possible irrotational flow fields?

(a) $\psi = \dfrac{-Ay}{x^2 + y^2}$ (b) $\psi = 2Axy$

(c) $\psi = \arcsin\left(\dfrac{x}{y}\right)$ (d) $\psi = \sinh(yx)$

(e) $\psi = Ax + By$ (f) $\psi = A \ln(xy^2)$

8-19. Determine the relation between the stream function ψ and the velocity potential ϕ when they both represent the same flow field.

8-20. In polar coordinates r and θ, the velocity components u_r and u_θ can be determined from the stream function by the relations

$$u_r = -\frac{1}{r}\frac{\partial \psi}{\partial \theta} \qquad u_\theta = \frac{\partial \psi}{\partial r}$$

Using these relations, determine the velocity components for the following stream functions

(a) $\psi = Ar^{\pi/\alpha} \sin\left(\dfrac{\pi\theta}{\alpha}\right)$ (b) $\psi = -\mu\theta$

(c) $\psi = -\mu \ln r$ (d) $\psi = Uy$

(e) $\psi = \dfrac{-AV_o}{r} \sin \theta$ (f) $\psi = V_o\left(r - \dfrac{a^2}{r}\right) \sin \theta$

8-21. Derive the conditions for irrotational flow in terms of the stream function.

8-22. A stream function ψ represents a certain flow field. At one point in the flow field the pressure is p_o and the velocity is q_o. Determine an expression for the pressure in terms of the stream function anywhere in the flow field.

8-23. Derive the continuity equation

$$\frac{1}{r}\frac{\partial(ru_r)}{\partial r} + \frac{1}{r}\frac{\partial u_\theta}{\partial \theta} = 0$$

in polar coordinates.

8-24. Using the continuity equation in polar coordinates in Problem 8-23, derive the Laplace equation in polar coordinates.

8-25. Sketch the flow net of the stream function

$$\psi = -\frac{H\theta}{2\pi} + V_o r \sin\theta$$

and locate the stagnation point.

8-26. In Problem 8-25 the pressure at $\theta = 0$, $r = \infty$ is p_∞. Calculate the pressure at $\theta = 0$, $r = H/\pi V_o$.

8-27. Determine the relation between μ and U so that there is only one stagnation point on the surface of the cylinder with circulation in a uniform stream.

ACOUSTIC VELOCITY

Frequently in this book we refer to the formula $a^2 = kp/\rho$ for acoustic or sonic velocity a in an isentropic expansion. In Appendix A we derive this equation using the momentum and continuity equations. The acoustic velocity is the velocity of propagation of a sound wave which is a pressure wave.

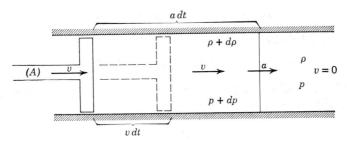

Sketch 40

For simplicity's sake we derive the acoustic velocity equation for a pressure wave in a tube of constant cross-sectional area. A piston at one end of the tube suddenly moves with a velocity v. The fluid in front of the pressure wave remains unchanged since it has not yet felt the movement of the piston. Thus, the properties in front of the wave are ρ, $v = 0$, and p; whereas between the wave and the piston the properties are $p + dp$, $\rho + d\rho$, and a new velocity v.

$$0 = \frac{d}{dt} \int_V \rho \, dx \, dy \, dz + \int_A \rho V \cos \theta \, dA \quad \text{(Continuity Equation)}$$

We choose as the control volume the face of the piston at time t, the cross section a distance $a \, dt$ down from the piston face, and the walls of the pipe between the two faces. No fluid crosses the boundaries of the control volume so that the term $\int_A \rho V \cos \theta \, dA$ is zero in time dt. Thus,

$$0 = \frac{d}{dt} \int_V \rho \, dx \, dy \, dz$$

or

$$\int_V \rho \, dx \, dy \, dz = \text{constant}$$

Therefore, the mass of fluid in the control volume does not change in the time dt. At time t the mass in the control volume is $\rho a \, dt \, A$. At time $t + dt$ the mass in the control volume is the product of the new density $\rho + d\rho$, and the new volume $(a - v) \, dt \, A$ in which the fluid is contained. The mass is

$$(\rho + d\rho)(a - v) A \, dt$$

Because the control volume mass does not change, we can equate the mass to get

$$\rho a A \, dt = (\rho + d\rho)(a - v) A \, dt$$

We simplify this to

$$0 = (a \, d\rho - \rho v - v \, d\rho) A \, dt$$

The velocity a of the wave is much greater than the velocity v of the fluid so that we can neglect the $v \, d\rho$ term to get

$$a \, d\rho = \rho v \tag{Z}$$

Next we apply the momentum equation to the control volume.

$$\sum F_x = \frac{d\mathbf{M}_x}{dt} + \int_A \bar{V}_x \rho V \cos \theta \, dA$$

The only external forces acting on the control volume are the pressure forces on one end, the force of the piston, and shear stresses from the walls of the tube. The shear stresses are small compared to the pressure forces so that we can neglect them. The pressure of the piston on the control volume is equal and opposite to the pressure which the piston exerts on the control surface. Thus, the force of the piston on the control surface is the product of the piston area and the pressure on the piston. The piston face acts on the control surface only at time t. During the rest of the time dt the piston rod A acts on the control surface with the same force as on the piston face. This force is the product of the pressure $p + dp$ which acts on the piston face and the cross-sectional area A of the piston face. Thus, the sum of the external forces ΣF_x is

$$\overset{+}{\rightarrow} \quad \Sigma F_x = (p + dp)A - pA = A\,dp$$

The term $\displaystyle\int_A \bar{V}_x \rho V \cos\theta\,dA$ in the momentum equation is zero because no fluid crosses the control surface.   Thus,

$$A\,dp = \frac{d\mathbf{M}_x}{dt} + 0 = \frac{d\mathbf{M}_x}{dt}$$

The term $d\mathbf{M}_x/dt$ is the rate of change of the momentum in the x direction of the fluid in the control volume.   The momentum in the x direction of the fluid inside the control volume at time t is zero since the velocity $\bar{V}_x$ of the fluid is zero.   At time $t + dt$ the momentum in the x direction is $(\rho A a\,dt)v$.   Thus,

$$\frac{d\mathbf{M}_x}{dt} = \frac{\rho A a\,dt\,v}{dt} = \rho A a v$$

We substitute this into the momentum equation to get

$$A\,dp = \rho A a v$$

We solve for v

$$v = \frac{dp}{a\rho}$$

and substitute it into Equation Z derived from continuity considerations.

$$a\,d\rho = \rho v = \rho\frac{dp}{a\rho}$$

We solve for a

$$a^2 = \frac{dp}{d\rho}$$

For an isentropic expansion

$$\frac{p}{\rho^k} = \text{constant} = K$$

or

$$p = K\rho^k$$

We differentiate this with respect to ρ to obtain

$$\frac{dp}{d\rho} = Kk\rho^{k-1}$$

Thus,

$$a^2 = \frac{dp}{d\rho} = kK\rho^{k-1} = \frac{kK\rho^k}{\rho}$$

but

$$K\rho^k = p$$

Therefore,

$$a^2 = \frac{kp}{\rho}$$

for an isentropic process.

CAVITATION

Unless the engineer is careful in the design of many types of liquid systems, the liquid pressure will drop below the vapor pressure causing small bubbles of the liquid vapor to appear in the liquid. When the liquid moves to another part of the system where the pressure is greater than vapor pressure, the vapor will condense and the pressure in the bubbles will go to zero. The condensed vapor takes a great deal less space than the vapor, causing reduction in the pressure which sets up a greater pressure in the liquid than in the bubble. The pressure difference accelerates the liquid from all directions toward the center of the bubble. The liquid rushes in and collapses the bubble to a smaller and smaller diameter.

The liquid moving from all directions collides at the center of the bubble and all the kinetic energy which the liquid has attained in rushing in to fill the bubble must be overcome by the compression of the liquid. The liquid has such a high bulk modulus that a tremendous pressure results at the center of the bubble.

In most hydraulics problems, gases that will come out of solution when the pressure is reduced are dissolved in the water. Some of the gases will come out of solution at much greater pressures than the vapor pressure. Thus, to be on the safe side, many engineers use a pressure for cavitation which is two to three times the vapor pressure.

In hydraulic propeller and turbine problems, there are many points where water flowing over the surface of the blades travels at high velocities, reducing the pressure to below the vapor pressure. The water carries the bubbles to points where the pressure is above the vapor pressure, causing cavitation. There are many examples of cavitation on blades where the cavitation pressures have been so great that chunks of the blade have been torn away. This reduces the efficiency of the system and eventually causes complete failure.

Where liquids flow in closed conduits, there are many ways to reduce pressure. When the height of the conduit increases without a decrease in velocity, the pressure drops. Cavitation begins if this drop in pressure is great enough. Large increases in velocity without change in elevation also will cause cavitation. Thus, the engineer must always check the points of high elevation, the points of high velocity, and the points where an increase in velocity and elevation combine. Cavitation in conduits can cause erosion of conduit walls in the same manner that the surface of the blades is destroyed.

The formation of gas bubbles in any flow destroys the continuum. Thus, all the equations which we developed using a continuum would no longer be valid. We see then that cavitation from both a theoretical and a practical standpoint must be avoided.

THERMODYNAMICS

To understand the flow of a compressible fluid, it is necessary to understand thermodynamics. After studying this appendix, we should know some of the terms and some of the relations among pressure, volume, and temperature, but we shall not have the knowledge of thermodynamics that is necessary for a complete understanding of compressible fluid flow. No attempt will be made to derive these relations, but some short explanation will be given.

For further information on thermodynamics, and further information is strongly recommended, any of the references on thermodynamics in Appendix E will be of great assistance.

A perfect gas is a gas which obeys the perfect gas law

$$pv^k = RT$$

where p = pressure, in $\mathrm{lb}_f/\mathrm{ft}^2$
v = specific volume, in $\mathrm{ft}^3/\mathrm{lb}_m$
R = universal gas constant, in $\mathrm{lb}_f\text{-ft}/\mathrm{lb}_m\ {}^\circ\mathrm{R}$
T = temperature, ${}^\circ\mathrm{R}$

We will change the perfect gas law so that the density in slugs per cubic feet is used in place of the specific volume. However, we must first derive the relation between pounds mass and slugs. A certain mass has a weight W expressed in terms of the mass by two formulae which differ only by a constant g_c.

$$W = (\text{slugs})(g)$$

$$W = \frac{1}{g_c}(\mathrm{lb}_m)(g)$$

The weights W are the same. Thus, we see that

$$(\text{slugs})\ g = \frac{1}{g_c}(\mathrm{lb}_m)g$$

329

or

$$\text{slugs} = \frac{1}{g_c} \text{lb}_m$$

We can rewrite v as

$$v = \frac{\text{ft}^3}{\text{lb}_m} = \frac{\text{ft}^3}{g_c \text{ slugs}} = \frac{1}{\rho g_c}$$

and substitute this in the perfect gas law to get

$$\frac{p}{\rho g_c} = RT$$

or

$$\frac{p}{\rho} = g_c RT$$

where ρ = density in slugs/ft^3

g_c = Newton's proportionality constant, in lb$_m$-ft/lb$_f$ sec^2

An isothermal process is one in which the temperature is constant. Thus, for a perfect gas an isothermal process is

$$\frac{p}{\rho} = \text{constant}$$

An isentropic process is a process which is adiabatic and reversible. Adiabatic means that there is no heat transfer, and reversible means that there is no friction. There are other limitations on the term reversible, but for our elementary use the limitation of no friction is adequate. The equation for an isentropic process is

$$\frac{p}{\rho^k} = \text{constant}$$

where $k = c_p/c_v$ the ratio of the specific heats c_p and c_v.

A polytropic process is one in which the equation of the relation between pressure and density is

$$\frac{p}{\rho^n} = \text{constant}$$

where n is a constant. Since n can be any constant, a polytropic process has no particular significance as the isentropic process has. The polytropic process is a statement of a very general relation between pressure and density.

BOUNDARY LAYER THEORY

appendix **D**

A surface moving with respect to a fluid has a layer of fluid adjacent to it called the boundary layer. The boundary layer is roughly described as that layer where the viscous effects are greater than the inertia effects. This description makes it difficult to determine the thickness of the boundary layer because it is almost impossible to determine at which point the inertia effects equal the friction effects. More exact methods of determining the thickness have evolved, and we shall discuss three of the methods here.

In using the boundary layer theory, we assume that all frictional effects occur inside the boundary layer and that the flow is frictionless outside it. We know this assumption is incorrect, and so it is not surprising that there exists more than one way to determine the thickness of this fictitious boundary layer. We shall discuss three different boundary layer thicknesses: the first is called the boundary layer thickness, the second the displacement thickness, and the third the momentum thickness.

We sketch (Fig. 90) the velocity profile in the region of a body that has been placed in a uniform stream moving with a velocity V_o. We see that the velocity of the fluid approaches asymptotically an external velocity V_e. If the edge of the boundary layer thickness is the point where the velocity v inside the layer equals the external velocity, the boundary layer thickness will be infinite. Since this is impossible, we define the boundary layer thickness as the thickness at the point where the velocity is a certain percentage of the external velocity. Two commonly used percentages are 95 per cent and 99 per cent. For our discussion we shall assume that the boundary thickness is the distance from the wall to the point where the velocity is 99 per cent of the external velocity.

The displacement thickness δ^* is based on continuity considerations. It amounts to saying that δ^* is the difference between the distance from the surface to infinity when for the same flow rate the velocity profile is used or a constant velocity V_e is used, which is another way of saying that δ^* is the normal distance the external streamlines are moved from the surface because of the boundary layer. This statement does not lend itself to mathematical treatment. Thus, we

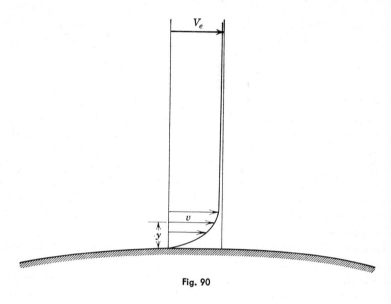

Fig. 90

mathematically define δ^* in the following manner:

$$V_e\delta^* = \int_0^\infty (V_e - v)\, dy \qquad\qquad \text{(D-1)}$$

The $(V_e - v)$ term approaches zero rapidly so that the value of the integral is finite. For a flat plate at zero incidence, δ equals approximately three times the displacement thickness.

In potential flow the momentum of the flow is greater than the momentum when we take into account the boundary layer. The loss of momentum due to the boundary layer is

$$\int_0^\infty \rho v(V_e - v)\, dy$$

The momentum thickness θ is the thickness of fluid moving at the external velocity which would be equal to the momentum loss. Thus,

$$\rho V_e{}^2\theta = \rho \int_0^\infty v(V_e - v)\, dy$$

The definition of θ is

$$\theta = \int_0^\infty \frac{v}{V_e}\left(1 - \frac{v}{V_e}\right) dy \qquad \text{(D-2)}$$

One of the most important equations in boundary layer theory is the momentum equation which we shall derive, following the method of von Karman,[1] and then use in the solution of a problem.   We sketch

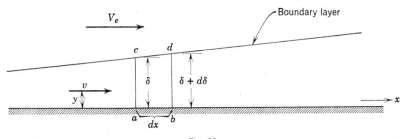

Fig. 91

the boundary layer along a surface (Fig. 91), choosing a fixed control value $abcd$ which is unit thickness normal to the sketch.   We apply the momentum equation to this control volume.

$$\sum F_x = \frac{dM_x}{dt} + \int_A \bar{V}_{xp}V \cos\theta \, dA \qquad \text{(4-5)}$$

The pressure on the surface ac is p, the pressure on the surface bd is $p + (\partial p/\partial x) \, dx$, and the shear stress τ acts on the surface ab. The pressure on the surface cd will have a component in the x direction.   We shall assume that the average of the pressure on the surfaces ac and bd acts on the surface cd.   This average pressure is $p + (\partial p/\partial x)(dx/2)$.   Thus, the summation of external forces in the x direction is

$$\sum F_x = p(\delta)(1) + \left(p + \frac{\partial p}{\partial x}\frac{dx}{2}\right) d\delta \,(1) - \left(p + \frac{\partial p}{\partial x}\,dx\right)(\delta + d\delta)(1)$$
$$- \tau_o \, dx \,(+1)$$

$$= -\frac{\partial p}{\partial x}\,dx\,\delta - \frac{\partial p}{\partial x}\,dx\,\frac{d\delta}{2} - \tau_o\,dx$$

We can neglect the $(\partial p/\partial x)(dx\,d\delta/2)$ term because it is of a higher

---

[1] Th. von Karman, Laminare und Turbulente Reibung, *Z. angew. Math. u. Mech.*, **1**, 235–236 (1921).   English translation, *NACA T.M.* 1092, 1946.

order. Thus, the summation of external forces is

$$\sum F_x = -\frac{\partial p}{\partial x}\,\delta\,dx - \tau_o\,dx \tag{D-3}$$

Next, we consider the $d\mathbf{M}_x/dt$ term in the momentum equation. This term is the rate of change of momentum of the fluid inside the control volume. The $\mathbf{M}_x$ of the fluid inside the control volume is

$$\mathbf{M}_x = \left(\int_0^\infty \rho v\,dy\right)dx$$

Thus,

$$\frac{d\mathbf{M}_x}{dt} = \frac{d}{dt}\left(\int_0^\infty \rho v\,dy\right)dx$$

or

$$\frac{d\mathbf{M}_x}{dt} = \int_0^\infty \rho\frac{dv}{dt}\,dy\,dx \tag{D-4}$$

The $\displaystyle\int_A \bar{V}_x\rho V\cos\theta\,dA$ term of the momentum equation must be evaluated at all surfaces of the control volume. The term is zero at the two end surfaces which are parallel to the sketch, and it is also zero at surface ab because $\theta = \pi/2$ at these surfaces. Thus,

$$\int_A \bar{V}_x\rho V\cos\theta\,dA = \int_{ac} \bar{V}_x\rho V\cos\theta\,dA$$

$$+ \int_{cd} \bar{V}_x\rho V\cos\theta\,dA + \int_{bd} \bar{V}_x\rho V\cos\theta\,dA$$

$$= -\int_0^\delta \rho v^2\,dy + V_e\int_{cd}\rho v\cos\theta\,dA$$

$$+ \int_0^{\delta+d\delta}\rho\left(v + \frac{\partial v}{\partial x}\,dx\right)^2 dy$$

$$\int_A \bar{V}_x\rho V\cos\theta\,dA = V_e\int_{cd}\rho V\cos\theta\,dA + \int_\delta^{\delta+d\delta}\rho v^2\,dy$$

$$+ \int_0^{\delta+d\delta}\left[2v\frac{\partial v}{\partial x}\,dx + \left(\frac{\partial v}{\partial x}\,dx\right)^2\right]dy \tag{D-5}$$

To evaluate the integral over the area cd, we must use the continuity equation for an incompressible fluid. Thus, from now on all equations will have the limitation of incompressibility.

$$\int_A \rho V\cos\theta\,dA = 0 \quad \text{(Continuity Equation)}$$

We apply this continuity equation to the control volume to get

$$\int_{ab} \rho V \cos \theta \, dA + \int_{cd} \rho V \cos \theta \, dA + \int_{bd} \rho V \cos \theta \, dA = 0$$

$$-\int_0^\delta \rho v \, dy + \int_{cd} \rho V \cos \theta \, dA + \int_0^{\delta+d\delta} \rho \left(v + \frac{\partial v}{\partial x} dx \right) dy = 0$$

$$\int_{cd} \rho V \cos \theta \, dA = -\int_\delta^{\delta+d\delta} \rho v \, dy - \int_0^{\delta+d\delta} \rho \frac{\partial v}{\partial x} dx \, dy \quad \text{(D-6)}$$

We substitute Equation D-6 into Equation D-5 to get

$$\int_A \bar{V}_x \rho V \cos \theta \, dA = -V_e \int_\delta^{\delta+d\delta} \rho v \, dy - V_e \int_0^{\delta+d\delta} \rho \frac{\partial v}{\partial x} dx \, dy$$
$$+ \int_\delta^{\delta+d\delta} \rho v^2 \, dy + \int_0^{\delta+d\delta} \rho \left[\frac{\partial v^2}{\partial x} + \left(\frac{\partial v}{\partial x} dx \right)^2 \right] dy \quad \text{(D-7)}$$

Between δ and $\delta + d\delta$ the velocity v is approximately the same as the external velocity V_e and so we can say

$$V_e \int_\delta^{\delta+d\delta} \rho v \, dy \approx \int_\delta^{\delta+d\delta} \rho v^2 \, dy$$

We substitute this relation into Equation D-7 and get the equation

$$\int_A \bar{V}_x \rho V \cos \theta \, dA = -V_e \int_0^{\delta+d\delta} \rho \frac{\partial v}{\partial x} dx \, dy + \int_0^{\delta+d\delta} \rho \frac{\partial v^2}{\partial x} dx \, dy$$
$$+ \int_0^{\delta+d\delta} \left(\frac{\partial v}{\partial x} \right)^2 dx^2 \, dy$$

The last term is a term of higher order. Therefore, we neglect it to get

$$\int_A \bar{V}_x \rho V \cos \theta \, dA = -V_e \int_0^{\delta+d\delta} \rho \frac{\partial v}{\partial x} dx \, dy + \int_0^{\delta+d\delta} \rho \frac{\partial v^2}{\partial x} dx \, dy$$

We take the differentiation outside the integration which changes the limits to give

$$\int_A \bar{V}_x \rho V \cos \theta \, dA = \frac{\partial}{\partial x} \int_0^\delta \rho v^2 \, dy \, dx - \frac{\partial}{\partial x} V_e \int_0^\delta \rho v \, dy \, dx \quad \text{(D-8)}$$

We make the final substitution of Equation D-8, D-4, and D-3 into the momentum equation and divide through by dx to get

$$-\delta \frac{\partial p}{\partial x} - \tau_o = \int_0^\delta \rho \frac{\partial v}{\partial t} dy + \frac{\partial}{\partial x} \int_0^\delta \rho v^2 \, dy - \frac{\partial}{\partial x} V_e \int_0^\delta \rho v \, dy \quad \text{(D-9)}$$

Equation D-9 is known as the momentum boundary layer equation, which is valid for two-dimensional, incompressible boundary layer flow.

We apply the momentum equation to the flow of a uniform stream over a flat plate at zero incidence as shown in Fig. 92. We sketch the

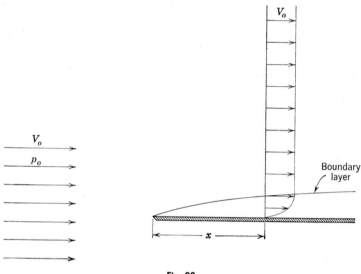

Fig. 92

velocity profile at distance x down from the leading edge and see that the external velocity at the top of the boundary layer equals the free stream velocity V_o. Thus, $V_e = V_o$ and is a constant. The flow outside the boundary layer is frictionless so that we can apply the Bernoulli equation to it. Thus,

$$\frac{V_o{}^2}{2} + \frac{p_o}{\rho} + g z_o = \frac{V_e{}^2}{2} + \frac{p_e}{\rho} + g z_e$$

We can neglect the changes in elevation as small so that $z_o = z_e$. We substitute this along with $V_e = V_o$ into the Bernoulli equation to get

$$\frac{p_o}{\rho} = \frac{p_e}{\rho} \quad \text{or} \quad p_o = p_e$$

This shows that the pressure does not vary in the x direction which means that

$$\frac{\partial p}{\partial x} = 0$$

We substitute $\partial p/\partial x = 0$ and $V_e = V_o$ into the momentum Equation D-9 and obtain

$$-\tau_o = \int_0^\delta \rho \frac{\partial v}{\partial t} \, dy + \frac{\partial}{\partial x} \int_0^\delta \rho v^2 \, dy - \frac{\partial}{\partial x} V_o \int_0^\delta \rho v \, dy$$

In this problem the flow is steady so that $\partial v/\partial t = 0$ which when we divide by ρ reduces the momentum equation to the following form:

$$-\frac{\tau_o}{\rho} = \frac{\partial}{\partial x} \int_0^\delta v^2 \, dy - V_o \frac{\partial}{\partial x} \int_0^\delta v \, dy$$

or

$$\frac{\tau_o}{\rho} = \frac{\partial}{\partial x} \int_0^\delta (V_o - v)v \, dy \qquad \text{(D-10)}$$

The shear stress at the surface can be calculated from the equation for laminar shear stress because of the laminar sublayer which exists at the surface.

$$\tau_o = \mu \frac{dv}{dy} \bigg|_{y=0} \qquad \text{(D-11)}$$

We can solve for τ_o and δ in terms of x when the shape of the velocity profile is known. We shall assume three different shapes of the velocity profile and see how sensitive the analysis is to changes in shape of the velocity profile. The first velocity profile we shall consider will be the linear profile $v = V_o(y/\delta)$. We substitute this velocity profile into Equations D-10 and D-11 to obtain

$$\frac{\tau_o}{\rho} = \frac{\partial}{\partial x} \int_0^\delta \left(V_o - V_o \frac{y}{\delta} \right) V_o \frac{y}{\delta} \, dy$$

$$= \frac{\partial}{\partial x} \left(\frac{V_o}{\delta} \right)^2 \int_0^\delta (\delta - y)y \, dy$$

$$\frac{\tau_o}{\rho} = \frac{\partial}{\partial x} \frac{V_o^2 \delta}{6} = \frac{V_o^2}{6} \frac{d\delta}{dx}$$

Since the term $V_o^2 \delta / 6$ is a function only of x, the partial derivative becomes the total derivative.

$$\tau_o = \mu \frac{dv}{dy} \bigg|_{y=0} = \mu \frac{V_o}{\delta}$$

We eliminate τ_o from these two equations to obtain

$$\mu \frac{V_o}{\delta} = \frac{\rho V_o^2}{6} \frac{d\delta}{dx}$$

We separate variables and insert the limits $x = 0$, $\delta = 0$, and $x = x$, $\delta = \delta$, and then integrate

$$\frac{6\mu x}{\rho V_o} = \frac{\delta^2}{2}$$

or

$$\delta = \sqrt{\frac{12\mu x}{\rho V_o}} = 2\sqrt{3}\, x\, \sqrt{\frac{\mu}{\rho V_o x}}$$

$$= \frac{3.46x}{\sqrt{R_x}}$$

where R_x is the length Reynolds number $\rho V_o x / \mu$. We substitute this value of the boundary layer thickness δ into the equation for the shear stress and get the following results:

$$\tau_o = \mu \frac{V_o}{\delta} = \frac{\mu V_o \sqrt{R_x}}{3.46}$$

$$= \frac{0.289\rho V_o{}^2}{\sqrt{R_x}}$$

Next, we try the velocity profile.

$$v = V_o \sin\left(\frac{y}{\delta}\frac{\pi}{2}\right)$$

We substitute this velocity profile in Equations D-10 and D-11 to get

$$\frac{\tau_o}{\rho} = \frac{\partial}{\partial x}[V_o{}^2\delta(0.137)]$$

$$\tau_o = \mu \frac{d}{dy}V_o \sin\left(\frac{y}{\delta}\frac{\pi}{2}\right)\Big|_{y=0} = \frac{\mu V_o}{\delta}\frac{\pi}{2}$$

We eliminate τ_o from these equations to obtain

$$\frac{\mu V_o}{\rho\delta}\frac{\pi}{2} = 0.137 V_o{}^2 \frac{d\delta}{dx}$$

We proceed as before to get

$$\delta = \frac{4.80x}{\sqrt{R_x}}$$

and

$$\tau_o = \frac{\mu V_o \sqrt{R_x}}{4.80x}\frac{\pi}{2} = \frac{0.328\rho V_o{}^2}{\sqrt{R_x}}$$

The last velocity profile we shall use is a modified Pohlhausen profile

$$v = V_o \left[2\left(\frac{y}{\delta}\right) - 2\left(\frac{y}{\delta}\right)^3 + \left(\frac{y}{\delta}\right)^4 \right]$$

We substitute this velocity profile into Equations D-10 and D-11 to get

$$\tau_o = \rho(0.12)V_o{}^2 \frac{d\delta}{dx}$$

$$\tau_o = 2\mu \frac{V_o}{\delta}$$

We solve these two equations for τ_o and δ which results in

$$\delta = \frac{5.77x}{\sqrt{R_x}}$$

$$\tau_o = \frac{0.346\rho V_o{}^2}{\sqrt{R_x}}$$

From the exact solution of this problem using the Prandtl boundary layer equations, we know that

$$\tau_o = \frac{0.332\rho V_o{}^2}{\sqrt{R_x}}$$

The value of the constant 0.332 is compared with the results using the three different velocity profiles.

	Velocity Profile	Value of Constant
1st	$v = V_o \dfrac{y}{\delta}$	0.289
2nd	$v = V_o \sin\left(\dfrac{y}{\delta}\dfrac{\pi}{2}\right)$	0.328
3rd	$v = V_o \left[2\left(\dfrac{y}{\delta}\right) - 2\left(\dfrac{y}{\delta}\right)^3 + \left(\dfrac{y}{\delta}\right)^4 \right]$	0.346

The last two velocity profiles give very close results within 4 per cent of the exact solution. The results of the first profile are poor, which is not surprising in view of the crudeness of the profile assumed. Almost any profile that has a shape near the actual shape gives results that are close.

We would not use this type of solution if we could get the exact solution for every problem. In fact, in the majority of the cases an exact solution does not exist so that we must use some selected velocity profile and the momentum equation.

REFERENCES

This book was written to introduce the theoretical approach to fluid mechanics. If the student should stop his formal fluid mechanics education with this book or with a course in which this book were the only one used, in the author's opinion, he would be making a grave mistake. The following books are listed for the student who cannot continue with additional course work in fluids or for one who has mastered this book. It is not a bibliography but a list of reference books for further study. Included are six catagories: elementary fluid mechanics, advanced fluid mechanics, gas dynamics, thermodynamics, potential flow, and special topics.

Any of the elementary fluid mechanics books might be used as a first book in fluids. Each would have a different emphasis and, in some cases, might well complement this book.

The books in the advanced fluid mechanics category are on a higher level than this one and deal with most of the topics in fields of fluid mechanics not mentioned here. All four are excellent, highly recommended references.

The books in the gas dynamics category all presuppose an understanding of thermodynamics. Gas dynamics has been defined as flow of a compressible fluid, which explains why thermodynamics is so important.

The exceedingly short list of books in the field of thermodynamics is to prepare the necessary background for the study of gas dynamics and should not imply a dearth of excellent thermodynamics titles.

The books listed under potential flow deal mainly with the mathematical potential theory, and, although some go further, they do not go far enough to be considered books about aerodynamics.

The special topics division includes subjects that do not fall directly into any of the other categories. The title of each book explains its specialty.

ELEMENTARY FLUID MECHANICS

Binder, R. C.: *Fluid Mechanics*, 3rd edition, Prentice-Hall, Englewood Cliffs, New Jersey, 1955.

Hunsaker, J. C., and B. G. Rightmire: *Engineering Applications of Fluid Mechanics*, McGraw-Hill Book Co., New York, 1947.

Murphy, G.: *Mechanics of Fluids*, 2nd edition, International Textbook Co., Scranton, Pennsylvania, 1952.

Rouse, H.: *Elementary Mechanics of Fluids*, John Wiley and Sons, New York, 1946.

Rouse, H., and J. W. Howe: *Basic Mechanics of Fluids*, John Wiley and Sons, New York, 1953.

Streeter, V. L.: *Fluid Mechanics*, 2nd edition, McGraw-Hill Book Co., New York, 1958.

Vennard, J. K.: *Elementary Fluid Mechanics*, 3rd edition, John Wiley and Sons, New York, 1954.

ADVANCED FLUID MECHANICS

Binder, R. C.: *Advanced Fluid Mechanics* (two volumes), Prentice-Hall, Englewood Cliffs, New Jersey, 1958.

Prandtl, L.: *Essentials of Fluid Dynamics*, Hafner Publishing Co., New York, 1952.

Prandtl, L., and O. G. Tietjens: *Applied Hydro- and Aeromechanics*, McGraw-Hill Book Co., New York, 1934.

Rouse, H. (editor): *Advanced Mechanics of Fluids*, John Wiley and Sons, New York, 1959.

GAS DYNAMICS

Cambel, A. B., and B. H. Jennings: *Gas Dynamics*, McGraw-Hill Book Co., New York, 1958.

Liepmann, H. W., and A. Roshko: *Elements of Gasdynamics*, John Wiley and Sons, New York, 1957.

Sauer, R.: *Introduction to Theoretical Gas Dynamics*, Edwards Bros., Ann Arbor, Michigan, 1947.

Shapiro, A. H.: *The Dynamics and Thermodynamics of Compressible Fluid Flow* (two volumes), Ronald Press, New York, 1953.

THERMODYNAMICS

Epstein, P. S.: *Textbook of Thermodynamics*, John Wiley and Sons, New York, 1937.

Fowler, R. H., and E. A. Guggenheim: *Statistical Thermodynamics*, University Press, Cambridge, 1952.

Keenan, J. H.: *Thermodynamics*, John Wiley and Sons, New York, 1941.

Mooney, D. A.: *Mechanical Engineering Thermodynamics*, Prentice-Hall, Englewood Cliffs, New Jersey, 1955.

Van Wylen, G. J.: *Thermodynamics*, John Wiley and Sons, New York, 1959.

POTENTIAL FLOW

Dryden, H. L., F. P. Murnaghan, and H. Bateman: *Hydrodynamics,* Dover Publications, New York, 1956.

Dwinnell, J. H.: *Principles of Aerodynamics,* McGraw-Hill Book Co., New York, 1949.

Goldstein, S.: *Modern Developments in Fluid Dynamics* (two volumes), Oxford University Press, New York, 1938.

Lamb, H.: *Hydrodynamics,* 6th edition, Dover Publications, New York, 1932.

Milne-Thomson, L. M.: *Theoretical Hydrodynamics,* 2nd edition, The Macmillan Co., New York, 1950.

Prandtl, L., and O. G. Tietjens: *Fundamentals of Hydro- and Aeromechanics,* McGraw-Hill Book Co., New York, 1934.

Rauscher, M.: *Introduction to Aeronautical Dynamics,* John Wiley and Sons, New York, 1953.

Streeter, V. L.: *Fluid Dynamics,* McGraw-Hill Book Co., New York, 1948.

SPECIAL TOPICS IN FLUID MECHANICS

AERODYNAMICS

Hayes, W. D., and R. F. Probstein: *Hypersonic Flow Theory,* Academic Press, New York, 1959.

Kuethe, A. M., and J. D. Schetzer: *Foundations of Aerodynamics,* John Wiley and Sons, New York, 1950.

von Karman, T.: *Aerodynamics,* Cornell University Press, Ithaca, New York, 1954.

von Mises, R.: *Theory of Flight,* McGraw-Hill Book Co., New York, 1945.

BOUNDARY LAYER THEORY

Schlichting, H.: *Boundary Layer Theory,* Pergamon Press, New York, 1955.

DIMENSIONAL ANALYSIS AND SIMILITUDE

Bridgman, P. W.: *Dimensional Analysis,* Yale University Press, New Haven, Connecticut, 1937.

Duncan, W. J.: *Physical Similarity and Dimensional Analysis,* Edward Arnold and Co., London, 1953.

Langhaar, H. L.: *Dimensional Analysis and Theory of Models,* John Wiley and Sons, New York, 1951.

Murphy, G.: *Similitude in Engineering,* Ronald Press, New York, 1950.

HYDRAULICS

Addison, H.: *A Treatise on Applied Hydraulics,* 4th ed., John Wiley and Sons, New York, 1954.

King, H. W.: *Handbook of Hydraulics,* McGraw-Hill Book Co., New York, 1954.

Rouse, H.: *Fluid Mechanics for Hydraulics Engineers,* McGraw-Hill Book Co., New York, 1938.

JET PROPULSION

Finch, V. C.: *Jet Propulsion—Turboprops*, The National Press, Millbrae, Calif., 1950.

Keenan, J. G.: *Elementary Theory of Gas Turbines and Jet Propulsion*, Oxford University Press, New York, 1946.

Sutton, G. P.: *Rocket Propulsion Elements*, 2nd edition, John Wiley and Sons, New York, 1956.

Zucrow, M. J.: *Principles of Jet Propulsion and Gas Turbines*, John Wiley and Sons, New York, 1948.

LUBRICATION

Hersey, M. D.: *Theory of Lubrication*, 1st edition, 2nd printing, John Wiley and Sons, New York, 1938.

Norton, A. E.: *Lubrication*, McGraw-Hill Book Co., New York, 1942.

PROPELLER THEORY

Glauert, H.: *The Elements of Aerofoil and Airscrew Theory*, Cambridge University Press, London, 1930.

Theodorsen, T.: *Theory of Propellers*, McGraw-Hill Book Co., New York, 1948.

Weick, F. E.: *Aircraft Propeller Design*, McGraw-Hill Book Co., New York, 1930.

TURBOMACHINERY

Church, A. H.: *Centrifugal Pumps and Blowers*, John Wiley and Sons, New York, 1944.

Dusinberre, G. M.: *Gas Turbine Power*, International Textbook Co., Scranton, Pennsylvania, 1952.

Spannhake, W.: *Centrifugal Pumps, Turbines and Propellers*, Technology Press, Cambridge, Massachusetts, 1934.

Stepanoff, A. J.: *Centrifugal and Axial Flow Pumps*, 2nd edition, John Wiley and Sons, New York, 1957.

Wislicenus, G. F.: *Fluid Mechanics of Turbomachinery*, McGraw-Hill Book Co., New York, 1947.

TURBULENCE

Batchelor, G. K.: *The Theory of Homogeneous Turbulence*, Cambridge University Press, London, 1955.

Hinze, J. O.: *Turbulence (An Introduction to its Mechanism and Theory)*, McGraw-Hill Book Co., New York, 1959.

Townsend, A. A.: *The Structure of Turbulent Shear Flow*, Cambridge University Press, London, 1956.

INDEX

Absolute pressure, 21
Acceleration, centrifugal, 90, 234
    constant, 50
    linear, 88
Acoustic velocity, 105, 194, 326
Adiabatic process, 330
Aerodynamics, 340, 342
Air, 47
Airfoil theory, 317
Angular momentum, 146, 147
Archimedes principle, 38
Atmosphere, isentropic, 48
    standard, 23
    temperature vs. height, 48
Atmospheric pressure, 22

Bernoulli's equation, application, to
    flow from orifice, 101–103
    to pipe flow, 94–96, 98–100
    to potential flow, 295–299, 303,
        316
    to submerged bodies, 96–98
    derivation of, 87–90
    dimensions of, 244
    limitations of, 109
Body force potential, 296
Body forces, 17, 296
Boundary layer, thickness, 331, 338
    transition, 217, 218, 233

Boundary layer separation, 232, 307
Boundary layer theory, 112, 141, 217,
    218, 227, 232, 276, 307, 308, 331,
    336, 338, 339, 342
    history of, 1, 3
Bulk modulus, 327
    definition of, 11
Buoyancy, 37

Capillarity, 175
Carburetor stall, 53
Cavitation, 11, 96, 327
Centrifugal pump, 155, 265
Channels, 235
Characteristic length, 263
Circulation, 312, 316, 318
Compressible flow, 89
Compressibilty effects, 104
Conservation of energy, 173
Conservation of matter, 71, 77
Continuity equation, 80, 97, 108, 154,
    189, 278, 323, 335
    differential form, 279, 280, 286, 300
    pipe flow, 83, 95
Continuum, 16
Control volume, application, for angu-
        lar momentum, 147, 152, 156,157
    for energy, 174, 176, 178–180, 181–
        182, 186, 192–193

Control volume, application, for
momentum, 124, 142–144
for continuity, 85, 95, 143, 144, 154,
158, 180, 183, 187, 323
definition of, 77
Critical pressure ratio, 192, 194
Curved surfaces, forces on, 33
Cylinder, flow around a, 301, 302
with circulation flow around a, 313,
317

D'Alembert's paradox, 307
Darcy equation, 220, 222, 253
Density, average, 4
definition of, 3, 4
Determinant, 256, 257, 258
order of, 258, 260
Dimensional analysis, 241, 245, 262,
342
applications, 241
Dimensional homogeneity, 241, 242,
249
Dimensionless ratio, see Pi term
Displacement thickness, 331, 332
Distorted model, 269
Doublet, 310, 315
Drag coefficient, 229
Drag force, 228, 229, 232, 306
Dynamic similarity, 263
incomplete, 267, 268

Electricity, 175
Energy, conservation of, 173
general equation of, 178, 179, 184,
192, 195
internal, 173
intrinsic, 176, 179, 185
kinetic, 175
potential, 175
principle of, 123
residual, 176
specific internal, 175
thermal, 259
Enthalpy, 193
Equilibrium, neutral, 43
stable, 43
unstable, 43
Equipotential lines, 288, 289, 293, 309,
311

Euler equation, comparison with
energy, 184
comparison with momentum, 160
modified, 103, 106, 109, 220, 222, 224

Flow, compressible, 89
frictionless, 89, 276
incompressible, 89
isentropic, 104, 106, 108, 188
laminar, 214, 215
Flow net, 286, 310, 311
Flow pattern, 72
Flow rate, 81, 223, 224
Fluid statics, 16
compressible, 47
fundamental equation of, 20
incompressible, basic equation of, 21
limitations on basic equation of, 16
Forces, body, 17, 296
pressure, 17, 87, 226, 229
shear, 17, 87, 226, 229
Forces on curved surfaces, 33
Friction, 202, 205, 214, 226
Friction factor, 220, 222, 225
Friction velocity, 222
Frictionless flow, 89, 276
Froude number, 229, 268
Fundamental dimensions, 242, 248, 250

Gage pressure, 21
Gas dynamics, 340
Gases, definitions, 2

Head loss, 184, 220, 221
Heat, 173, 181, 185
Hydraulics, 342
history of, 1

Ideal fluid, 276
Incompressible flow, 89
Irrotational flow, 284, 286, 298, 300
Isentropic expansion, 323, 325, 330
Isentropic flow, 104, 106, 108, 188
Isothermal process, 13, 106, 107, 330

Jet propulsion, 343
Joukowski transformation, 317

Kinetic energy, 175
of molecules, 4

Kinematic viscosity, 208
Knudsen number, 271

Laminar flow, 214, 215
Laminar sublayer, 218, 227, 337
Laplace equation, 286, 287, 290, 291, 300, 302, 317
    polar coordinates, 308, 317
Lift, 315
Liquids, definition of, 2
Lubrication, 343

Mach number, 105, 191, 229
Magnetism, 175
Manometry, 20
Mass, 242
Mass system, 123, 147, 174
Matrix, 255, 256
Metacenter, 43
Mixing length, 216
Model studies, 262
Modulus of elasticity, 12
Momentum, 123
Momentum, angular, 146, 147
    equations of angular, 149, 150, 160
Momentum equation, boundary layer, 333, 335, 337
Momentum equations for control volume, 125, 126, 160, 325, 333
Momentum thickness, 331, 332, 333

Neutral equilibrium, 43
Newton's proportionality constant, 178, 330
Newton's second law, 71, 86, 90, 123, 150, 160, 242, 296
Newtonian fluids, 208
Non-Newtonian fluids, 208
Nozzle, 188, 194
Nusselt number, 270, 271

One-dimensional flow, 74

Path line, 72
Peclet number, 270
Perfect fluid, 74
    definition, 3
Perfect gas, air, 47
Perfect gas law, 13, 47, 178, 329
Pipe bend, force, 127

Pipe flow, 217, 219, 222
Pipe losses, minor, 223, 224, 225
Pi term, 247, 251, 253, 263, 267
Pi terms, determination of minimum number, 254
Plane surfaces, forces on, 27
Pohlhausen profile, 339
Polar coordinates, 305, 308
Polytropic process, 330
Potential energy, 175
Pounds mass, 329, 330
Power, 137
Prandtl, 216
Prandtl number, 270
Pressure, absolute, 21
    atmospheric, 22
    definition of, 5
    direction of, 7
    effect on viscosity, 207
    gage, 21
    stagnation, 98
    vapor, 11
Pressure forces, 17, 87, 226, 229
Pressure on cylinders, 305, 307
Pressure ratio, critical, 192, 194
Pressure wave, 323
Pressure work, 176, 177
Propeller theory, 343
Prototype, 262, 263
Pumps, 151

Relative roughness, 220
Reversible process, 330
Reynolds' experiments, 213
Reynolds number, 214, 225, 254, 268, 307, 338
    critical, 214
Rivers, 235
Rocket problem, 144
Rotation, 281, 284
Rotation of a liquid, 53

Schiller, 215
Secondary flow, 233
Separation, boundary layer, 232, 307
Shear forces, 17, 87, 226, 229
Shear stress, 151, 203, 218, 221, 233, 338
    definition of, due to molecular action, 205
    due to turbulence, 216

Shear stress, turbulent, 233
Shock waves, 5, 200, 201
Sink, 310
Sinuous flow, 213, 214
Slugs, 329, 330
Sonic velocity, 105, 194, 326
Sound wave, 323
Source, 309
  strength of, 309
Specific gravity, definition, 4
Specific heat, 330
Specific internal energy, 175
Specific volume, definition, 4
Specific weight, definition, 4
Spring, hydraulic, 12
Stable equilibrium, 43
Stability, floating submerged bodies, 42
Stagnation point, 98, 315
Stagnation pressure, 98
Stanton diagram, 219, 220, 223, 225
Statics, fluid, *see* Fluid statics
Steady flow, 72, 89, 151, 178
Steady motion, 80
Stream function, 299, 301, 302, 318
Streamline, 72, 87, 213, 288, 289, 293, 309, 311
Streamlines as solid boundaries, 295, 301
Stream tube, 72, 90
Submerged body, 96
Subsonic flow, 191
Supersonic flow, 191
Surface tension, angle of, 9
  definition, 7

Temperature, atmospheric, 48
  definition, 4
  effect on viscosity, 205, 207

Thermal conductivity, 259
Thermal energy, 259
Thermodynamics, 329, 340
  first law of, 173, 188
Three-dimensional flow, 76
Torque, 150, 151, 153, 155, 210
Turbines, 151, 327
Turbomachinery, 343
Turbulence, 343
Turbulent effects, 127
Turbulent flow, 214, 216
Two-dimensional flow, 75, 76

Unstable equilibrium, 43
Unstable flow, 214
Unsteady flow, 72, 89

Vane problems, 135
Vapor pressure, 96, 327
  definition, 11
Velocity, at a surface, 74, 202
  acoustic, 105, 194, 326
Velocity potential, 285, 286, 291, 293, 301, 318
Velocity profile, 73, 331, 337, 338, 339
Vena contracta, 91, 92, 93
Venturi meter, 116
Viscosity, coefficient of, 203, 207
  kinematic, 208
Von Karman, 333
Vortex, 311
  strength of, 313, 315

Wake effects, 308
Water hammer, 5
Wave formation, 267
Weber number, 270
Work, 173